AN ELEMENTARY CHEMISTRY

BY

ERIC JOHN HOLMYARD

M.A., M.Sc., D.Litt., F.I.C.

HEAD OF THE SCIENCE DEPARTMENT, CLIFTON COLLEGE,
EXAMINER IN CHEMISTRY (HIGHER CERTIFICATE) TO THE NORTHERN
UNIVERSITIES' JOINT MATRICULATION BOARD
AND FORMERLY TO THE UNIVERSITY OF BRISTOL,
MEMBRE CORRESPONDANT DU COMITÉ INTERNATIONAL
D'HISTOIRE DES SCIENCES

LONDON
EDWARD ARNOLD & CO.

First Published 1925; *Reprinted* 1925 (*twice*), 1926 (*twice*), 1927
Second Edition 1928; *Reprinted* 1928, 1929, 1930, 1931, 1932
Third Edition 1934; *Reprinted* 1935, 1937, 1940, 1942, 1943, 1944, 1945

Printed in Great Britain by
Butler & Tanner Ltd., Frome and London

PREFACE TO THE FIRST EDITION

As the syllabuses in chemistry set for the various First School Certificate Examinations in this country are now very well standardized, and differ very little from that in the London Matriculation, it has seemed desirable to write a book specially to meet the requirements of candidates at these examinations. Writing to syllabus is sometimes to be deprecated, but I have had no hesitation in doing so in this instance, since there appears to be a general feeling among science teachers that it would be difficult to improve the present syllabuses materially. With this feeling I am in agreement, yet I have not confined myself strictly within the prescribed limits.

The arrangement of the book calls for a few words of explanation. By grouping all the theoretical work at the beginning I do not, of course, imply that it should be *taught* in bulk. Since, however, there are as many different courses in elementary chemistry as there are teachers, it appeared to be most convenient to adopt a scheme which could easily be adapted to the methods of various schools. For the same reason, I have written the descriptive part in such a way that it can, I hope, be made to harmonize, without much difficulty, with the teacher's own particular views as to how the subject should be presented.

A certain amount of repetition will be observed in several places. This is deliberate: it is hopeless to expect a young student to grasp an important fact or principle the first time he meets with it, and he would be an optimist who believed that boys conscientiously look up all the references to other pages with which they meet.

The first chapter, *What is Chemistry?*, has been introduced in order to supply boys and girls who are not "going on with chemistry" an answer to that frequent question, "What is the good of it?"

In preparing the MS. of this book for the press, I have had great assistance from Mr. F. P. Dunn, F.I.C., to whom I am glad to take this opportunity of expressing my gratitude. The preparation of the numerical calculations has been the laborious task of my friend and former pupil, Mr. B. E. Berry, B.A., of Gonville and Caius College, Cambridge. The alacrity with which I accepted his offer to perform this labour is the measure of my thanks to him for having so ably accomplished it. I have pleasure also in thanking Messrs. G. Bell & Sons, Ltd., for having generously permitted me to quote several passages from my *Practical Chemistry*, which they published in 1923. The Tables of Logarithms and Anti-Logarithms are reprinted from Professor J. Perry's *Practical Mathematics* by permission of the Controller of H.M. Stationery Office.

E. J. HOLMYARD

CLIFTON COLLEGE, BRISTOL.

PREFACE TO THE THIRD EDITION

For the third edition of this book, the type has been entirely re-set, a fact that has enabled the text to be brought up to date throughout. Though little change in the general arrangement of the book has been found necessary, manufacturing processes have been described in accordance with modern methods, and the general atmosphere of the book has been given those modifications which recent teaching practice appears to favour. Minor additions have been made in several places, and new sections have been added on magnesium, nickel, chromium, aluminium and mercury—metals which the elementary student may not require to study in detail, but which he is constantly encountering in the laboratory and in daily life.

The author would once again thank the public most sincerely for the continued and gratifyingly extensive support they have given to the book, and hopes that, in its new edition, it may continue to win approval. He is also very grateful for the appreciative letters received, over several years, from some hundreds of correspondents, and equally so for those which have contained suggestions and criticisms.

E. J. HOLMYARD

CLIFTON COLLEGE, BRISTOL.

CONTENTS

LIST OF PLATES

ELEMENTARY CHEMISTRY

CHAPTER I

WHAT IS CHEMISTRY?

There is a proverb which says that the child is father of the man, meaning that a man is only a boy on a larger scale, and that he behaves in the same kind of way and likes the same kind of thing. There is a good deal of truth in the saying, for a man no doubt gets the same sort of satisfaction from sucking at his pipe as the infant gets from his bottle. The likeness is, however, even plainer in the curiosity and inquisitiveness which grown-ups and children both possess to an unlimited extent. We have all investigated the inside of a clock with a hammer and screw-driver, "just to see how it works" and what it is made of. If that model engine, given to us last Christmas by Aunt Matilda, now exists only in the model engines' Paradise, its scattered remains nevertheless bear silent witness to the overwhelming curiosity of the youth of mankind.

A man's curiosity in mechanical toys seldom gets less as he grows up, for how many a father (I myself plead guilty for one) has bought his son a box of Meccano and then, locked in his study, played with it himself? But as we grow older, our curiosity looks round for fresh sources of satisfaction. It is no longer content with cogs and cams or nuts and bolts. These are all very well in their way, but for most of us they do not go far enough. "The world is a strange place," said Lord Rayleigh, "and perhaps the strangest thing of all is that we are here to discuss it." It is certainly full of the most wonderful things, which attract and hold our attention and make the words "why?" and "how?" and "what?" spring unbidden to our lips.

When you are playing football, you know that the best way to success lies in team-work supplemented by individual brilliance. The same is true when the game is not football, but the infinitely more exciting one of unravelling the secrets of Nature. The steady and persistent inquiries of thousands of lesser men make the way ready for the great genius who suddenly appears and with an irresistible rush scores a try—or, in other words, makes a discovery of the greatest importance. And just as a brilliant player often renders possible, by his strategy, more efficient progress by the rest of the team, so does the great discoverer point the way for future spade-work by the rank and file—spade-work, but nevertheless work which may be of enormous value to the human race.

To solve some of the problems, then, which the world around sets us, we have to make use not only of our own curiosity and intelligence, but also of those of our fellow-men. This organized curiosity, with its special methods of asking questions of Nature, and its carefulness in recording her replies, is what we call science. Science is not a collection of occasionally interesting, but more often dull, facts: it is a voyage of discovery with this remarkable characteristic—that the farther the voyagers go the more and ever more they perceive there is to be discovered. They never find that they have completed the circuit, like Magellan or Drake.

Now, just as no one would dream of setting out on an exploration without getting himself into training, so the scientist is not content with his curiosity in its idle and casual form. He understands that his inquisitiveness must be trained to leave no clue unfollowed, "no avenue unexplored," no spoor untracked, and at the same time to confine itself strictly to the problem in hand. If you want to understand how the scientist works, you cannot do better than read a good detective story, such as the "Dr. Thorndyke" stories, by R. Austin Freeman, or the Sherlock Holmes stories themselves if you have not already devoured them. The detective first of all observes the scene of the crime very closely and carefully, and looks for " clues " or signs from which he can get some idea of the criminal. The end of a cigarette, the dust in a bowler hat, a thread of cloth—any one of a thousand details which the untrained man would overlook—may put the detective on the track of his quarry at once. It is the same in science. Every detail must be carefully observed : nothing is too insignificant to be worth attention. When you pour dilute sulphuric acid upon zinc, imagine that you are the first person who has ever done it, and *look*, as though your life depended upon it. No one in the world, not even the greatest Professor of Chemistry, knows everything that happens even in this simple experiment ; you may discover something that has hitherto been unnoticed. Many a great discovery has been made by a man who observed a little more closely than anyone had done before.

The scientist has one great advantage over the detective. The latter may think he knows how the crime was committed, but he cannot have it done over again to see if he is right. The scientist, however, can make as many guesses about his problem as he likes, and he can *make experiments* to test them. If the first guess is not right he can begin all over again, and keep on trying until he finds one which is satisfactory. If you think you have missed something in your sulphuric acid and zinc experiment, you can take some more zinc and sulphuric acid and try again until you are satisfied. We shall learn a good deal more about the methods of science later on. Meanwhile we must find out why " Science " is split up into a number of branches which are called chemistry, physics, botany, zoology, and so on.

In prehistoric times, every man was his own butcher, carpenter, stone-mason, tailor, soldier and shepherd. When men came at length to live together in groups, however, it was found to be better to let one man be responsible for the carpentering, another for the tailoring, and so on, and thus we may imagine the various trades and professions to have grown up. It is not every one who would make a good tailor, and the good tailor may prove to be a failure as a stonemason. In exactly the same kind of way there are people who are better at dealing with animals than with rocks and minerals, and others who prefer to spend their lives in finding out all they can about plants. When there is a subject we are particularly interested in, we like to give it a high-sounding name. If, for example, we collect stamps, we say that our hobby is philately, while if we have a passion for rare and curious coins we call ourselves numismatologists—it sounds so much better than "coin-collectors"! Well, those people who study animals call their occupation the science of *zoology*; *botany* is the science of plants; *geology* deals with the formation of rocks and rivers, mountains and glaciers; *astronomers* study the stars. *Physics* is chiefly concerned with the way in which things move, with the nature of light and electricity, with magnets and generators, while *chemistry*, the science with which we have to become acquainted, investigates the various substances of which the air, the sea, and the earth's crust are composed, and tries to find out what they are made of, how they may be changed into other substances, and what happens during the changes.

In spite of this convenient separation into various branches, science is really an undivided whole. The botanist, for example, cannot study his plants properly unless he knows something of chemistry, for plants are made up of the same substances that the chemist investigates. The chemist, too, often finds that he and the physicist are tunnelling the same hill, but from opposite ends; while they both combine to enable the astronomer to discover what the stars are composed of. In return, the astronomer sometimes finds a substance in the sun or stars which the chemist has overlooked upon the earth. In olden days, the knowledge of Nature which men had won was comparatively small, so that it was possible for one man to be fully acquainted with all of it. But with the progress of time the bounds of knowledge were widened, and nowadays a man cannot hope to become expert in more than one, or at most two, of the various branches of science. This, however, must not prevent him from trying to get a satisfactory elementary knowledge of the rest, for unless he does so he will have a very one-sided view of the world. He would be like a man in a room with several windows who refused to look out except through a particular one. If this one happened to overlook the sea, he might conclude he was living upon a rocky islet, when a glance through the others would show him that he was in reality upon the mainland.

In other words, science is our effort to find out all we can about the world around us. We split science up into various branches simply in order to make progress more quickly and easily, but all scientists are working for the same objects, and use the same methods. When he sees a buttercup in a field the chemist says, "What is that green stuff in its leaves made of?" The botanist says, "What is the flower for?" The zoologist says, "Why do these insects keep on visiting it?" The geologist says, "What sort of soil are its roots growing in?" The physicist says, "Why doesn't the wind blow it over?" These, or questions like these, are the kinds that the various scientists mentioned would put to themselves. We see that what strikes one man does not interest the others so much, but who is to say which is the most important? We cannot understand all about the buttercup until we have asked and answered questions of all kinds, and what is true of the buttercup is true of the world at large. All the various groups of scientists are continually asking questions of Nature; when she has answered them all we shall find that although we have travelled by many different paths we have arrived all together at the same terminus.

Chemistry, then, is one particular way of asking questions of Nature. It attracts some men more than others, but it attracts almost all boys and girls because they are all interested in the questions it asks and the methods it uses to get an answer. The chief question in chemistry is "What is it made of?" Now, that is practically the same thing which we want to know about the clock. The clock has certain peculiarities which interest us: it makes a noise and its hands move. We therefore cannot rest until we have found out what there is in the clock which makes it exhibit this peculiar behaviour.

What do we do? Well, we take it to pieces and examine the parts. Do we know all about the clock now? Perhaps we think we do, but we can easily find out whether our confidence is justified, *by putting the parts together again.* If we can do this, we are satisfied. Similarly, when the chemist meets with a substance which is new to him, he first of all splits it up or takes it to pieces, a process which he calls *analysis.* He is thus able to get some idea of its structure. He is not satisfied, however, until he can take the parts and put them together again so as to regain the original substance —a process which he calls *synthesis.* Like the boy with a clock, the chemist often finds that it is easy to break a substance up into many parts, but much more difficult to build up those parts again into the original substance. Analysis is generally a simpler task than synthesis, but only when he has been able to synthesize a substance is the chemist certain that his knowledge of it is adequate.

Some substances absolutely refuse to be split up. Thus, although we can easily split up, or analyse, water into two gases called hydrogen and oxygen, no one has ever been able to split up hydrogen or oxygen into other substances. Substances which no one has so far been able to split up into other substances are called *elements.* About ninety-two elements are known, and all the other substances of which the world is composed are made up of these elements. You will see a list of the elements on page 437.

The Uses of Chemistry.—You may perhaps ask of what use chemistry is to yourself and to the human race. Suppose we consider the second of the two first. Practically the whole of our modern civilization is built up upon the work of chemists. The great machines which do so much of the world's work could never have been made if the chemist had not studied the properties of iron and steel and discovered how to extract iron from its ores. The use of coal-gas, now universal in civilized countries, depends for its success upon chemical processes. The dyes which make our surroundings full of colour are prepared by chemists from substances which are found in coal-tar. Even the "silk" stockings with which our sisters and our cousins and our aunts deck themselves are made by chemists from ordinary wood. The margarine which is used for food is turned out from the laboratory rather than from the dairy. The gas with which the dentist mercifully makes us unconscious of his tortures, the iodine with which we sterilize cuts, the aspirin we take to cure a headache, the vulcanite of our fountain-pens, the fireworks for November 5, the artificial manures to increase the wheat crop, the table-salt which does not get damp, the celluloid of which films are made—all these things and innumerable others represent the work of the chemist.

But it is not only in these wonderful applications that chemistry is of value. Perhaps its chief importance lies in the fact that it both stimulates and satisfies our intellectual curiosity. The average chemist does not set about his work in order to make some discovery which shall be of practical value: he toils unceasingly for no other purpose than to find out as much as he can about the substances that interest him. If he discovers something which can be turned to account in the practical affairs of daily life, he usually leaves the inventor or the man of business to make use of it: his own work lies in the actual discovery of new facts. According to the great Greek philosopher, ARISTOTLE (384–322 B.C.), there is no nobler occupation than the pursuit of knowledge for its own sake; if this is true, then there can be no nobler occupation than science. When you study chemistry, then, you do so not chiefly in order to know such things as how to prepare copper sulphate, but rather to gain some idea of how man seeks to understand and to control the world of Nature and to turn it to his own advantage. The spirit of chemistry is everything; the bare facts, although they may be interesting in themselves, are of far less importance. Chemistry is a fascinating branch of human activity, and from it we can gather as much information concerning man himself as about the various substances and changes it investigates.

Thus, even if you do not propose to become a chemist or a doctor or an engineer after you leave school, chemistry will help to equip your mind for your adult life, and will give you an outlook on the world which it is essential for you to have and which you can scarcely gain in any other way. That is why we who teach chemistry in schools think that all boys and girls must know something of the aims and methods of chemistry. We do not think that it will make any difference to you to know that the equivalent of magnesium is 12·16, but we do think that you cannot live your mental life fully if you are completely ignorant of the beauty which chemistry unfolds, and of that side of truth to the search for which generation after generation of chemists have devoted their lives.

Questions

1. What have chemists done to make our daily life (*a*) safer and (*b*) more comfortable ?

2. Go through last week's daily papers, and write short notes on those items of news for a correct understanding of which it is necessary to have some knowledge of chemistry.

3. Of what use do you think a knowledge of chemistry would be to (*a*) a doctor, (*b*) an engine-driver, (*c*) a clergyman, (*d*) a poet, (*e*) a musician, (*f*) a plumber, (*g*) a lawyer, (*h*) a stockbroker, (*k*) a teacher of Latin and Greek ?

4. What do you regard as the chief aims of chemistry ?

5. Explain the words *analysis* and *synthesis*.

6. Is chemistry worth studying simply because of the material benefits it brings ?

CHAPTER II

HOW CHEMISTRY AROSE

When, with "delighted eyes," we "turn to yonder oak," we do not always stop to think that it was once an insignificant acorn, struggling for its life in darkness and amidst noxious weeds. And a man from a foreign clime might well find it difficult to believe that the apparently lifeless oak of the winter months will in a short time bear a mass of green foliage. In the same way, a boy who begins to study chemistry may not realize that the science started in a very humble way and has reached its present proud position only after centuries of struggle: sometimes it was nearly smothered, at others it appeared to be dead, and occasionally it tasted a brief spell of prosperity only to relapse into a state of grave ill-health.

It will be interesting, therefore, to glance briefly at some of the adventures which chemistry has undergone from its earliest days. It will also be useful, for we cannot really understand what chemistry is, nor what it is likely to become, unless we know what it has been in the past. If we were presented with a chick, and did not know anything about eggs and hens, we should find it impossible to gain any adequate idea of what the chick really was, and should certainly not be able to predict anything about its future. Chemistry has had a very eventful history, which for thrills, mystery and excitement beats many a romance of fiction. We cannot here deal with it fully, but we can glance quickly at some of the chief events and gain as light acquaintance with some of the most celebrated men.

To discover the origin of chemistry takes us back some 5,000 or 6,000 years to the early days of ancient Egypt. In this land, blessed with a wonderful climate and irrigated every year by the Nile flood, civilization is generally believed to have originated. One of the most important causes of the great advance made by man in these remote times was the discovery ot copper, which led to the manufacture of copper chisels and other tools. With these instruments at his disposal, man was able to progress in rapid strides. The wonderful pyramids and other buildings that the Egyptians erected

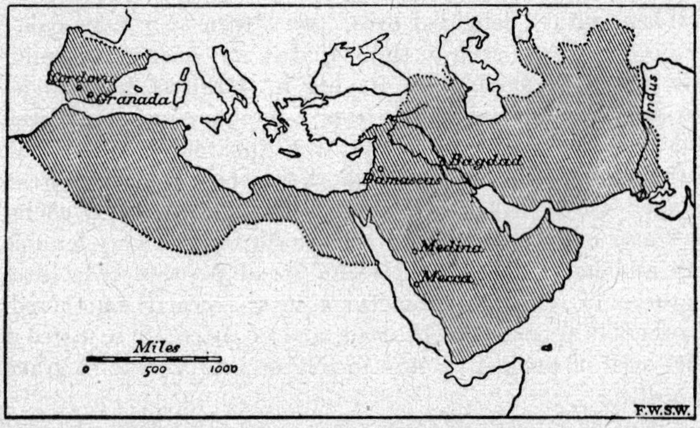

FIG. 1.—Map to show extent of Empire of Islam in the Eighth Century A.D.

remain to this day to bear witness to the skill and prowess of the dwellers by the Nile.

Copper was by no means the only metal which the Egyptians knew. They prized gold as much as we do, and they knew also silver, lead, and tin. The last they obtained from mines in Persia, and by mixing it with copper they were able to make the alloy *bronze*, which is much harder than copper, and therefore more suitable for cutting-tools. They also knew iron, for pieces of iron have been found in the masonry of the Great Pyramid.

Besides the metals, the Egyptians used various minerals

such as malachite (a copper ore), turquoise, quartz, mica, etc. They knew how to make glass and soap, and they used salt as well as resins and oils in the embalming or mummification of human bodies. Many substances were employed as medicines and as poisons, while in the manufacture of pigments and dyes the ancient craftsmen attained to a remarkable degree of proficiency.

Most of this knowledge appears to have been kept as secret as possible by the priests, who worked in laboratories attached to their temples.

When the Greeks and Romans visited Egypt, they were impressed by the skill which the Egyptians showed in working metals and in similar operations, and called these various arts the "Art of Egypt." Now the Egyptian word for "Egypt" is *Kemi*, which is written

and means "The Black Land"—no doubt in reference to the black colour of the mud left behind when the waters of the Nile receded after the yearly flood. The "Art of Egypt" therefore became "The Art of Kemi," and from *Kemi* we get our present word "*chemistry*," through the intermediate Arabic word *kimia*.

For chemistry to advance, it is not sufficient merely to carry out practical operations. It is necessary also to *think* about these operations, and this is what the Egyptians seem never to have done. However, on the other side of the Mediterranean, the ancient Greeks were so busy thinking that they had no time to conduct experiments. On the basis of a few observations they set out to explain the whole world—nay, the whole universe—and they evolved many wonderful schemes, some of which have proved very useful to scientists of a later time. Still, if it is impossible for chemistry to advance by practical operations alone, it is equally impossible for it to make any real progress by theories or imagination alone, so that for centuries after the ancient Empires of Egypt and Greece had ceased to exist, chemistry remained in a very backward state. The philosophers went on philosophizing, and the craftsmen went on with their labours in the workshops, but there was no connection between the two.

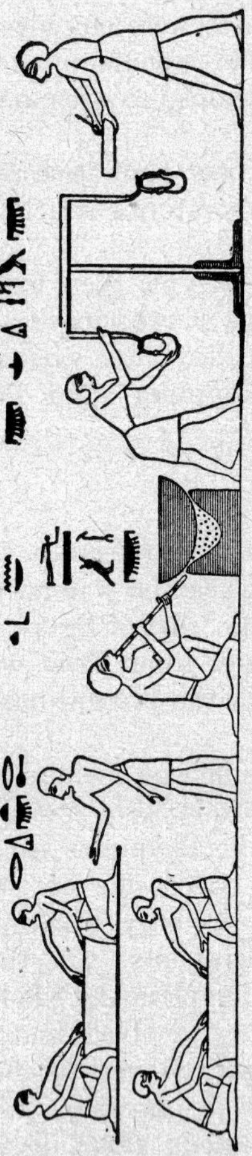

FIG. 2.—Ancient Egyptians working Gold.

Fortunately, in the seventh century of our era, an event occurred that caused the theoretical and the practical sides to be brought together, and thus the science of chemistry was set upon a firm footing. This event was the rise of Muhammadanism, or, to give it its proper name, Islam. Arabia has been inhabited from time immemorial by wandering tribes of Bedouin, and up to the beginning of the seventh century they had all been idolaters and were continually fighting with one another. The Prophet MUHAMMAD, however, preached the One God to them, and converted them from their idolatrous practices. In their enthusiasm for this new religion they forgot their feuds with one another, and became welded into a strong and united nation. After the Prophet's death, they set out on a war of conquest, and very soon the banners of Islam were floating over all the countries surrounding the Mediterranean, from the Atlantic Ocean to the River Indus.

When the Muslim conquerors had settled down, they started to encourage learning as much as they possibly could. Trains of camels were sent to Constantinople and other towns to bring back to Baghdad all the books and manuscripts that could be procured, and the Caliphs founded

وقد صار العبد المكتوف ملكا من ملوك الروم وفضله ظاهر غير مكتوم فلما راى
خضوع القاضي وذلته قبل راسه ورجليه واخذ في الشكر والثنا عليه وابتدا يعرفه
ما فعل به من الجميل لكونه صار ملكا بعد ما كان عبدا ذليل صورة رجل لباسه
اصفر والمركب بين يديه على القامين وقد ابيض وتحته نار الفتيله
وفوق جسمه ابيك املا الانا وقدامه هذه الاحرف البرباوي والعبد ملكا جالس على
كرسي والقاضي قدامه

ج لك يا كريم الجوهر ويقيناه لك مزج احمر يا من لا يرد فعله في الناس احدا
يا محيل الجسد روحا والروح جسدا يا سيد الجواهر الخالده بحدته يا مصلح
الارواح الغير خالده لفرط فضيلته يا ايها الجوهر الفاعل في الكائنات
الفاسدات يا مبدي العجايب ومظهر الخفيات يا من لولاه لم يتزوج الحيوان
البري والبحري يا من جعل زحل في جوف شدته بحري يا من زوج العربيه ببحر النجاج
يا من جعل الرمل الدهيم مع قوته زجاج يا مصلح بين الاعادي بخراج

PAGE OF ARABIC CHEMICAL MANUSCRIPT.

colleges and observatories, libraries and hospitals all over the Empire. In this zeal for learning, chemistry was not forgotten, but the Muslims were in the happy position of being able to use both the Greek wisdom and the practical arts of ancient Egypt, for they soon established themselves in the latter country.

Under the Caliph of the Arabian Nights, HARUN AL-RASHID [1] (786–809), there lived the first truly great chemist. He was born in Persia, and his name was JABIR IBN HAYYAN; in Europe, however, he is generally known as GEBER. He wrote many books on chemistry, which show that he was an accomplished chemist, both in practice and in theory.

It was in Spain that the Muslims came into closest contact with Western Europe. During the time that they were in possession of the country (711–1492), their universities were the best in the world, and European students used to flock to Cordova and Toledo and other towns to learn from the Muslim professors. When they had learnt what they could they were naturally anxious to pass on their knowledge to their fellow-countrymen, and so they began translating books of all kinds from Arabic into Latin. One of these translators, an Englishman, ROBERT OF CHESTER, performed a double service: he not only translated the chief Arabic work on *algebra*, and thus introduced this branch of mathematics to Europe, but he also translated a book on chemistry. This was the first book on chemistry to appear in a European tongue, and the translation of it was finished on February 11, 1144. More translations followed, and soon European scholars were able to make progress by themselves.

For some centuries, however, comparatively little was done, since chemists were practically all engaged in a fruitless search for some substance—the *elixir*—which should enable them to convert metals like lead and copper into gold and silver. From this idle dream they were roughly awakened by the Swiss chemist, PARACELSUS (1493–1541), who publicly

[1] Accent on the last syllable of "Rashid."

burnt the books of his predecessors and made a fresh start. He was a bombastic fellow, but he stirred chemistry up, which was just what it needed at the time. According to Paracelsus, the chief aim of chemistry was to be the preparation and investigation of drugs for use in medicine, and from his time to the end of the seventeenth century, chemistry did in fact mainly concern itself with medical problems of this kind.

The HONOURABLE ROBERT BOYLE (1627-91), however, broke free from these fetters, and he and other chemists scarcely less brilliant succeeded in raising chemistry to its proper rank. During the eighteenth century, chemists rapidly increased their skill, and with improving means of communication they were able to keep themselves informed on what their brethren in other parts of the world were doing. This interchange of ideas and information was probably one of the chief causes of the great progress which chemistry made during this period. The principal chemists of the time were BLACK (1728-99), PRIESTLEY (1733-1804), CAVENDISH (1731-1810), SCHEELE (1742-86), LAVOISIER (1743-94), and DALTON (1766-1844).

Lavoisier and Dalton deserve special mention, for the former was the first to put forward the modern explanation of what happens when things burn (*viz.* that they combine with the oxygen of the air), while Dalton founded the Atomic Theory, about which you will read in Chapter VII. On the Atomic Theory of Dalton rests all the marvellous chemistry of the nineteenth century.

From Dalton's time to our own is little more than 100 years, yet that century has witnessed a greater advance than did the preceding 2,000 years. We need not describe that advance here, for in its main ideas the chemistry since Dalton's time has not changed very much, and you will get a bird's-eye view of it from your present course. At the end of the book (p. 449) there are some details about the lives of a few famous chemists, and a list of books from which you can get further information if you would like to have it.

OF THE IMPERFECTION OF THE Chymist's DOCTRINE OF QUALITIES.

By the Honourable
ROBERT BOYLE Esq;
Fellow of the *R. Society.*

LONDON,
Printed by *E. Flesher*, for *R. Davis*
Bookseller in *Oxford.* 1675.

Questions

1. Why must we know something about the history of chemistry when we are studying this science?

2. How did chemistry arise?

3. Mention some of the chemical facts and processes known to the Ancient Egyptians.

4. Look up in an encyclopædia or other books of reference the way in which bodies were mummified. Then write a list of the chief substances required, and find out whence the Egyptians could have got them.

5. Find out all you can about the atomic theories of Democritus, Empedocles, Lucretius, and other ancient philosophers.

6. Explain how it was that the Muslims were able to establish chemistry on a sound basis.

7. Who was the chief Muslim chemist? When did he live?

8. What is the origin of the word *chemistry*?

9. What do you know of Robert of Chester?

10. Who was Paracelsus? What service did he render to chemistry?

11. What was the Elixir?

12. Mention some of the chief chemists of the eighteenth century.

13. Who founded the Atomic Theory?

14. From reference books, make a list of the scientific discoveries that we owe to the Hon. Robert Boyle.

CHAPTER III

THE CHEMIST'S TOOLS AND WHAT HE DOES WITH THEM

The carpenter, the surgeon, the dentist, and the photographer all have special tools with which to carry on their work. A dentist could, no doubt, use an ordinary pair of pincers, and the surgeon could borrow a saw from his neighbour the carpenter, but they would not find them as easy to work with as those which are specially designed for dentistry or surgery. The same thing is true of the vessels and instruments which are used in chemistry. These pieces of *chemical apparatus* are made so as to enable the chemist to carry out his experiments with greater ease and efficiency, and as they are designed for this particular purpose, they have advantages which ordinary pots and pans, bottles and pipes, burners and funnels do not possess. You could, of course, carry out many experiments in jam-jars or empty salmon-tins, and one of the greatest of all chemists, JOHN DALTON, was so poor that he had to use ink-bottles instead of flasks and the stems of churchwarden pipes instead of glass tubing. As long as you realize that fact, and do not imagine that chemistry cannot be carried on without elaborate erections of coiled tubes and stoppered tap-funnels, there is no reason why you should deny yourself the benefit of the convenient apparatus which has been designed. There is no merit in using a tumbler if a beaker is more suitable.

At the same time, it is a very good rule not to use a complicated piece of apparatus when a simple one will do: the famous German chemist, BAEYER, who made many notable advances in chemistry, found that the humble test-tube was practically all he required even in the wonderful researches that made him celebrated all over the world. A keen eye and a nimble finger are worth more to a chemist than all the apparatus in the catalogue.

When you see a picture of a chemist in an advertisement in the newspapers or magazines, you will invariably find the piece of apparatus which is shown in Fig. 3. This vessel, which appeals so much to the public imagination, is the *retort*. It deserves to be mentioned first, as it is one of the oldest of the chemist's tools, although it is not quite the same in shape now as it was in early days. Then it consisted of two parts, a lower one which was called the gourd or pumpkin from its shape, and an upper one called the *alembic*. The two parts were joined together by a ring of clay, so that when it was set up ready for use an ancient retort had the appearance shown in Fig. 4. A retort is used for heating a substance, or mixture of substances, which gives off vapours that can easily be condensed. The vapours are cooled in the top part of the retort and the liquid so formed runs down the tube to the opening at A, where it can be collected in a suitable vessel, which is called the *receiver*. You will use a retort when you are making nitric acid (see p. 269).

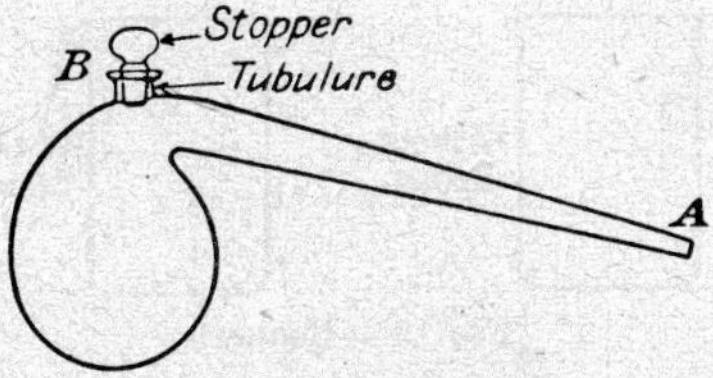

FIG. 3.—Modern Retort.

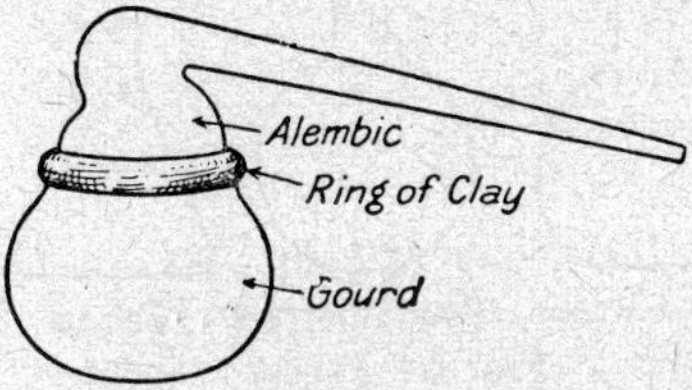

FIG. 4.—Ancient Retort.

Beakers are vessels made of thin glass. They are used to hold liquids which may have to be heated. All glass apparatus which may have to be heated is made with *thin* walls, because glass is a poor conductor and expands as it becomes hot. If the walls were thick, the part next the source of heat would begin to expand before the heat had had time to get right through the wall. You can imagine what would happen. If one part of the glass tried to expand while the neighbouring parts were still cold and therefore not expanding, a strain would be produced and the glass would crack.[1] Sometimes apparatus is made of fused silica, that is, sand which has been melted and then moulded into the required shape. The advantage of silica ware is that sudden changes of temperature do not make it crack, since silica does not expand very much when it is heated. You can make a silica beaker red-hot and then plunge it into cold water without cracking it. Unfortunately, silica vessels are very brittle and comparatively expensive, otherwise they would be used much more.

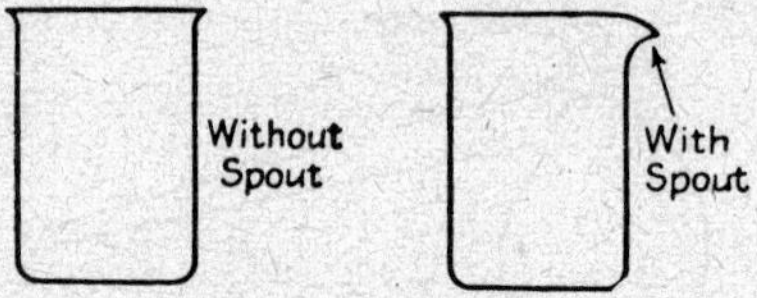

FIG. 5.—Beakers.

Flasks are glass vessels with long necks. They are used for boiling liquids. Some are flat at the bottom, while others are round (Fig. 6). The round ones are more inconvenient than the flat, since the latter will stand on a bench without support, but we generally prefer the round-bottomed ones, since they are not so liable to crack when heated. If you heat a flat-bottomed flask you will often find that it cracks round the edge of the flat piece at the bottom. *Conical flasks*, sometimes called *Erlenmeyer flasks*, after the man who invented them, are shown in Fig. 6. They will stand heat, and are used chiefly in analysis.

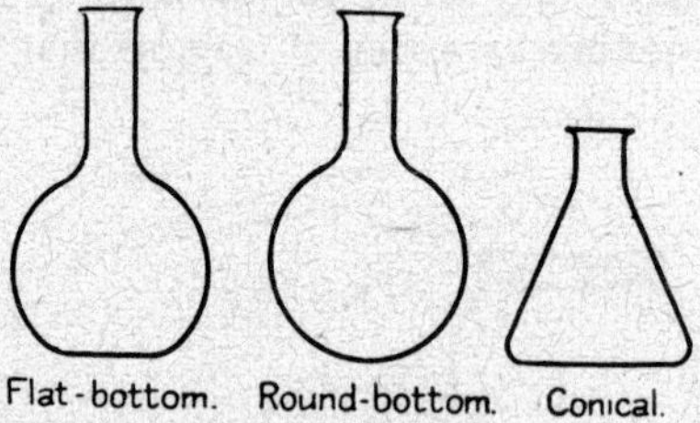

FIG. 6.—Flasks.

[1] As Chaucer says,

"*Ful ofte it happeth so,*
The pot to-breketh, and farewel! al is go!"

Funnels.—There is not much to say about funnels. They are of the usual shape, but are made of glass, and have a solid angle of 60°. This is so that a filter-paper, when folded into quadrants and then opened, as shown in Fig. 7, will exactly fit them. Funnels are used in pouring a liquid into a vessel, and also in filtering. Some funnels have a different shape. They may have a head shaped like a thistle (*thistle-funnels*)

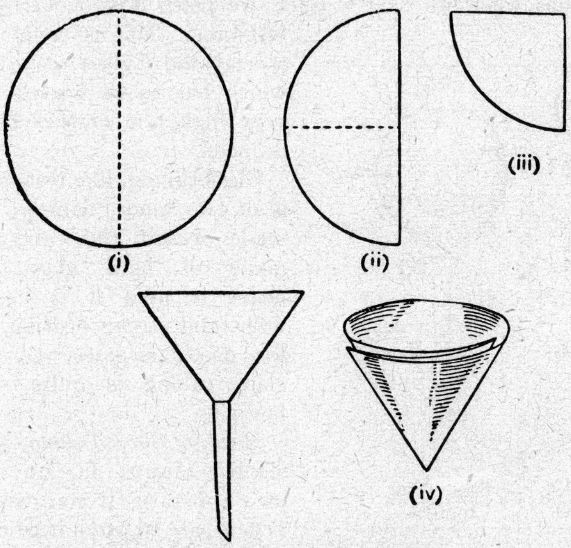

FIG. 7.—Funnel and Filter-paper.

(Fig. 8A), or they may be of the kind shown in Fig. 8B. The latter are called separating or tap funnels, and are used to separate from one another two liquids that do not mix, such as oil and water. In the figure, the top layer in the funnel is oil, and the lower one water. If the tap is turned on and the stopper removed, water runs through, and when it has all passed the tap the latter may be closed. In this way the oil can be separated from the water.

Of all the glass apparatus the *test-tube* is the most useful. As we could guess from its name, it is a tube in which we may make tests or experiments. You should note this carefully for it will save you from the mistake of spelling the word "testube." Ordinary test-tubes are made of soft glass, that is, glass which will melt fairly easily when heated. These may be used for experiments in which heat is not required, or for heating *liquids* in. They should not be used to heat *solids* in, since they would melt. If we want to find what happens when we heat a solid, we place it in a *hard-glass* test-tube. This is made of a special kind of glass (see p. 350) which has to be heated to a very high temperature before it melts.

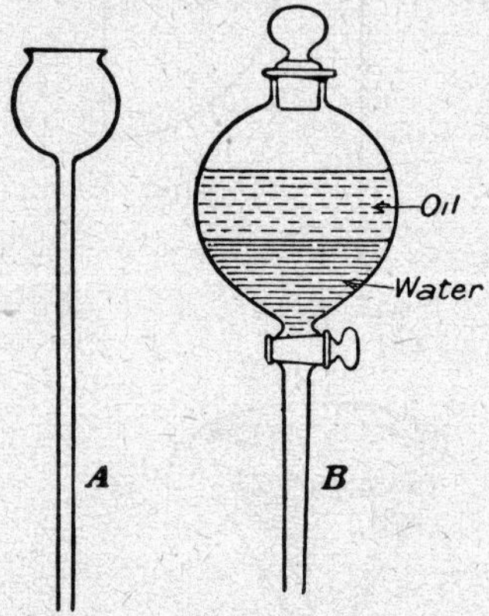

FIG. 8.
Thistle Funnel. Separating Funnel.

Glass tubing, like test-tubes, is of two kinds, namely, that made of soft glass and that made of hard glass. The latter is used if it has to withstand strong heating, but for most purposes the soft-glass tubing is quite satisfactory.

Bending Glass Tubing.—You should always fit up your own apparatus if you can: it is not safe to leave it to other people. You must therefore practise the art of bending glass tubing. The simplest exercise is to make a right-angle bend; this is done as follows. Take a piece of soft-glass tubing, about 4 or 5 millimetres internal diameter, and about a foot in length. See that it is quite dry, inside and out. If there is any moisture inside the tube, remove it by blowing hot air through. You will find in the laboratory a pair of hand-bellows for this purpose: they blow air through an iron tube which is heated by a row of gas-burners. To the end of the iron tube is connected a piece of rubber tubing to which you can attach the piece of glass tubing which you want to dry.

When your glass tubing is dry it is ready for bending. Get a fish-tail burner, that is, one which gives a flat and luminous flame—not an ordinary Bunsen burner—and heat the glass tubing in the flame, holding it at the ends with your hands *underneath* and twisting it round and round continuously

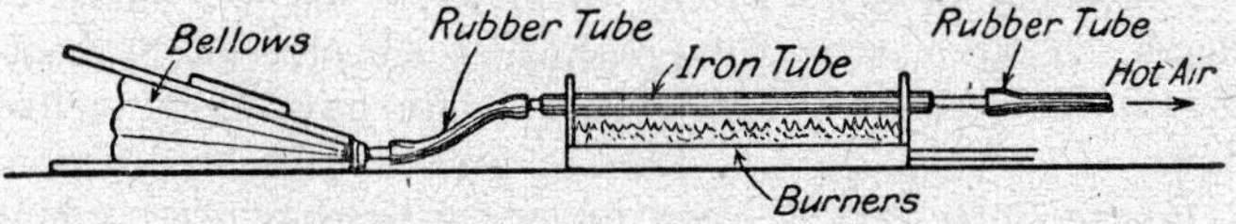

FIG. 9.—Apparatus for drying Glass Tubing, etc.

so as to get it evenly heated. (See Fig. 10.) Go on heating until you feel that the glass in the flame is quite soft, then take the tubing out of the flame and let one end gradually sink by its own weight (do not force it) until the required bend is produced. Before the glass has hardened, make

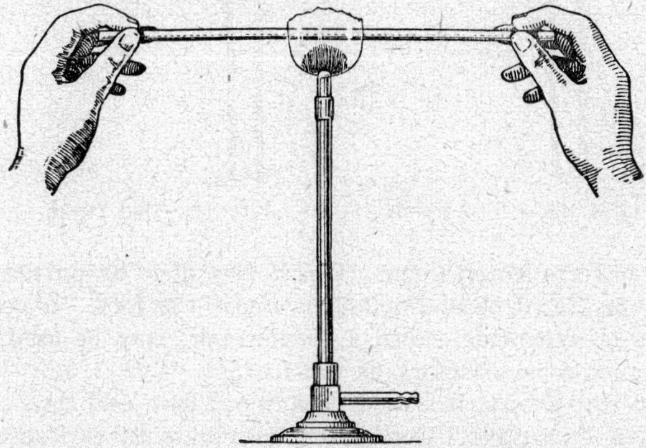

FIG. 10.—Method of holding Tube in Flame.

quite sure that both arms of the bend are in the same plane: try this by putting it down on a piece of asbestos and observing whether it lies flat. If it does not, bend it till it does, gently re-heating if necessary.

If your bend has been well made, the diameter of the tube

in the actual bend will be the same size as that of the rest of the tube (Fig. 11). If, however, you did not get the glass soft enough, or if you got it too soft, or if you forced it round, you will probably find that the tube has partly collapsed, and formed a bad bend such as that shown in Fig. 12.

The edges of glass tubing must never be left sharp or rough. They must be fire-polished, or smoothened by heating in the flame until the sharp edges have been melted down.

Boring Corks.—It is often necessary to pass glass tubing or thermometers through corks, and to make corks fit flasks, tubes, etc. New corks are hard, and will not fit well, so we

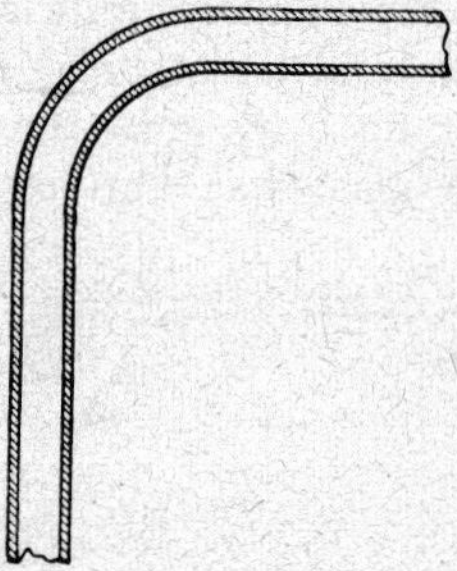

FIG. 11.—Good Bend.

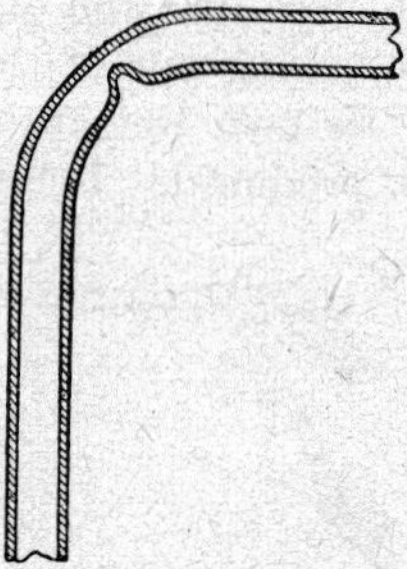

FIG. 12.—Bad Bend.

first have to soften them. This is best done by putting the cork on the floor and rolling it under the foot. A special piece of apparatus, called a cork-presser, may be used, but it is not so satisfactory as the foot.

To bore a cork, it should be softened first, and then bored with a cork-borer. Cork-borers are brass tubes sharpened at the end. They are of various sizes, to make holes for tubes of various diameters. To find which size to use, take your piece of glass tubing and choose a borer which will almost but not quite pass over the tube. Then hold the cork in the left hand, stick the borer in, perpendicularly to the face of the cork, and screw it round gently until it goes right through. *Do not force it through,* or it will tear the cork, and instead of getting a clean cylindrical hole you will get merely a gaping rent.

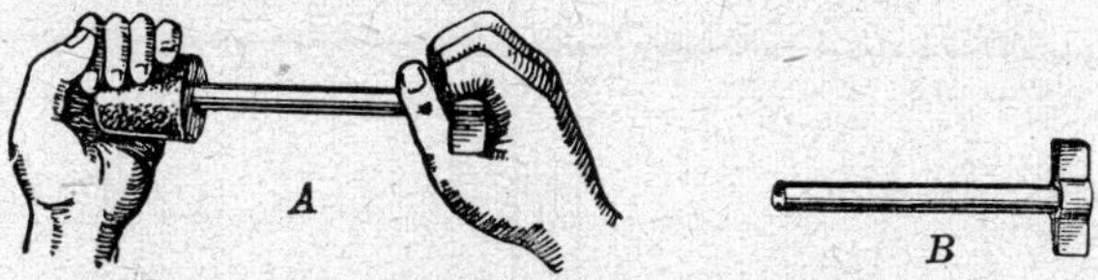

FIG. 13.—*A*. Boring a Cork. *B*. Cork Borer.

After you have bored the cork, push the plug of cork out of the borer by means of the metal rod which you will find in the box of borers.

Rubber Tubing.—Rubber tubing is used for connecting two pieces of glass tubing together. When you are using it for joins in this way, see that the two pieces of glass tubing touch one another inside the rubber (Fig. 14).

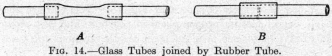

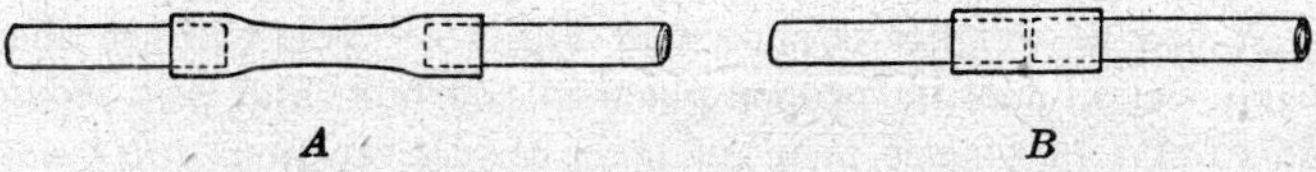

FIG. 14.—Glass Tubes joined by Rubber Tube.
A. Wrong way. *B*. Right way.

The Balance.—The balance is the chemist's chief instrument. It is a delicate piece of work, and should be treated with the utmost respect, as it is very expensive and very easily damaged. It consists of (i) a beam, swinging on a steel or agate knife-edge, and (ii) two scale-pans attached one to each end of the beam by means of metal stirrups. Each stirrup rests on a knife-edge on the beam. From the centre of the beam a pointer projects vertically downwards, its lower end moving over a graduated scale (Fig. 15).

At the ends of the beam are small screws which can be screwed in or out; these are for adjusting the balance so that when both pans are unloaded the pointer comes to rest exactly over the middle of the scale. In order to save the knife-edge, when the balance is not in use the beam is lowered by the handle H and rests on the screws S.

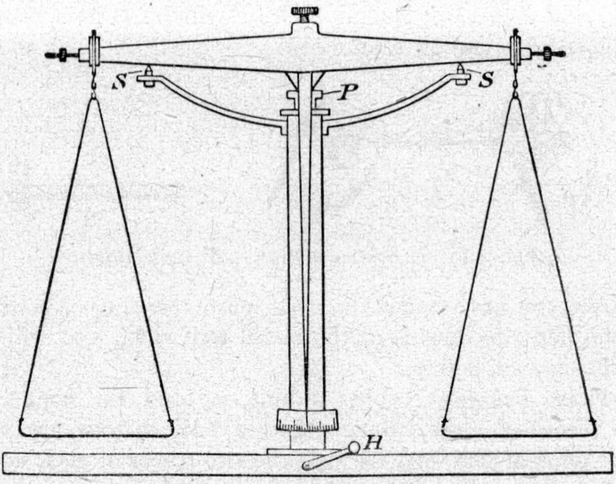

FIG. 15.—A Chemical Balance.

A box of weights is shown in Fig. 16. You will see that each weight has its proper place in the box, and *you should be careful to replace them in their correct positions after use.*

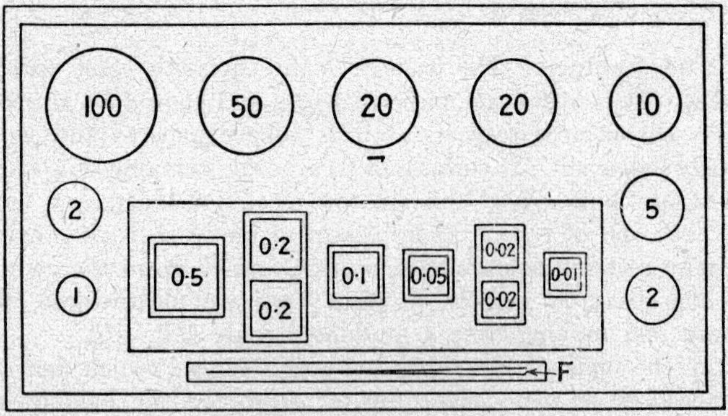

FIG. 16.—Box of Weights.

The use of the balance will be explained to you in the laboratory, but the following rules must be read and observed:

RULES FOR THE USE OF THE BALANCE.

1. No chemicals, however harmless they may appear, are to be weighed directly on the pans, *or on paper*. They must be weighed on watch-glasses or in basins or in some other glass or porcelain apparatus. *There are no exceptions to this rule.*

2. Counterpoising with bits of paper, shot, etc., is forbidden. If the balance is not properly adjusted, *do not attempt to adjust it yourself*, but report to the master or to the laboratory assistant.

3. Never attempt to weigh anything hot.

4. Do not put on or take off weights while the beam is swinging.

5. Unless you are left-handed, put the object to be weighed on the left-hand pan, and the weights on the right-hand pan.

6. Replace the weights in the box *in the proper positions* after use.

7. Weights must be picked up with the forceps, and *not* with the fingers.

8. Close the balance-case after you have finished weighing, or if you have to leave the balance (even if for only a short time).

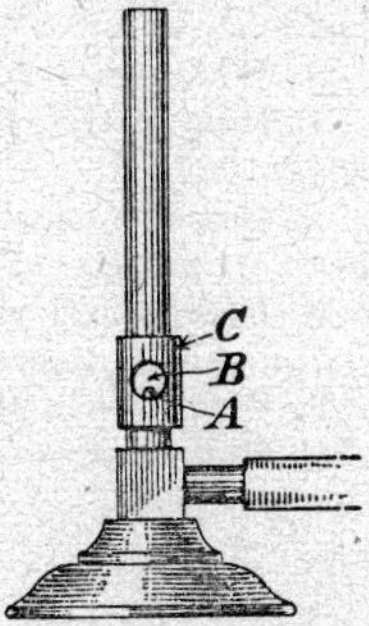

FIG. 17.—Bunsen Burner.

The Bunsen Burner.—After the balance, perhaps the most important piece of apparatus in the laboratory is the Bunsen burner. This was invented by ROBERT BUNSEN (1811–99), a German chemist, and is shown diagrammatically in Fig. 17.

The gas enters through the fine jet *A*, where it mixes with air drawn in through the large hole *B*. *B* may be partly or completely covered by turning round the ring of metal, *C*, which surrounds the base of the tube. At the top of the tube a mixture of gas and air comes off, and when this is lit it burns with a blue non-luminous flame. If all the air is cut off at *B*, the gas will then burn with a luminous flame, while if *B* is fully opened, a very hot, roaring flame is produced. For ordinary purposes, *B* is half open, and the flame is then quite quiet, non-luminous, and not excessively hot. You will find more about "Flame" on p. 345.

The other common pieces of apparatus present no difficulty, and as you will soon meet them all in the laboratory, nothing need be said about them here.

Questions

1. Some people say that when boys and girls are doing practical chemistry they should use jam-jars, saucepans, broken plates and saucers, and so on, instead of the usual apparatus. Do you agree with this or not? Give reasons for your answer.
2. Draw and describe a *retort*. How does it differ from the old-fashioned *alembic*?
3. What are beakers? Why are they made of thin glass?
4. How would you separate from one another two liquids which do not mix?
5. Describe exactly how you would proceed to make a right-angled bend in a piece of glass tubing.
6. How would you bore a cork?
7. Draw a diagram of a balance to show the principal parts.
8. Write down the rules for the use of the balance.
9. Make a drawing of a Bunsen burner and explain how it works.

CHAPTER IV

CHEMICAL AND PHYSICAL CHANGES.

ELEMENTS, COMPOUNDS AND MIXTURES

The changes that matter may undergo are so numerous that the chemist does not attempt to investigate all of them. Those that involve merely a change in position—such as the flight of a bullet or the fall of an apple—he leaves to the physicist. So, again, he is not much interested in the changes that take place when a liquid boils and turns into a gas or vapour, or when a solid melts and turns into a liquid. What the chemist is concerned with is the kind of change which results in one sort of matter being turned into another sort. We shall therefore have to consider at once the distinction that is made between *chemical* changes and *physical* changes.

When a piece of platinum wire is heated in a flame it becomes red-hot or white-hot, and gives out light. On cooling, however, it returns to its original condition, and it has been nothing but platinum all the time. Similarly, when we take a piece of iron and magnetize it, we alter it in some way, for after magnetization it is able to attract other pieces of iron, which it could not do before. If we drop it on the floor several times, we shall find that its magnetism is destroyed, and it becomes as it was originally. Here again, the iron is still iron even when it is magnetized, and remains iron after its magnetism has been removed. Such changes as these are called *physical changes*.

Again, when water is cooled it turns into ice, and when it is boiled it becomes steam. If we analyse ice, water, and steam, we find that they are all of exactly the same composition; in other words, no new sort of matter is formed when water is turned into ice or steam, and so we call this kind of change a physical change too. Solid, liquid, and gas are called three *physical states* of matter, and most substances can be obtained in all three states under appropriate conditions. Thus a solid can usually be melted, forming a liquid, while a liquid may be boiled and so converted into a gas. A gas, too, may be converted into a liquid by cooling, and into a solid by further cooling. Even ordinary air can be turned into a colourless liquid if it is cooled sufficiently, while if liquid air is still further cooled it freezes to a colourless solid. Change of physical state, then, which is merely a matter of adding or removing heat, causes no change in the *composition* of the substance concerned, and is therefore said to be a physical change.

You will notice that it is usually easy to *reverse* a physical change. For example, if you have white-hot platinum, it is easy to get ordinary platinum simply by cooling, while, as we have seen, magnetized iron may be demagnetized merely by dropping it on the floor a few times.

Suppose we take a piece of sulphur and heat it. First of all it melts, and then the liquid sulphur boils. If we cool the vapour we can get liquid sulphur back again, and then solid sulphur. The changes are, in fact, physical ones. But if we heat the sulphur more strongly, and let air get at it, we shall find that it takes fire and burns with a blue flame, giving off a choking gas with a very characteristic smell. After a time, all the sulphur will have disappeared. If we collect the gas which is formed, we shall notice that it is colourless, and that on cooling it to ordinary temperature it does not change in any way. We cannot, in fact, get sulphur back from it merely by reversing the conditions; it is a new sort of matter altogether. This kind of change is therefore different from those we have previously considered; it is, in fact, a *chemical* change. If we weighed the sulphur before we started, and weighed the gas which was formed, we should find that an *increase in weight* had occurred. This is different from what happens in a physical change, for if we freeze 10 grams of water we get 10 grams of ice, and if we magnetize a piece of iron weighing 30 grams we find that the iron after magnetization still weighs 30 grams.

Other examples of chemical changes are the rusting of iron and other metals, the burning of coal, wood, oil, gas, and so on, the decomposition of potassium chlorate by heat, and other reactions which you will carry out in the laboratory. You will find it very easy to distinguish between chemical and physical changes, so we need not talk about them at length here. It will be useful, however, to summarize the chief characteristics of the two kinds of change, so that you can remember them easily:

Physical Changes	Chemical Changes
1. May be merely a change of state, from solid to liquid, liquid to gas, etc.	1. Mere change of state does not involve a chemical change.
2. No new sort of matter formed.	2. New sort or sorts of matter formed.
3. No change in weight.	3. Although the *total* weight of all the substances taking part is unchanged, the *separate* weights of the different substances change. Thus if we take 32 grams of sulphur and burn it in 32 grams of oxygen, we get 64 grams of a new substance, sulphur-dioxide, and 0 grams of sulphur and 0 of oxygen left.
4. Generally easily reversible.	4. Only seldom reversible; generally irreversible.
5. Excluding latent heat, little heat is usually taken in or given out.	5. A chemical change is generally accompanied by the production of heat (and often of light). Sometimes heat is absorbed.

To decide, therefore, whether a given change is physical or chemical, what we really have to do is to find out whether a *new sort of matter* is formed. If so, the change is a chemical one. Suppose, for example, we burn a piece of magnesium ribbon. It burns with a brilliant light, and the residue consists of a white powder very different from the original magnesium. The change is therefore chemical. If we weighed the magnesium we should find that every 24 grams of magnesium gave 40 grams of the white powder.

It might appear, therefore, that in a chemical change, matter is produced out of nothing. Chemists have, however, investigated this question very closely, and their conclusions may be summed up in the words *Matter can neither be created nor destroyed.* This statement is known as the *Law of the Conservation of Matter*, and we shall see that it is of great importance in chemistry.

Let us return to the case of the magnesium. We started, let us suppose, with 24 grams of magnesium, and we got 40 grams of the white powder formed. What is the cause of the increase of weight? We can get a clue to this problem by trying to burn the magnesium in a vacuum. If we attempt to do this, we find that the magnesium refuses to burn. It seems clear, therefore, that we must look for the source of the increase in weight, which takes place when magnesium is burnt in the air, *in the air itself.* If this is so, then if we burn a piece of magnesium in a closed flask, the flask as a whole ought to weigh the same afterwards as before, since what is gained by the magnesium will be lost by the air in the flask. This experiment has been tried by chemists, and the expected result has always been found. You yourselves may carry out similar experiments in the laboratory.

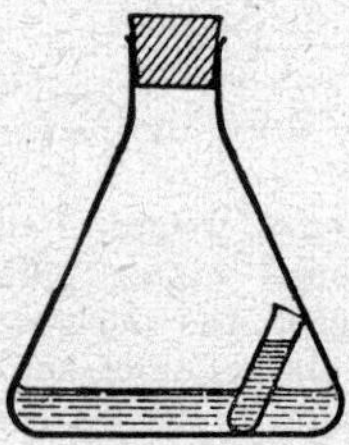

FIG. 18.

(i) Take a clean conical flask and fit it with a rubber stopper. Into the flask put about 20 c.c. of common salt solution, and a small test-tube containing silver nitrate solution (Fig 18). Replace the stopper and weigh the apparatus as accurately as possible. Then tilt the flask so that the two solutions mix. You will find that a chemical action takes place, resulting in the formation of a white precipitate of silver chloride. Weigh the apparatus again.

(ii) Take a clean dry round-bottomed flask, fitted with a rubber stopper, and in it place a *small* piece of yellow phosphorus which you have dried between filter-paper. Replace the stopper firmly. Weigh the apparatus as carefully as you can. Ignite the phosphorus by dipping the bottom of the flask into hot water. Put your thumb on the stopper to make certain that it is not blown out. Allow the flask to cool after the reaction is over, dry it with a clean cloth, and weigh again.

If you find that in these two experiments there is no change in weight, you will be able to conclude that, in these two cases at least, no matter has either been created or destroyed, so that the Law of the Conservation of Matter is confirmed. Of course, some one might object that your balance was not sensitive enough to let you be *quite* certain that no change in weight had occurred. All you can reply to this is that, up to the present, no chemist has been able to detect the creation or destruction of matter, even with the most delicate balance ever constructed. LANDOLT, for example, could find no change in weight even when his apparatus was sensitive enough to detect a loss or gain of one part in ten million. Hence we are perfectly justified in assuming that it cannot be done. However complicated the change may be, it is always found that the *total weight* of all the substances started with is *exactly* equal to the *total weight* of all the substances formed. If this were not so, chemistry could not exist, for chemists would never know what was going to happen.

Various Kinds of Chemical Change.—There are many different kinds of chemical change, the most important of which are—

(i) Combination.
(ii) Decomposition.
(iii) Replacement or Substitution.
(iv) Double Decomposition.

It is easy to understand the difference between them by considering definite examples, all of which will be shown to you in the lectures.

(i) *Combination.*—When two or more substances react

together to form only *one* product, they are said to *combine.* Thus if magnesium is burnt in oxygen, we get a white powder, called magnesium oxide, and nothing else. Magnesium oxide is, in fact, composed of magnesium and oxygen. We may express the change by a chemical "equation"—

Magnesium + oxygen = magnesium oxide.

Other examples are—

(*a*) Phosphorus + iodine = phosphorus iodide.
(*b*) Hydrogen + chlorine = hydrogen chloride.
(*c*) Ammonia + hydrogen chloride = ammonium chloride.

(ii) *Decomposition.*—When one substance splits up into two or more substances it is said to decompose. Thus if mercuric oxide is heated it splits up into mercury and oxygen—

Mercuric oxide = mercury + oxygen.

Other examples are—

By action of heat:
(*a*) Potassium chlorate = potassium chloride + oxygen ↑
(*b*) Sodium bicarbonate = sodium carbonate + water + carbon dioxide ↑.
(*c*) Lead nitrate = lead oxide + oxygen ↑ + nitrogen peroxide ↑.

(iii) *Replacement or Substitution.*—If one substance takes the place of another in a compound, the action is called a replacement. Thus when we add zinc to copper sulphate solution, the zinc turns out the copper, which is precipitated, and we are left with a solution of zinc sulphate—

Copper sulphate + zinc = copper + zinc sulphate.

Other examples are—

(*a*) Copper sulphate + iron = copper + iron sulphate.
(*b*) Silver nitrate + zinc = silver + zinc nitrate.

(iv) *Double Decomposition.*—If we have a compound AB that reacts with another compound CD in such a way that two new compounds, AD and CB, are formed, the action is called a double decomposition. Thus if we add sodium chloride solution to silver nitrate solution, we get a white precipitate of silver chloride, while sodium nitrate is left in solution—

Sodium chloride + silver nitrate
= silver chloride ↓ + sodium nitrate.

Other examples are—

(*a*) Mercuric chloride + potassium iodide
= mercuric iodide ↓ + potassium chloride.

(*b*) Sodium sulphate + barium chloride
= barium sulphate ↓ + sodium chloride.

(*c*) Sodium hydroxide + iron chloride
= iron hydroxide ↓ + sodium chloride.

The reactions given as examples in § iv are all carried out by mixing solutions of the substances on the left-hand side. The sign ↓ indicates that the substance immediately in front of it is insoluble in water, and comes down as a precipitate, *i.e.* is thrown out of the solution as a solid. The sign ↑ indicates that the substance comes off as a gas.

Elements, Compounds and Mixtures

The substances of which the world is composed are divided by chemists into three groups, *elements*, *compounds* and *mixtures*. All three of these names are probably quite familiar to you, but in chemistry they have quite definite meanings, different from those which are attached to them in the everyday language of the people. Thus, when a poet talks about the "strife of the elements" we know he is referring to fire, air, earth, and water. By using the word in this sense, he shows that he is still under the influence of a chemical theory elaborated by Aristotle some 2,000 years ago. According to Aristotle (384–322 B.C.), the greatest scientist of ancient Greece, the multitudinous substances which go to make up the world of nature are each and all composed of four simple substances, *fire*, *air*, *earth* and *water*; these he called the Four Elements. Gold, according to Aristotle, consists of these four elements in a certain proportion; silver also consists of fire, air, earth and water, but in a different proportion, and the same he believed to be true of all other substances. The views of Aristotle were accepted throughout the ages right up to the time of King Charles II, and, as we have seen, traces of them are to be found even at the present day.

However, towards the end of the seventeenth century, the HONOURABLE ROBERT BOYLE wrote a book, called *The Sceptical Chymist*, in which he showed that Aristotle's opinions on the composition of matter were unsatisfactory. Boyle proposed another definition of an element—a definition which has since been universally adopted by chemists. *The Sceptical Chymist* was published in 1661. In it the author says: "I mean by *elements*, as those chymists, that speak plainest, do by their principles, certain primitive and simple, or perfectly unmingled bodies; which not being made of any other bodies, or of one another, are the ingredients of which [all other substances] are immediately compounded, and into which they are ultimately resolved." In other words, an element is a single substance, which cannot be split up into simpler substances.

This is exactly our modern idea of elements. We regard as an "element" any substance which, up to the present, has not been decomposed into two or more constituents. Of course, future research may show that some of those bodies which we regard as elements are not really so; in time to come a chemist may perhaps split up iron, for example, into simpler bodies. This kind of thing has often happened in the past, so that we have learnt to be cautious, and instead of saying "an element is a substance which *cannot* be split up into simpler ones," we say "an element is a substance which has not *yet* been split up."

About 92 elements are known. A table of them is given on p. 437. Common elements are oxygen, hydrogen, carbon, sulphur, gold, silver, iron, lead, tin, copper, mercury and aluminium.

Mixtures and Compounds.—Here, again, you must be careful to understand what exactly the *chemist* means by "mixtures" and "compounds." In everyday life people often use the words as if they meant the same as one another, while you may even see a cough syrup described as a "compound mixture." The chemist, on the other hand, distinguishes between these two classes of substances very carefully indeed, and you must make quite certain that you yourselves can do so. In the laboratory you will carry out experiments on the subject, but meanwhile we can discuss it shortly here: it is by no means difficult, and examiners are very fond of it. In the words of Robert of Chester, *what should I say more?*

Suppose you took a number of thieves and a number of policemen and crowded them all together (without disclosing their identity). Well, you would then have a *mixture* of thieves and policemen. You will see at once (*a*) that the policemen are not attached to the thieves, (*b*) that there is no necessary connection between the number of policemen and that of the thieves, and that therefore (*c*) we could mix any number of thieves with any number of policemen, and (*d*) we could separate the two classes without difficulty. For example, we could draw the thieves out of the crowd by holding up a few diamond tiaras on the outskirts, while immediate separation would occur if we were to blow a whistle in the neighbourhood, the policemen moving rapidly towards the whistle and the thieves distinctly more rapidly in the immediately opposite direction.

In exactly the same way, if we stir up some iron filings with some sulphur powder, we get a *mixture* of the two. With a lens we can still see the particles of each substance —they have not changed in any way. Moreover, there is no limit to the weight of iron which we can mix with a given weight of sulphur, and *vice versa*. Finally, we can separate the iron from the sulphur by passing a magnet over the mixture, which has the same effect on the iron-sulphur mixture as holding up diamond tiaras has on the thieves-policemen mixture. We see another resemblance between the two cases, for the thieves and the policemen, though they happen to be close to one another, have not changed in any way— the thief is still a thief and the policeman a constable.

Now, suppose the policemen were suddenly made aware of the fact that their companions in the crowd were all "wanted." Combination would occur at once. Let us suppose that *one* policeman could manage *one* thief. Then if there were more thieves than policemen, the excess would evaporate, while if there were more policemen than thieves then there would be some policemen left unemployed. During the combination of the thieves with the policemen, heat would probably be evolved: the mass would get white-hot with excitement, and we might expect to see sparks. What would the product be? It would clearly be a collection of particles each consisting of one thief united firmly by handcuffs to a policeman. Note that the *weight* of the thieves need not be the same as the *weight* of the policemen, but if one of the latter weighed 16 stone and a thief 10 stone, then the policeman-thief particle would weigh 26 stone.

How does one of these particles differ in properties from the two "elements" of which it is composed? In the first place, it will no longer be attracted by a diamond tiara, the properties of the thief having been changed by his combination with the policeman. In the second, we can no longer separate the thieves from the policemen merely by blowing a whistle. To separate thieves from policemen we should now have to cut the bond which unites them, *i.e.* to cut through the handcuffs.

Let us now return to the iron and sulphur. If we heat the mixture the iron and sulphur appear to become acquainted with the fact that they are in close proximity, and they *combine* together, the mass becoming incandescent. Each extremely minute particle of iron (the *atoms* of iron, about which you will read in Chapter VII) captures one atom or minute particle of sulphur, and a new substance is formed, the tiny particles of which each consist of one particle of sulphur and one of iron. Now, if there are more sulphur atoms than iron atoms, the excess of sulphur will vaporize and be driven off, while if there are more iron atoms than sulphur atoms, the excess of iron atoms will be left. You see that the parallel with the thieves and policemen is very close.

The new substance which is formed is *iron sulphide*. What

properties does it possess? In the first place, it is no longer attracted by a magnet, just as the combination thief + policeman is no longer attracted by a tiara. The fact that the thief is closely bound to the policeman alters his properties, and the fact that an iron atom is closely bound to a sulphur atom alters the properties of the iron atom.

We saw, above, that if a thief weighs 10 stone and a policeman 16 stone, every stone of thief is equivalent to 1·6 stone of policeman. Hence if we had 100 stone of thieves to capture we should want 160 stone of policemen to do it, supposing that all thieves are alike in weight and all policemen similarly. The same sort of thing is true about the iron and the sulphur. Each iron atom weighs $1\frac{3}{4}$ times as much as a sulphur atom. Hence, if we want to convert 1 gram of sulphur into iron sulphide we must use 1·75 grams of iron, or else we shall have some sulphur or some iron left over.

Finally, although the thief-policeman compound contains both thief and policeman, they cannot easily be separated from one another. They are held together by a bond. So are the iron and sulphur in iron sulphide. The bond in this case is called *chemical force*. What exactly this force is we do not know. We do know, however, that to snap the chemical bonds between substances cannot be done by any mechanical means, such as magnetic force, or by using a pair of forceps, or by dissolving in water and filtering, etc. To break chemical bonds we have to bring about a chemical change, either by the action of heat or by making the substance react with other substances.

We are now in a position to sum up the main differences between mixtures and compounds.

1. *The composition of a mixture may vary, but the composition of all specimens of the same compound is always the same.*

If we mix sand and salt, no chemical reaction occurs, and the proportion in which we mix the two substances can be varied at will. Similarly, if we mix hydrogen and oxygen we can do so in any proportion we like; but if we make hydrogen and oxygen *combine* to form a compound, water, we shall find that they do so in certain definite proportions by weight (1 of hydrogen to 8 of oxygen) which it is quite beyond the power of any chemist to alter.

2. *The constituents of a compound can never be separated by mechanical means, while those of a mixture may be.*

This is because the constituents of a compound are bound together by chemical force, whereas those of a mixture are not.

3. *In a mixture, each constituent retains its own properties, but the properties of a compound are different from those of its constituents.*

Thus, sand is a gritty substance insoluble in water, and sugar is a sweet substance soluble in water. If we taste a mixture of sugar and sand we can detect both the gritty sand and the sweet sugar, while if we add some of the mixture to water, the sugar dissolves and the sand does not. We should expect this, for by merely mixing the sand and the sugar together we have not altered the particles of either, and therefore we should be surprised if either of them showed any alteration in chemical properties.

When, however, we *combine* hydrogen with oxygen, we get a *new sort of substance* altogether, and we find that the properties of water differ considerably from those of hydrogen and from those of oxygen.

4. *Compounds are the product of chemical reaction.* Now chemical reaction is usually accompanied by evolution of heat (in a few cases by absorption of heat). To split up a compound into its constituents we should therefore expect to have to supply at least as much heat as was given out when it was formed. This is found to be the case. *If, in practice, we find that on adding one substance to another, heat is evolved* (or, rarely, absorbed) we suspect that a chemical reaction has occurred, and that the product is a *chemical compound.* There are many other factors to consider here, but we shall be safe in taking evolution of much heat as a rough indication of chemical change. (Evolution of heat due to the condensation of a vapour or the freezing of a solid must, of course,

be neglected; these changes do not involve the formation of new substances.)

Mixtures, then, are composed of two or more substances not held together by chemical force. They may be *mixtures of elements*, or *mixtures of elements and compounds*, or *mixtures of compounds.*

Compounds are substances composed of two or more elements bound together by chemical force.

[*On revising, read the following paragraph:*

When you have studied the atomic theory, you will realize that *elements* consist of one kind of *atom* only, compounds consist of one kind of *molecule* only, and mixtures consist of *at least two different kinds of molecules.* Now, to separate a molecule into its constituent atoms we have to overcome the chemical force which holds those atoms together. To do this requires a chemical action; in other words, if the constituents of a compound are regarded as the elements of which it is composed, it is impossible to separate that compound into its constituents by purely *mechanical* means, *i.e.* means which do not involve a chemical reaction. The constituents of a mixture, however, if we regard these as the various substances which have been mixed together, are not bound together by chemical force, and therefore can, in theory, always be separated by merely mechanical means, since there is no chemical force to overcome. In practice, certain mixtures may prove difficult to separate mechanically into their constituents, because there may be no suitable mechanical means available; such a separation is, however, always theoretically possible, whereas the decomposition of a *compound* into its constituents by mechanical means is theoretically and practically *impossible.*]

In the laboratory, you will conduct experiments on the separation of mixtures such as sand and sugar, gunpowder, aniline and benzene, water and alcohol, iron and sulphur, into their constituents. You should refer also to the discussion on the nature of *air*, p. 190.

Questions

1. What are the chief characteristics of (*a*) physical changes, (*b*) chemical changes ?

2. State whether the following are physical changes or chemical changes, giving your reasons in each case :

(*a*) Magnetization of iron.
(*b*) Burning of magnesium in air.
(*c*) Melting of ice.
(*d*) Condensation of steam to water.
(*e*) Explosion of a mixture of hydrogen and oxygen.
(*f*) Dissolving salt in water.
(*g*) Conversion of sugar into barley-sugar.

3. State the *Law of the Conservation of Matter,* and describe experiments to illustrate its truth.

4. How may chemical changes be classified ? Mention two examples of each type.

5. Define the term *elements.* Who first invented the modern definition of an element ?

6. What were Aristotle's ideas on the structure of matter ? Criticize them in the light of your own knowledge of chemistry.

7. What are the principal differences between mixtures and compounds ?

8. Is gunpowder a mixture or a compound ? Give your reasons.

9. How would you attempt to find out whether a given substance was a mixture or a compound ?

CHAPTER V

THE GAS LAWS

If you place a toy balloon, fully inflated, in front of the fire, your carelessness is startled by an explosion—the balloon has burst. In order to find out why it burst, try the experiment again with another balloon; but this time watch it and see what happens. You will find that, like the frog in the fable, the balloon begins to swell, and continues until at last the skin can withstand the pressure no longer and suddenly breaks. From this pleasant scientific investigation you can gather a very important fact, namely, that *gases expand when they are heated.* On the other hand, when gases are cooled, their volume becomes smaller: in other words, they *contract.*

Roughly, then, we may say that, if we are dealing with a given weight, or mass, of a gas, its volume will depend upon the temperature. The higher the temperature the greater the volume will be, and conversely. Numerous experiments by many different chemists have shown that this is true for *all* gases, whatever they may be, and the French scientist, CHARLES, made it his business to find out *how much* the volume of a gas was changed by changes of temperature. He and later workers finally discovered that *the volume of a given mass of gas varies directly as the Absolute temperature if the pressure is kept constant* (*i.e.* not allowed to change). This statement is known as **Charles's Law,** though Charles himself expressed the law differently.

What exactly does this Law mean? In the first place, let us settle the question of "Absolute Temperature." On the ordinary Centigrade scale, the freezing-point of water is

0° and its boiling-point 100°. The Absolute scale has degrees of the same size, *i.e.* there are 100 of them between the freezing- and boiling-points of water, but it starts 273° lower than the Centigrade scale. Hence, 0° C. is 273° Abs., and — 273° C. is 0° Abs. All we have to do, therefore, to find the Absolute temperature of a substance is to add 273 to the temperature in degrees Centigrade. Suppose the temperature of a gas was 15° C. What would its Absolute temperature be? Well, $15 + 273 = 288$, so that its Absolute temperature would be 288°.

The next point is: what does "varies directly as" mean? Two quantities are said to *vary directly* as one another when, if one of them is increased or decreased in a certain proportion, the other is also increased or decreased in the same proportion. Thus, the number of buns you can buy in the break varies directly as the number of pennies you have to spend. If you double the number of pennies, you double the number of buns; if you halve the number of pennies, you halve the number of buns, and so on.

In exactly the same way, two quantities are said to vary inversely as one another when, if one of them is *increased* in a certain proportion, the other is *decreased* in that proportion, and conversely. Thus, the number of the aforesaid buns which you can get for a shilling varies inversely as their price. If (*absit omen!*) the price of buns is doubled you can get only half as many for a shilling as you could before; if, taking a more optimistic view, the price of buns were to be halved, you could get twice as many for a shilling as you did originally. The sign which the mathematicians use to save themselves the trouble of writing "varies as" is $\propto$, so that $a \propto b$ means "a varies directly as b." On the other hand, $a \propto \frac{1}{b}$ is a short way of saying "a varies inversely as b."

The only other thing to notice in Charles's Law is that the pressure must be kept constant if the law is to hold. This is because changes of pressure in themselves affect the volumes of gases, so that clearly we must not allow the pressure to change if we want to find the effect of change of temperature only. Similarly, when we are investigating the effect of change of pressure upon the volume of a gas, we must keep the temperature constant.

To express Charles's Law simply, we may write that, for a given mass of gas,

$$V \propto T \text{ when } P \text{ is constant,}$$

V being the volume, T the ABSOLUTE temperature, and P the pressure.

Let us now apply the Law.

EXAMPLES.—(i) A gas occupies 72 c.c. at 15° C. What will be its volume at 100° C.?

The first thing to do is to change the Centigrade temperatures to Absolute temperatures. 15° C. = (273 + 15)° Abs. = 288° Abs.; 100° C. = (273 + 100)° Abs. = 373° Abs.

Now, we are taking the gas from 288° to 373°, *i.e.* we are heating it. Hence it will expand, and so its final volume will be greater than its original one. By Charles's Law, since the temperature has been increased by $\frac{373}{288}$, the volume must also be increased in the same proportion.

$$\therefore \text{ New volume} = \text{original volume} \times \frac{373}{288}$$

$$= \frac{72 \times 373}{288} \text{ c.c.}$$

$$= 93{\cdot}3 \text{ c.c.}$$

(ii) A gas occupies 1,000 c.c. at 0° C. To what temperature must it be heated so that it may occupy 2,000 c.c.?

Change the temperature to ° Abs. 0° C. = (273 + 0)° Abs. = 273° Abs.

Let $x°$ = new temperature Abs.

Then $$\frac{1{,}000 \times x}{273} = 2{,}000, \text{ by Charles's Law.}$$

$$\therefore x = 546° \text{ Abs.}$$

$$= (546 - 273)° \text{ C.} = 273° \text{ C.}$$

(iii) A gas occupies 450 c.c. at 27° C. What will its volume be at − 171° C.?

Change the temperatures to ° Abs.

$$27° \text{ C.} = (273 + 27)° \text{ Abs.} = 300° \text{ Abs.}$$

$$-171° \text{ C.} = (273 - 171)° \text{ Abs.} = 102° \text{ Abs.}$$

As the gas is to be cooled it will contract; therefore the larger of the two temperature numbers must go at the bottom in the expression.

$$\text{New volume} = \frac{450 \times 102}{300}$$
$$= 153 \text{ c.c.}$$

In all three of these examples, it has of course been assumed that the pressure was constant throughout.

Boyle's Law.—The "father of chemistry, and brother of the Earl of Cork," was the HONOURABLE ROBERT BOYLE who in 1662 discovered how the volume of a gas changes with variations in pressure. He showed (*Boyle's Law*) that the *volume of a given mass of gas varies inversely as the pressure upon it, if the temperature is constant.* Gas pressure is measured in terms of the length of a column of mercury which the pressure could support. Thus, a "pressure of 100 mm." means a pressure which could support a vertical column of mercury 100 mm. high. For higher pressures, a larger unit, the "*atmosphere,*" is used; it is equal to the average pressure of the earth's atmosphere at sea-level, viz. 760 mm. The pressure of 760 mm. is also called *Normal* or *Standard* Pressure.

If we assume Boyle's Law, we can calculate what volume a gas would occupy at any desired pressure, if we know what its volume is at one particular pressure. Suppose a gas to occupy 100 c.c. at 500 mm. pressure. What volume would it occupy at 760 mm.? Since the pressure will be *greater*, the volume will be *less*, and therefore we must put the larger pressure at the bottom in the expression.

$$\text{New volume} = \frac{100 \times 500}{760} = 65{\cdot}7 \text{ c.c.}$$

If you always ask yourself first whether the final volume, in calculations on Boyle's and Charles's Laws, will be greater or smaller, and arrange the factors of your expression accordingly, you will never go wrong.

Boyle's Law may be shortly expressed thus:

$$V \propto \frac{1}{P} \text{ if T is constant.}$$

The Honourable Robert Boyle.

It follows from Boyle's Law and Charles's Law together that the *pressure exerted by a gas is directly proportional to the* ABSOLUTE *temperature if the volume is constant,* or P $\propto$ Abs. T if V is constant.

Normal or Standard Temperature and Pressure.—We have seen that normal or standard pressure is taken as 760 mm. of mercury. Normal or standard temperature is taken as 0° C., the temperature of melting ice; this is, of course, 273° Absolute.

N.T.P. or S.T.P. is used as a contraction for normal or standard temperature and pressure, *i.e.* 0° C. and 760 mm.

Correction of the Volume of a Gas saturated with Water-vapour.—If a gas is allowed to stand in contact with water, it finally becomes saturated with water-vapour. It is therefore no longer pure, but a mixture of the gas with water-vapour. The total pressure of a gas in this condition will therefore be made up of two pressures, *viz.* (*a*) the pressure of the gas itself, and (*b*) the pressure of the water-vapour. Now the pressure of water-vapour in contact with liquid water is found to be constant at constant temperature. Tables have been drawn up giving the "pressure of aqueous vapour," or "vapour pressures of water" at different temperatures, and by reference to them we can at once find the pressure of the water-vapour in a gas saturated with the latter at a known temperature. If the gas is collected under atmospheric pressure, the real pressure of the gas itself will be the atmospheric pressure *minus* the pressure of water-vapour at the temperature concerned.

EXAMPLE.—Suppose we have 100 c.c. of a moist gas at 15° C. when the barometer reads 770 mm. What will be its volume *dry* at N.T.P.? First, look up the pressure of water-vapour at 15° C. This is found to be 12·7 mm. Therefore the true pressure of the gas is 770 — 12·7 = 757·3 mm. The rest of the correction is then made in the usual way.

N.B.—It takes some considerable time for a gas collected over water in the usual way to become saturated with water-vapour, so that it is generally better *not* to apply this correction in ordinary laboratory experiments (except in examinations, where examiners always expect you to do it).

Questions

1. State Boyle's Law and Charles's Law.

2. What do you mean by Normal Temperature and Pressure ?

3. A gas occupies a volume of 19·0 c.c. at a pressure of 800 mm.; what volume will it occupy at a pressure of 760 mm. if the temperature is kept constant ?

4. The volume of a gas in a cylinder is 35·0 c.c. when the pressure is 720 mm. If the pressure is increased to 750 mm., the temperature being kept constant, what will be the new volume of the gas ?

5. When subjected to a pressure equivalent to 700 mm. of mercury, a gas occupies a volume of 11·0 c.c. The pressure is now increased until the volume is reduced to 10·0 c.c. ; what is this final pressure, assuming that the temperature remained constant throughout the experiment ?

6. A volume of gas at a pressure of 729·5 mm. occupies 124·0 c.c. ; what volume will it occupy at 760 mm. pressure if the temperature is kept constant ?

7. What volume will a gas occupy at 760 mm. pressure if it occupies 51·2 c.c. when the pressure is 789·4 mm., the temperature being kept constant ?

8. If a gas occupies 25·0 c.c. at a temperature of 27° C., what volume will it occupy at 0° C. if the pressure remains constant ?

9. A gas occupies 96·0 c.c. at 15° C. Find its volume at 0° C. if the pressure remains constant.

10. At 45° C. a gas occupies 214·0 c.c. ; what will its volume be at 0° C. if the pressure is the same ?

11. A volume of gas at a temperature of 80° C. occupies 21·0 c.c. The temperature is now lowered, the pressure being kept constant, until the volume of the gas has been reduced to 18·0 c.c. Find the final temperature.

12. Find the volume at 0° C. of a gas which occupies 106·0 c.c. at 28° C., the pressure being the same at both temperatures.

13. Find the volume at S.T.P. (0° C. and 760 mm.) of a gas which occupies 102·0 c.c. at 33° C. under a pressure of 780 mm.

14. At 27° C. and under a pressure of 750 mm., a gas occupies a volume of 38·0 c.c. Find its volume at N.T.P.

15. At 12° C. and 775 mm. pressure a gas occupies 361·0 c.c. Find its volume at N.T.P.

16. A gas occupies a volume of 22·6 c.c. at a temperature of 18° C. and a pressure equivalent to 754 mm. of mercury ; what will its volume be at 0° C. and 760 mm. pressure ?

17. Find the volume at 0° C. and 760 mm. pressure of a gas which occupies 51·2 c.c. at 23° C. and 765 mm. pressure.

18. A volume of gas collected over water was found to measure 38·0 c.c. at atmospheric pressure. The temperature of the water

was 12° C., and the height of the barometer was 760·51 mm. Find the volume of the gas at S.T.P. (0° C. and 760 mm.) to the nearest c.c.

19. A gas collected over water at 21° C. occupied 133·0 c.c. at atmospheric pressure, the height of the barometer being 792·12 mm. Find the volume of the gas at S.T.P.

20. What volume will a gas occupy at N.T.P. if it is found to occupy 57·4 c.c. when standing over water at 15° C., the levels being equated so that the gas was at atmospheric pressure? The height of the barometer was 775·58 mm.

21. Find the volume at N.T.P. of a gas which, collected over water, occupies 156·2 c.c. at 14·5 C. and atmospheric pressure. The height of the barometer was 761·98 mm.

22. The following data were obtained in a Victor Meyer experiment:

Volume of air in graduated tube after levelling	64·9 c.c.
Temperature of water	17·2 C.
Height of barometer	767·41 mm.

Find the volume of the air reduced to N.T.P.

23. A volume of gas collected in a graduated cylinder over water measured 22·6 c.c. when the levels of the water inside and outside the cylinder were the same. The temperature of the water was 11·2° C., and the height of the barometer was 769·17 mm. Find the volume of the gas at S.T.P.

CHAPTER VI

EQUIVALENTS

When I send the lab.-boy to the grubber [1] in break to get me a couple of buns, I find that it is necessary to provide him with threepence every time. It is, unfortunately, not possible to obtain an unlimited supply of buns for one threepenny-bit : two buns are strictly *equivalent* to three pennies. This is an example of a great truth which applies also in the less vitally important subject of chemistry. For example, when I dissolve magnesium in dilute sulphuric acid I find that a definite quantity of sulphuric acid—say 98 grams of the pure acid—will not go on dissolving magnesium for ever. This quantity of acid will dissolve up to 24 grams of magnesium, but there it stops, and the reason is not far to seek—at this point there is none of the acid left. The 24 grams of magnesium and 98 grams of sulphuric acid have been converted into hydrogen and magnesium sulphate. If we measure the volume of hydrogen, we shall be able to calculate its weight, since 1 litre of hydrogen at N.T.P. weighs 0·09 grams ; in this case we should find that exactly 2 grams were obtained. Similarly, the weight of magnesium sulphate could be determined by suitable means : it would be found to be 120 grams. Proportionate weights of sulphuric acid would dissolve proportionate weights of magnesium, and yield proportionate weights of hydrogen and magnesium sulphate.

The same sort of thing is true of all chemical reactions —you will do experiments in the laboratory to convince yourselves that it is so. Substances, in fact, react with one another in perfectly definite weights, and it would be as

[1] Or tuckshop.

fruitless to expect 98 grams of sulphuric acid to dissolve more than 24 grams of magnesium as to hope to get more than twelve pennies for one shilling. The laws of the Medes and Persians are not to be compared in rigidity to this law of chemistry.

In order to express the fact that 24 grams of magnesium require just 98 grams of sulphuric acid to dissolve them, and that the products are 2 grams of hydrogen and 120 grams of magnesium sulphate, we say that 24 grams of magnesium are *equivalent* to 98 grams of sulphuric acid or to 2 grams of hydrogen or to 120 grams of magnesium sulphate. The given weights of all the above substances are, in fact, severally equivalent to one another.

Now, in daily life, in order to have some standard by which to compare the values of different substances—in order, for example, to know how many pounds of potatoes are equivalent to one Rolls-Royce, or how many tons of coal are equivalent to an orchestra stall at Drury Lane, we have to adopt a certain unit in terms of which we can express the " equivalents " of all the various objects concerned. This unit is the pound sterling (£). If we know that the equivalent of a Rolls-Royce on this system is £2,000, and that the equivalent of a pound of potatoes is £0·005, it follows that one Rolls-Royce is equivalent to 400,000 pounds of potatoes. In the same way we can express the " equivalents " of any other objects in terms of the £. The convenience of such an arrangement is obvious, and its merits are so great that we have adopted an analogous system in chemistry.

Definition of Equivalent.—We take as our standard substance the lightest known element, hydrogen, and define the equivalent of any other substance as *that* **number** *of units of weight of it which will react either directly or indirectly with one of the same units of weight of hydrogen.* On this system the equivalent of sulphuric acid is 49, since when hydrogen is liberated from sulphuric acid, 49 grams of the acid always yield 1 gram of hydrogen; or when 49 ounces (or tons) of the acid are used, they yield 1 ounce (or ton, as the case may be) of hydrogen, and so on.

Note that the equivalent of a substance is a *number* only; it is incorrect to say that the equivalent of sulphuric acid is 49 *grams*—it is NOT 49 *grams* but just 49. When we say that the equivalent of sulphuric acid, then, is 49, we mean that 49 grams, grains, ounces, pounds or tons of it will react with evolution of 1 gram, grain, ounce, pound or ton respectively of hydrogen. Similarly, the equivalent of oxygen is the *number* of units of weight of it which will combine with one of the same units of weight of hydrogen. Thus, although the unit of weight commonly used in chemistry is the gram, the equivalent of a substance is a *number* only. When we mean a definite *weight* of the substance, we talk about its *gram*-equivalent, *i.e.* its equivalent expressed in grams. Thus, the equivalent of potassium is 39, but its *gram*-equivalent is 39 *grams*. We can also use *ton*- or *ounce*-equivalents if we like, but this is not often necessary, as we usually work in grams. Once again, therefore, remember that

Equivalent = a **Number** only.

Gram-Equivalent = a **Weight**—*viz.* the equivalent expressed in grams.

Methods of Determining Equivalents.

(i) Some elements, such as oxygen and chlorine, combine directly with hydrogen. The equivalents of these elements may therefore be determined by taking a known weight of the element, converting it into its compound with hydrogen, and finding the weight of the compound. From the figures so obtained the equivalent can be calculated.

EXAMPLE.—9·85 *grams of an element A were made to combine with hydrogen. The weight of the compound so formed was* 11·08 *grams. What is the equivalent of A?*

If 9·85 grams of A yield 11·08 grams of its compound with hydrogen, then 9·85 grams of A have combined with 11·08 — 9·85 grams of hydrogen = 1·23 grams.

Now the equivalent of A will be the *number* of grams of it which combine with 1 gram of hydrogen.

$\therefore$ since 1·23 grams of hydrogen combine with 9·85 grams of A,

1 gram „ „ combines „ $\frac{9 \cdot 85 \times 1}{1 \cdot 23}$ „ „

= 8 grams.

8 grams is therefore the *gram*-equivalent of A, and the *equivalent* of A is 8.

Alternatively, this method could be employed in the reverse direction, that is, a known weight of the compound of A with hydrogen could be taken and treated in such a way that the hydrogen was removed and the element A left. If the residual weight of A were found, we should have all the necessary figures, and could work out the equivalent in the way shown above.

(ii) Some elements again—such as zinc and magnesium—will dissolve in a dilute acid, liberating hydrogen in the process. Here, we could determine the equivalent of the element by taking a known weight of it, dissolving it in a dilute acid, and finding the weight of hydrogen liberated. From our results we could work out the number of grams of the element required to liberate 1 gram of hydrogen and hence get the equivalent.

EXAMPLE.—0·304 *grams of a metal were dissolved in dilute sulphuric acid. The weight of the hydrogen liberated was found to be* 0·008 *grams. What is the equivalent of the metal?*

0·008 grams of hydrogen were liberated by 0·304 grams of the metal,

$\therefore$ 1 gram „ „ would be „ by $\frac{0 \cdot 304 \times 1}{0 \cdot 008}$ „ „ „

= 38 grams.

The *gram*-equivalent of the metal is therefore 38 grams, and its *equivalent* 38.

It is, of course, much easier to measure the *volume* of the hydrogen which comes off than its *weight*, but since we know that 1 litre of hydrogen at N.T.P. weighs 0·09 grams, we can easily *calculate* the weight of any volume of hydrogen if we know its temperature and pressure.

EXAMPLE.—0·57 *grams of a metal yielded* 105 *c.c. of hydrogen, measured at* 15° *C.* 740 *mm. pressure. What is the equivalent of the metal?*

105 c.c. at 15° C. 740 mm. become $\frac{105 \times 273 \times 740}{288 \times 760}$ at N.T.P.

= 96·9 c.c.

∴ 1,000 c.c. of hydrogen at N.T.P. weigh 0·09 grams.

∴ 96·9 „ „ „ „ $\frac{0{\cdot}09 \times 96{\cdot}9}{1{,}000}$ grams.

Since $\frac{0{\cdot}09 \times 96{\cdot}9}{1{,}000}$ grams of hydrogen are liberated by 0·57 grams of metal,

∴ 1 gram of hydrogen would be liberated by $\frac{0{\cdot}57 \times 1{,}000}{0{\cdot}09 \times 96{\cdot}9}$ „ „

= 65·4 grams.

The *gram*-equivalent of the metal is therefore 65·4 grams, and its *equivalent* 65·4.

(iii) Many elements, however, will neither combine directly with hydrogen nor liberate it from a dilute acid. In these cases we attack the problem by an indirect method. Oxygen will combine with hydrogen, and we can therefore measure its equivalent directly. Experiments have shown that 8 grams of oxygen will combine with 1 gram of hydrogen; therefore the equivalent of oxygen is 8. Now, although it may be impossible to get an element to combine with hydrogen or to liberate hydrogen from a dilute acid, it is almost always possible to make it combine with oxygen, and the number of grams of it which will combine with 8 grams of oxygen is taken as its equivalent, since 8 grams of oxygen combine with 1 of hydrogen. In short, we assume that *the weights of two substances which are separately equivalent to a constant weight of a third are also equivalent to one another.* Is this assumption justifiable? Well, we can test its validity in some instances. For example, 12 grams of carbon are combined with 32 grams of oxygen in carbon dioxide. We therefore assume that the equivalent of carbon is $\frac{12}{4}$ (*i.e.* 3), since the equivalent of oxygen is 8. Now we can also get carbon to form a compound with hydrogen, and by analysis of this substance we can calculate the equivalent of carbon directly. By this method it is found to be 3—the same value as we obtained before. Hence our assumption was justified in this instance, and it has been justified in many other cases as well. It has never been known to fail, in fact, so that even in those cases where we cannot test it we may feel confident that it still holds good.

EXAMPLES.—(i) 0·374 *grams of a metal yielded* 0·446 *grams of its oxide. What is the equivalent of the metal? Equivalent of oxygen* = 8.

0·446 grams of the oxide contain 0·374 grams of the metal.

Hence the weight of oxygen they contain is 0·446 − 0·374 = 0·072 grams.

If 0·072 grams of oxygen combine with 0·374 grams of metal,

$$\therefore \quad 8 \quad ,, \quad ,, \quad ,, \quad ,, \quad \frac{0{\cdot}374 \times 8}{0{\cdot}072} \quad ,, \quad ,,$$

$$= 41{\cdot}6 \text{ grams.}$$

The equivalent of the metal is therefore 41·6.

(ii) 0·256 *grams of an element combined with* 0·183 *grams of chlorine. What is the equivalent of the element? Equivalent of chlorine* = 35·5.

If 0·183 grams of chlorine combined with 0·256 grams of the element,

$$\therefore \quad 35{\cdot}5 \quad ,, \quad ,, \text{ would combine with } \frac{0{\cdot}256 \times 35{\cdot}5}{0{\cdot}183} \quad ,, \quad ,,$$

$$= 49{\cdot}6 \text{ grams.}$$

The equivalent of the element is therefore 49·6.

Equivalents of Compounds.—The idea of equivalents is not confined to elements; compounds, too, may cause hydrogen to take part indirectly or directly in a chemical change, and hence their equivalents may be determined. Like that of an element, the equivalent of a compound is the number of units of weight of it which will react either directly or indirectly with one of the same units of weight of hydrogen.

The equivalent of a compound is determined by making use of some convenient reaction in which the compound takes part. Thus, the equivalent of sulphuric acid is the number of grams of it which will yield 1 gram of hydrogen, *e.g.* on treatment with zinc. If the equivalent of sulphuric acid be known, then the number of grams of caustic soda which the equivalent in grams of sulphuric acid will neutralize is the equivalent of caustic soda. By continuing this process, the equivalent of any compound may be discovered. It follows that, if two substances react together, they will do so in the proportion by weight of their equivalents, since their equivalents have been determined in this way. This property is made use of in volumetric analysis, experiments on which you will carry out in the laboratory. A *normal solution* of a substance, for instance, is one which contains the gram-equivalent of the substance in a litre of solution. Hence, *equal volumes of all normal solutions are exactly equivalent to one another*, and the same applies to equal volumes of all *deci-normal* $\left(\frac{N}{10}\right.$, *i.e.* tenth-normal) solutions, and so on. Thus, 10 c.c. of N-hydrochloric acid will neutralize exactly 10 c.c. of N-caustic soda or N-caustic potash, or 100 c.c. of $\frac{N}{10}$ caustic soda or potash; and 25 c.c. of $\frac{N}{2}$, or half-normal sodium carbonate, will neutralize exactly 25 c.c. of $\frac{N}{2}$ sulphuric acid or $\frac{N}{2}$ nitric acid or $\frac{N}{2}$ oxalic acid or $\frac{N}{2}$ hydrochloric acid, and so on.

The equivalent of sulphuric acid is 49; therefore 1 litre of N-sulphuric acid contains 49 grams of the acid, while 1 litre of $\frac{N}{10}$ sulphuric acid contains $\frac{49}{10}$, or 4·9 grams of the acid. Similarly, 1 litre of N-caustic soda solution contains 40 grams of caustic soda, since the equivalent of caustic soda is 40. You will realize in the laboratory how much time, labour and thought are saved by using this idea of "normality." If you share the common human weakness for doing things with the minimum amount of labour, you will find that the time is very well spent in which you make yourselves familiar with the principles of normal solutions. For one thing, you will be saved endless calculation, and (unless you have a passion for logarithms) you will probably think this is very much to be desired.

The equivalents of some common substances are given below. The formulæ in the second column you will understand after you have read Chapter IX. Neglect them when you are reading the chapter for the first time.

Substance.	*Formula.*	*Equivalent.*
Sulphuric acid	H_2SO_4	49
Hydrochloric acid	HCl	36·5
Nitric acid	HNO_3	63
Oxalic acid crystals	$H_2C_2O_4.2H_2O$	63
Oxalic acid anhydrous	$H_2C_2O_4$	45
Sodium hydroxide	$NaOH$	40
Potassium hydroxide	KOH	56
Sodium carbonate anhydrous . .	Na_2CO_3	53
Potassium permanganate . . .	$KMnO_4$	31·6
Potassium dichromate	$K_2Cr_2O_7$	49
Silver nitrate	$AgNO_3$	170
Iodine	I	127
Ferrous ammonium sulphate . .	$(NH_4)_2SO_4.FeSO_4.6H_2O$	392
Sodium thiosulphate	$Na_2S_2O_3.5H_2O$	248
Ammonia	NH_3	17

It is often possible to find the equivalent of a compound from inspection of its formula (Chapter IX), but you must be careful not to suppose that the equivalent of a compound is always the sum of the equivalents of its constituent elements. It often is, but often is not.

It should be noted that occasionally a substance may have more than one equivalent, according to the reaction in which it takes part or to the compound in which it is found. The different equivalents of a particular substance are, however, always simply related to one another numerically. Thus the equivalent of copper in black copper oxide is 31·8, while in brown copper oxide it is 63·6, the ratio of the two being $\frac{63\cdot6}{31\cdot8}$ or 2 : 1. The explanation of this phenomenon in the case of elements is that an element may have more than one valency (see Chapter VIII); in the case of a compound the existence of more than one equivalent is due to the fact that the compound may behave in different ways in different reactions. To take a definite example, let us consider the case of potassium chloride. This is a compound of chlorine and potassium. By analysis we can find the percentage by weight of chlorine it contains, and thus calculate what number of grams of it contains the gram-equivalent of chlorine (35·5); this will be the equivalent of potassium chloride, and is found to be 74·5. Now potassium chloride is formed, together with oxygen, when potassium *chlorate* is heated (p. 172), and we find that for every 48 grams of oxygen liberated, 74·5 grams of potassium chloride are left. Hence in this case the gram-equivalent of potassium chloride (*viz.* that weight of it which has reacted with 8 grams of oxygen) is $\frac{74 \cdot 5}{6} = 12 \cdot 4$ grams, ∴ its equivalent here is 12·4. In stating the equivalent of a compound, therefore, we ought to specify the particular reaction concerned in order to be strictly accurate. However, in most cases no difficulty arises, and by the time you meet with compounds which have more than one equivalent you will be so expert at chemistry that they will give you no sleepless nights.

Details of Methods of Finding Equivalents of Elements.

Since you will carry out many determinations of equivalents in the laboratory, the experimental details of the methods employed will not be given here in full.

Equivalents of Metallic Elements.—The chief methods available for the purpose are the following :—

(i) If the metal is soluble in a dilute acid (or in a solution of an alkali) with liberation of hydrogen, take a known weight of it, dissolve it in a suitable dilute acid (or alkaline solution) and find the weight of hydrogen evolved.

(ii) If the metal is not soluble in a dilute acid, convert a weighed quantity of it into its oxide, and find the weight of oxygen taken up (= increase in weight). Then calculate the number of grams of it which would combine with 8 grams of oxygen.

(iii) If neither of the above methods is suitable, convert a weighed quantity of the metal into its chloride. Weigh this and calculate the number of grams of the metal which would combine with 35·5 grams of chlorine, since 35·5 is the equivalent of chlorine (Example on p. 59). *Methods ii. and iii. may also be used in the reverse way, that is, reduction of the oxide or chloride to the metal.*

(iv) The equivalent of a metal may often be conveniently found by displacement of it from a solution of one of its salts by means of a weighed quantity of another metal of known equivalent. Then the equivalent of the first metal is the number of grams of it displaced by the gram-equivalent of the second.

(v) By electrolysis. It was shown by FARADAY that in electrolysis the weights of substances liberated at the electrodes are in the ratio of their equivalents. By measuring, therefore, the weight of a metal deposited in an electrolytic cell and the weight of hydrogen liberated by the same quantity of electricity, the equivalent of the metal may be found. In this connection, see Chapter X, on Electrolysis (p. 126).

EXAMPLES OF SOME OF THE ABOVE METHODS.

(i) The first method is suitable for finding the equivalents of magnesium, zinc, iron and aluminium, using dilute hydrochloric or sulphuric acid for the first three elements, and *hot* hydrochloric acid for aluminium, which will not dissolve in dilute sulphuric acid or in *cold* hydrochloric acid.

Magnesium.—Use the apparatus shown in Fig. 19.

First see that the apparatus is air-tight. Remove the bottle A, open the clip E, and fill the syphon-tube F by blowing through C. Close the clip and replace A. Open the clip. If the apparatus is air-tight a little water will run into G, but the flow will stop in a few seconds. If the apparatus leaks, however, the water will continue to flow into G; in this case examine all the corks and glass tubing, and if necessary replace them. When you have made the apparatus air-tight close the clip E and remove the bottle A.

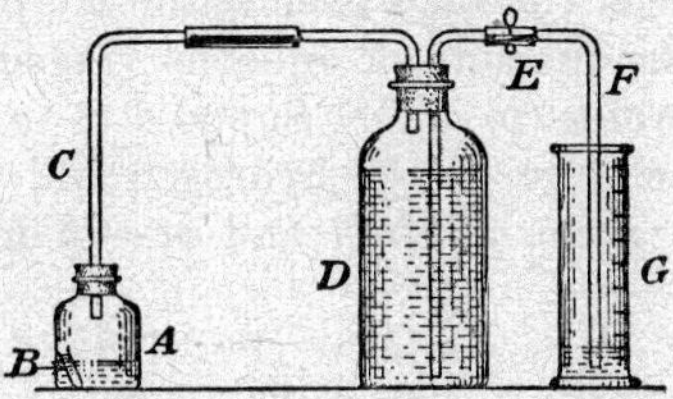

FIG. 19.

Weigh out accurately about 30 cm. of clean magnesium

ribbon and place it in A. Cover it with a layer of water. Then put into A a small test-tube, B, filled with concentrated hydrochloric acid, and fix A on to C. Now open the clip and note the level of the water in G; it should not be more than 10–20 c.c. if the cylinder is less than 300 c.c. in capacity. Tilt the bottle A and allow the acid in B to flow out. The hydrogen which is evolved displaces its own volume of water into the graduated cylinder G. After the action is over let the apparatus stand, with the clip still open, until the level of the water in G no longer changes. Close the clip, take the tube F out of G, and read the volume of the water in the cylinder. Subtract the volume of the water originally present; the difference is the volume of the water displaced by the hydrogen, and therefore of the hydrogen itself.

Take the temperature of the water, look up in the tables the pressure of water-vapour at that temperature, read the barometer, correct the volume of the hydrogen to N.T.P., and work out the equivalent of magnesium as shown below.

Let x be the volume of the hydrogen evolved, *i.e.* the volume of the water driven over into the cylinder. Suppose that the temperature of the water is $t°$, and the height of the barometer m millimetres. Then since the hydrogen has been collected over water the pressure on it will be m minus the pressure of aqueous vapour at $t°$. Look this up in the tables (p. 457). Suppose it to be p mm. Then the actual pressure on the hydrogen will be $m - p$.

x c.c. at $t°$ C. and $m - p$ mm. pressure will become

$$\frac{x \times (m - p) \times 273}{760 \times (273 + t)} \text{ c.c. at N.T.P.} = n \text{ c.c.}$$

Now the weight of this volume of hydrogen $= \dfrac{n \times 0{\cdot}09}{1{,}000}$ grams.

Suppose that the weight of magnesium taken $= w$ grams.

Then, since $\dfrac{n \times 0{\cdot}09}{1{,}000}$ grams of hydrogen are given by w grams of magnesium, 1 gram of hydrogen would be given by

$\frac{w \times 1,000}{n \times 0{\cdot}09}$ grams, and this is the gram-equivalent of magnesium.

The same apparatus may be employed for zinc and iron, though in the case of the latter the action is slow.

Aluminium.—Aluminium does not readily dissolve in dilute hydrochloric acid in the cold, although it does so on heating. A modified form of apparatus is therefore used; this is shown in Fig. 20.

A round-bottomed flask of about 300 c.c. capacity is fitted with a cork carrying a delivery-tube D and a piece of glass tubing connected to a funnel C by means of a piece of rubber-

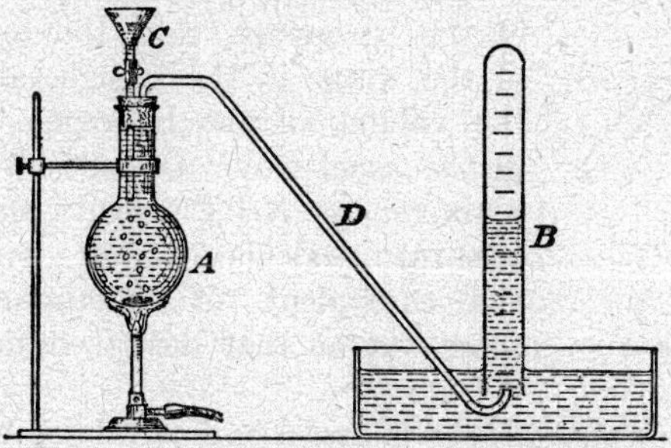

FIG. 20.

tubing. The latter can be closed by means of a clip. The delivery-tube D leads to a graduated tube B (of at least 100 c.c. capacity) inverted in a pneumatic trough. About 0·05 grams of aluminium foil (not more) is weighed accurately and then placed in the flask A. The whole of the apparatus—funnel, flask and delivery-tube—is then filled with water which has been freshly boiled (to drive out dissolved air). The end of the delivery-tube in the cork must end flush with the lower surface of the cork (Fig. 21), to prevent hydrogen from collecting under the latter.

See that the clip is closed, and then run out the water from the funnel and fill the latter with concentrated hydrochloric acid. Open the clip and allow nearly all the hydrochloric acid to run into the flask ; do not let it all in or you may admit some air as well. Now close the clip and heat the flask. Fill the graduated tube with water and invert it over the end of the delivery-tube.

The aluminium dissolves in the hydrochloric acid and hydrogen is evolved, part of which passes over into the graduated tube. When the aluminium has completely dissolved heat the flask until the water boils vigorously. The current of steam will drive over the rest of the hydrogen. After boiling for 5 minutes, remove the flame and open the clip.

Transfer the graduated tube to a deep trough of water, level, and read the volume of the hydrogen. Note the height of the barometer, take the temperature of the water in the trough, and correct the volume of the hydrogen to N.T.P. in the usual way. Given that 1 litre of hydrogen at N.T.P. weighs 0·09 grams, you can calculate from your results the equivalent of aluminium in the same way as that described under magnesium.

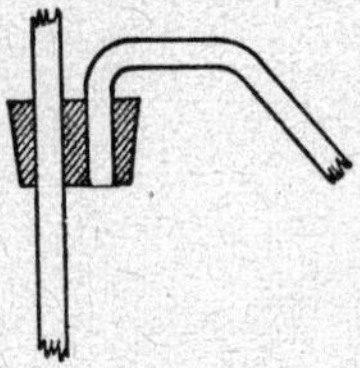

FIG. 21.

(ii) The second method is useful in determining the equivalents of copper, tin and lead. These metals are not conveniently converted into their oxides by direct action of oxygen upon them, but the oxides can easily be made in the following way. Nitric acid contains a great deal of oxygen (48 parts by weight out of every 63) and readily parts with it. When it acts upon a metal it sometimes converts it directly into the oxide (*e.g.* tin), and sometimes into the *nitrate* of the metal. Now many nitrates (*e.g.* those of tin and lead) split up on heating and give off gases, while a residue of the metallic oxide is left. Hence in finding the equivalents of copper, tin and lead, we act upon a known weight of the metal with nitric acid, heat until nothing but the metallic oxide is left, and then weigh again. The increase in weight is the weight of oxygen taken up by the weight of metal used, and hence we can calculate what weight of the metal would combine with 8 grams of oxygen, and this will be the gram-equivalent of the metal.

In finding the equivalent of copper, for instance, proceed in the following way. Take a clean dry test-tube and weigh it. Introduce about half a gram of copper foil and weigh again. The difference gives the weight of the copper. Now add concentrated nitric acid drop by drop. At first there is a vigorous reaction, but after a time the copper will have completely dissolved and further addition of acid will then cause no effect. When this is so, carefully heat the blue solution of copper nitrate until it is evaporated to dryness. Then heat more strongly until all the blue copper nitrate has been decomposed and converted into black *copper oxide*. Allow the test-tube to cool, and when it is cold weigh it again. Heat again, cool, and re-weigh, continuing this process until the weight is constant: in this way only can you be *sure* that all the copper nitrate has been converted into the oxide. You now have the following weights:

(ii) Weight of test-tube + copper = grams.
(i) ,, ,, ,, = grams.

∴ (iii) Weight of copper = grams (say x grams).

(iv) Weight of test-tube + copper oxide, when constant = grams.
(i) ,, ,, ,, = grams.

∴ (v) Weight of copper oxide = grams (say y gms.).

The equivalent of oxygen is 8.

$y—x$ grams of oxygen have combined with x grams of copper.

∴ 8 ,, ,, ,, would combine with $\frac{8x}{y-x}$,, ,, ,,

and this is the gram-equivalent of copper.

Reversal of Method ii.—In the method just described we determined the equivalent of copper by a building-up or *synthesis* of its oxide. We could, however, start with the oxide and convert it into the metal, *i.e.* we could *analyse* the oxide. It is clear that we should get exactly the same sort of figures, namely, weight of oxide and weight of metal, and hence could calculate the equivalent in the same way.

Conversion of the oxide of a metal into the metal itself is called reduction. It can often be brought about by simply heating the oxide in a stream of hydrogen, when the oxygen of the oxide combines with the hydrogen to form steam and the metal is left. The equivalents of copper, lead, nickel and many other metals may be found in this way.

EXAMPLE.—*Equivalent of copper by reduction of its oxide.* Take a clean porcelain boat, heat it in the Bunsen flame, and allow it to cool in a desiccator. Put into it about 0·5

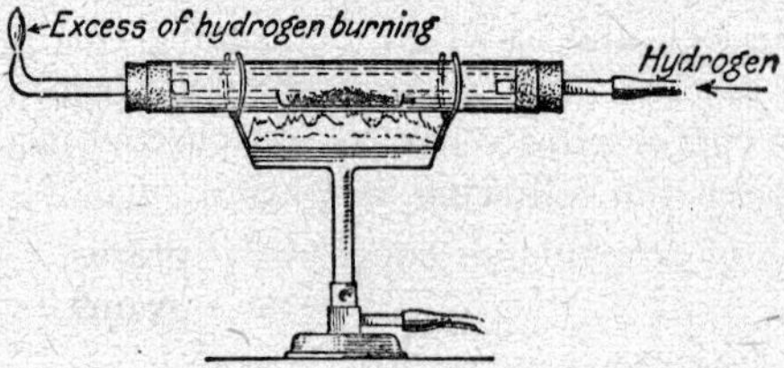

FIG. 22.—Equivalent of Copper by reduction of its Oxide.

grams of pure black copper oxide, heat it gently to drive off moisture from the oxide, allow it to cool in a desiccator, and re-weigh. The difference is the weight of copper oxide.

Place the boat and contents in a piece of hard-glass tubing arranged as in Fig. 22, heat, and pass a stream of hydrogen through the tube. Light the excess of hydrogen which issues from the other end of the tube so as to get some idea of the rate at which it is passing through the apparatus.

The copper oxide is gradually reduced by the hydrogen, and the progress of the reduction can be followed by observing the change in colour of the substance in the boat, from the black of copper oxide to the reddish brown of copper. When you think the reduction is complete allow to cool in the current of hydrogen, and remove the boat when it is cold. Weigh. Replace in the tube and heat in hydrogen for another

5 minutes. Cool and re-weigh. Repeat until the weight is constant.

The loss in weight of the boat and contents is the weight of oxygen contained in the copper oxide taken. The difference between the weight of the boat + copper and that of the boat alone gives the weight of the copper. From your results you can calculate the equivalent of copper in the usual way.

(iii) The third method is useful in finding the equivalent of silver.

Silver will not displace hydrogen from a dilute acid, and its oxide is unstable. Its equivalent is therefore determined by converting it into its chloride, which is quite stable and easy to prepare.

Weigh accurately about 0·4 grams of silver and dissolve it in dilute nitric acid in a beaker. Add an excess of hydrochloric acid to the solution of silver nitrate so obtained. The white curdy precipitate which is formed is *silver chloride*—

Silver nitrate + hydrochloric acid
= silver chloride ↓ + nitric acid.

Dilute the solution considerably with water, then filter off the silver chloride, wash it well, and dry it and weigh it.

The equivalent of chlorine is 35·5, and you have the following weights:

(i) Wt. of silver, say x grams.
(ii) Wt. of silver chloride, say y grams.

∴ Wt. of chlorine which has combined with x grams of silver = $y - x$ grams.

If $y - x$ grams of chlorine have combined with x grams of silver,

$$\therefore 35{\cdot}5 \text{ ,, } \quad \text{ ,, } \quad \text{would combine with } \frac{35{\cdot}5x}{y - x} \text{ ,, ,,}$$

and this is the gram-equivalent of silver.

(iv) The method of displacement is not often used in actual practice, but it is interesting as a laboratory experiment. When iron is put into copper sulphate solution, copper is deposited and iron goes into solution as iron sulphate—

Copper sulphate + iron = iron sulphate + copper ↓.

You can easily test this by dipping the blade of your

pocket-knife into copper sulphate solution ; you will find that it becomes coated with copper. This is one of the reactions which led ancient chemists to believe that metals could be *transmuted* or changed into one another ; they thought that here the iron was actually changed into copper, as they did not realize that the copper was originally present in the blue solution.

Now, when iron replaces copper in this way, the *equivalent* of iron will precipitate the *equivalent* of copper. Hence, if we find the weight of iron which dissolves and that of the copper which is deposited, we can calculate the equivalent of copper if we know that of iron (28).

EXAMPLE.—*Equivalent of silver by displacement with zinc.* When zinc is added to silver nitrate solution, silver is deposited and zinc nitrate is left in solution. The equivalent of zinc is 32·5. Weigh accurately about 0·3 grams of thin zinc foil, put it into a beaker, and add excess of silver nitrate solution. Allow to stand until all the zinc has dissolved. Filter off the grey precipitate of metallic silver, wash, dry and weigh. You then have the following weights :

i. Wt. of zinc, say x grams.
ii. ,, silver, say y ,,

If x grams of zinc displace y grams of silver,

then 32·5 ,, ,, would displace $\frac{32{\cdot}5y}{x}$ gms. of silver,

and this is the gram-equivalent of silver.

(v) *Electrolytic Method.*—Like method (iv), the electrolytic method is not much used in practice. It may be illustrated in the following way.

EXAMPLE.—*Determination of equivalent of copper electrolytically.* Fit up in series a water-voltameter and an electrolytic cell, with copper electrodes, containing copper sulphate solution (Fig. 23). (Cf. Chapter X, on Electrolysis.)

Carefully clean and dry the copper cathode of the electrolytic cell, and then weigh it. Connect up, and pass the current until about 50 c.c. of hydrogen have collected in the graduated tube over the cathode in the voltameter. Then switch off the current, level the hydrogen and read its volume. Note also the temperature of the water in the voltameter and read the height of the barometer. Take out the copper cathode from the electrolytic cell, wash it, dry it, and weigh it. You then have the following data:

Height of barometer	$= h$ mm.
Temperature	$= t°$ C.
Volume of hydrogen	$= v$ c.c.
Original wt. of copper cathode	$= w$ gms.
Final ,, ,, ,,	$= n$ gms.

$\therefore$ Wt. of copper deposited $= n - w$ gms., say x gms.

Now correct the volume of hydrogen to N.T.P. in the usual

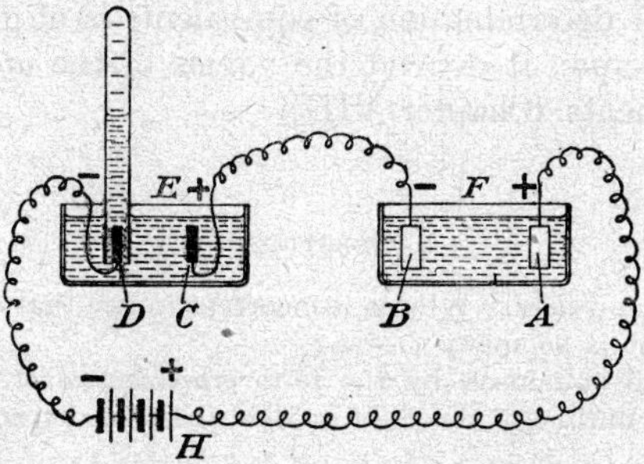

FIG. 23.—Electrolytic Method of finding Equivalent of Copper.

way, not forgetting to subtract from the height of the barometer the pressure of aqueous vapour at $t°$ C.

Let the corrected volume of the hydrogen be y c.c..

Since 1 litre of hydrogen at N.T.P. weighs 0·09 grams,

$\therefore$ y c.c. ,, ,, weighs $\frac{0{\cdot}09 \times y}{1{,}000}$ grams.

Then if $\frac{0{\cdot}09 \times y}{1{,}000}$ grams of hydrogen are liberated in the same time as x grams of copper,

$\therefore$ 1 gram of hydrogen would be liberated in the same time as $\frac{x \times 1{,}000}{0{\cdot}09 \times y}$ grams of copper,

and this will be the gram-equivalent of copper.

Equivalents of Non-Metallic Elements.—The determination of the equivalents of non-metals, while equally simple in theory, is usually more difficult in practice, since so many of the non-metallic elements are gases, which need more skill in manipulation.

(i) By direct combination of the element with hydrogen, when the equivalent may be calculated from the weight of the element taken and the weight of the product.

(ii) By formation of the oxide or chloride.

Details of the determination of the equivalents of various non-metallic elements will be found in the descriptive part of this book.

The exact determination of equivalents is of great importance, since upon it depend the values of the *atomic weights* of the elements (Chapter VIII).

Questions

1. Define *equivalent.* Why is it incorrect to say that the equivalent of an element is so many *grams* ?

2. What do you mean by the term *gram-equivalent* ?

3. Give an outline of the chief methods used in determining equivalents.

4. How would you proceed to find the equivalent of (*a*) copper, (*b*) zinc, (*c*) silver ?

5. How may the equivalents of the following elements be determined—iron, magnesium, lead, tin ?

6. Describe an experimental method of finding the equivalent of aluminium.

7. What is a *normal solution* ? What volume of $\frac{N}{2}$ caustic soda would be required to react with 105·7 c.c. of $\frac{N}{10}$ nitric acid ?

8. 10·9 c.c. of N-potassium hydroxide are found to neutralize a certain volume of bench dilute sulphuric acid. What volume of $\frac{N}{5}$ caustic soda would neutralize the same volume of this acid ?

9. 0·40 grams of magnesium when dissolved in hydrochloric acid liberated 0·033 grams of hydrogen. What is the equivalent of magnesium ?

10. 0·58 grams of a metal when dissolved in a dilute acid liberated 0·021 grams of hydrogen. Find the equivalent of the metal.

11. The following data were obtained in an experimental determination of the equivalent of a metal by solution in a dilute acid:

Weight of metal taken = 0·35 grams.
Weight of hydrogen evolved = 0·0107 grams.

Calculate the equivalent of the metal.

12. 0·250 grams of a metal when dissolved in a dilute acid liberate 46·8 c.c. of hydrogen (measured dry at S.T.P.). Calculate the equivalent of the metal. (1 litre of hydrogen at S.T.P. weighs 0·09 grams.)

13. 0·0746 grams of a metal, dissolved in dilute hydrochloric acid, gave 91·8 c.c. of hydrogen, measured dry at S.T.P. Calculate the equivalent of the metal.

14. An experiment for the determination of the equivalent of a metal gave the following results:

Weight of metal dissolved in dilute acid = 0·1232 grams.
Volume of hydrogen liberated, collected over water at atmospheric pressure = 119·6 c.c.
Temperature of the water = 12° C.
Height of the barometer = 762·7 mm.
Find the equivalent of the metal.

15. A known weight of a metal was dissolved in caustic soda solution, and the liberated hydrogen collected and measured. From the following data calculate the equivalent of the metal.

Weight of metal = 0·0714 grams.
Vol. of hydrogen over water at atmospheric pressure = 92·45 c.c.
Temperature = 15° C.
Height of barometer = 774·1 mm.

16. 0·654 grams of a metal on oxidation gave 0·814 grams of oxide. What is the equivalent of the metal?

17. 0·5883 grams of a metal on oxidation gave 0·7363 grams of the oxide. Find the equivalent of the metal.

18. 1·529 grams of a metal on oxidation gave 1·651 grams of the oxide. Find the equivalent of the metal.

19. 0·8433 grams of a metallic oxide were reduced in a current of hydrogen. The weight of metal produced was found to be 0·7384 grams. What is the equivalent of the metal?

20. 0·8351 grams of a metallic oxide when reduced gave 0·7359 grams of the metal. Find the equivalent of the metal.

21. An experiment shows that 0·5260 grams of zinc will displace 0·5116 grams of copper from a solution of copper sulphate. Assuming that the equivalent of zinc is 32·7, find that of copper.

22. 0·4100 grams of copper displace 1·391 grams of silver from a solution of silver nitrate. What is the equivalent of silver, assuming that the equivalent of copper is 31·8?

23. 0·7920 grams of iron were found to displace 0·9020 grams of

copper from a copper sulphate solution. Assuming that the equivalent of copper is 31·8, find that of iron.

24. In determining the equivalent of a metal it was found that 100·0 parts by weight of the metal combined with 34·27 parts by weight of chlorine. What was the equivalent of the metal, assuming that of chlorine to be 35·5 ?

25. 0·4260 grams of silver were dissolved in nitric acid, and the silver then precipitated as chloride by hydrochloric acid. The weight of silver chloride formed was 0·5662 grams. What is the equivalent of silver if that of chlorine is 35·5 ?

26. 1·820 grams of a liquid chloride of phosphorus were decomposed by excess of water. Silver nitrate was added to the solution, and the precipitated silver chloride was collected and weighed. This weight was found to be 5·691 grams. Assuming that the equivalents of silver and chlorine are 107·9 and 35·5 respectively, calculate the equivalent of phosphorus.

27. An electric current is passed simultaneously through the following solutions: acidulated water; copper sulphate; and silver potassium cyanide. The weight of hydrogen evolved from the acid solution is found to be 0·0132 grams; 0·421 grams of copper are deposited from the copper sulphate solution, and 1·429 grams of silver from the silver solution. What are the equivalents of copper and silver from these data ?

CHAPTER VII

THE ATOMIC THEORY

In Chapter II it was mentioned that the ancient Greek philosophers made many speculations about the structure of the universe. One of them, THALES (about 600 B.C.), thought that all matter was composed of water, while according to ARISTOTLE (384–322 B.C.), the four "elements" of which all other substances are composed are Fire, Air, Earth, and Water. Certain other thinkers, such as DEMOCRITUS (fifth century B.C.) and the Roman LUCRETIUS (about 98–55 B.C.), evolved what was known as an *atomic* theory, which in short is this: that if we were to take a piece of gold, for instance, and cut it up into small parts, and then cut these into still smaller parts, and so on, we could not continue to do so for ever. After a time, they said, we should get down to particles so small that they could not be split up any further, even if we had eyesight keen enough and tools accurate enough for the purpose. These tiny particles, which they supposed to be eternal, invisible and indivisible, they called *atoms* (*i.e.* in Greek, something which cannot be cut up). All matter, then, was considered to be composed of these extremely minute atoms.

Now, this is more or less what we believe at the present day. However, we must not imagine that our modern atomic theory is directly due to the Greeks, for the chief point about the ancient theories is that they were too vague to be tested, and were not based upon any experimental evidence. Perhaps the ancient idea of atoms would have had a much better and greater influence upon chemistry if circumstances had been different. Aristotle, however, strongly opposed it, and since practically all mediæval chemists firmly believed in everything that Aristotle said, the idea that matter is composed of atoms was very slow in gaining general acceptance. Even if it had, it is difficult to see what use chemists could have made of it until they had begun to realize that, in chemistry, it is absolutely essential to carry out experiments *quantitatively*, that is, to *weigh* and *measure* the amounts of matter which undergo change.

By the end of the eighteenth century, however, this quantitative aspect of chemistry had become general, so that when John Dalton (1766–1844) revived the atomic theory he was able to think of ways of *testing* it in the laboratory. All the earlier theories, as we have seen, were very vague, and were not put forward in such a form that they could have been tested. Moreover, even if they had been, chemists had not acquired sufficient skill for the purpose. Hence, although the idea of atoms is extremely ancient, chemists look upon Dalton as the true founder of the theory because he re-shaped it into such a form that it was capable of being tested experimentally.

Dalton published his views in his famous book *A New System of Chemical Philosophy* (Part I, 1808; Part II, 1810). You will see the title-page of Part II on page 81. He said: Let us suppose the following:

1. Matter is composed of a great number of extremely minute particles, which cannot be split up any further. These we will call *atoms*.

2. All the atoms of the same element are exactly alike, in weight and in every other respect, and are different from the atoms of other elements.

3. Atoms are indestructible and cannot be created.

4. In the formation of compounds, combination occurs between *small* whole numbers of the atoms of the elements concerned.

5. All the "compound atoms" (molecules) of a compound are exactly alike.

Nowadays, we reserve the name "atoms" for the ultimate

DALTON COLLECTING MARSH GAS.

From the mural painting by FORD MADOX BROWN, *by permission of the Town Hall Committee of the Manchester Corporation*

particles of elements. It is clear that the smallest particle of a *compound* must contain at least *two* atoms, since a compound cannot consist of less than two elements, and there cannot be less than 1 atom of each of those elements in the tiniest particle of a compound. Hence, the smallest particle of a compound is still capable of division, for we can split it up into the atoms of its constituent elements. It is, therefore, not strictly correct to call it an *atom* ("indivisible") at all, so chemists call the tiniest particles of compounds by another name, *viz. molecules* (*i.e.* "little masses").

Another point which we may consider here is that, as a rule, the atoms even of elements do not go about *singly*. They like company, and generally join up together in pairs, or in groups of 3 or 4, or more, atoms. To the smallest particle of an element which, under ordinary circumstances, goes about by itself, we also apply the term molecule. There are some exceptional elements, such as helium and argon, whose atoms are very unsociable, and prefer to lead a solitary existence. In this case it is clear that the smallest possible particle of the element ("atom") is also the smallest particle of the element which, under ordinary circumstances, goes about by itself ("molecule"); in other words, the atom and the molecule of these elements are identical.

Let us sum up what we have learnt about atoms and molecules, and put our ideas of them into *definitions.*

Atom.—An atom is the smallest, chemically indivisible, particle of an element.

Molecule.—A molecule is the smallest particle of an element or compound which can normally lead a separate existence.

We can thus have *atoms* of *elements only*, but *molecules* of both *elements* and *compounds*. The smallest number of atoms that the molecule of a *compound* can contain is obviously two, since, as has been pointed out above, a compound must contain at least two elements, and the smallest number of atoms of each element that its molecule can contain is 1. There is no upper limit to the number of atoms the molecule of a substance may contain. Thus the starch molecule contains at least 10,000 atoms, and that of albumen (white of egg) probably a much larger number.

Atomicity.—*The atomicity of an element or compound is the number of atoms contained in its molecule.*

EXAMPLES:

Substance.	Element or Compound.	Atomicity.	Composition of Molecule.
Helium	E	1	1 atom of helium
Hydrogen	E	2	2 atoms of hydrogen
Ozone	E	3	3 ,, ,, oxygen
Phosphorus vapour .	E	4	4 ,, ,, phosphorus
Sulphur ,, .	E	6	6 ,, ,, sulphur
Water	C	3	{ 2 ,, ,, hydrogen 1 atom of oxygen
Sulphuric acid . . .	C	7	{ 2 atoms of hydrogen 1 atom of sulphur 4 atoms of oxygen

Molecules consisting of 1 atom are said to be *mon*-atomic.
,, ,, 2 atoms ,, ,, *di*-atomic.
,, ,, 3 atoms ,, ,, *tri*-atomic.
,, ,, more than 3 atoms ,, ,, *poly*-atomic.

CHEMICAL LAWS

If the assumptions made by Dalton are true, we shall see on consideration that certain conclusions can be drawn from them which we ought to be able to test in the laboratory.

(i) If all matter is composed of atoms, and atoms are indestructible and cannot be created, then matter itself can neither be created nor destroyed. In other words, in any chemical reaction whatsoever, the total weight of the substances started with ought to be exactly equal to the total weight of the substances formed.

As we have seen already (p. 34), this expectation is borne out in practice. No chemist has ever been able to find a reaction in which the total weight of the original substances is different from the total weight of the products.

A

NEW SYSTEM

OF

CHEMICAL PHILOSOPHY.

PART II.

BY

JOHN DALTON.

Manchester:

Printed by Russell & Allen, Deansgate,

FOR

R. BICKERSTAFF, STRAND, LONDON.

1810.

This fact we can sum up and express as a general statement or "law," the Law of the Conservation of Matter.

Law of the Conservation of Matter.—*Matter can neither be created nor destroyed.*

The word "law" here means something different from that which it means in such an expression as "laws of the country." Laws in science are not *rules*, made by scientists, which substances *have* to obey under penalty: they are descriptions of the way in which substances *do* behave as a matter of fact. Since they are only descriptions, some of them are more accurate than others. When the description is very accurate, and describes the facts very well, we say that the "law" is "obeyed" strictly. Other facts are more difficult to describe with accuracy. In this case we say that the "law" is "obeyed" sometimes, or that it is a "rough law." The Law of the Conservation of Matter is an example of an extremely accurate description of the facts with which it deals. Not the slightest exception to it has ever been found. Dulong and Petit's Law, however (p. 105), is only a very rough law, and exceptions to it are numerous.

A scientific law is useful to us in this way. If we have always found it to be "obeyed" strictly in the past, we believe that it will probably hold in those cases which we have not actually tried. Thus, although no one can possibly tell that, to-morrow or next week or next year, the fact that no matter is created or destroyed in a chemical reaction will still continue to be true, we should be extremely surprised if it did not, and we act as though we were certain that it will. Besides being descriptions, then, scientific laws can be used as rules to help us and guide us in our dealings with Nature.

With increasing knowledge, we are able to describe facts more and more accurately, and so our descriptions of these facts, that is, our scientific laws or "laws of Nature," are themselves becoming more accurate and more trustworthy.

(ii) A second conclusion we can draw from Dalton's assumptions is that each and every specimen of the same compound should have exactly the same composition, *i.e.* they should all consist of the same elements in a constant proportion by weight. This follows from assumption 5, that all the molecules of a particular compound are exactly alike, *i.e.* composed of the same numbers of the same atoms.

We can easily test this conclusion in the laboratory. For example, we could take as many different specimens of common salt as we could manage to procure, purify them, and analyse them. This has actually been done by chemists, who have found that salt *always* consists of the two elements *sodium* and *chlorine*, in the proportion by weight of 23 of sodium to 35·5 of chlorine.

Similarly, analysis of water has shown that water invariably consists of *hydrogen* and *oxygen*, in the proportion by weight of 1 of hydrogen to 8 of oxygen.

No exceptions to this kind of behaviour have ever been discovered, so we describe our results in a " law " :—

The Law of Constant Composition (or Definite Proportions).—*The same compound always consists of the same elements in a constant proportion by weight.*

(iii) A third conclusion is this : that *when two elements combine to form more than one compound, then the weights of one of those elements which combine with a constant weight of the other are in a simple ratio to one another.* This also is borne out in practice, and is known as the **Law of Multiple Proportions.** It follows from assumption 4, *viz.* that when atoms combine to form a molecule they do so in *small* whole numbers. Suppose, for example, that the elements A and B unite together to form two different compounds. The simplest imaginable case will be when in one of the compounds 1 atom of A combines with 1 atom of B, and in the other compound 1 atom of A combines with 2 atoms of B. Since, in one " compound atom " of each of the two compounds there is 1 atom of A, it follows, from Dalton's assumption 2, that the weight of A is constant in these two " compound atoms." The weights of B, on the other hand, will be in the ratio of the number of atoms of B present in each " compound atom " : in this case, 1 : 2. This is a simple ratio, and if the molecules of compounds are always composed of *small* numbers of atoms, the ratio always *must* be simple. It does not matter of which element we take the constant weight, nor what weight we take as the constant weight, as long as we find the *ratio to one another of the weights of the other element* which have combined with this constant weight. Thus, suppose in the above instance we take the weights of A which have combined with a constant weight of B. Let 1 atom-weight of B be the constant weight of B. Then in the first compound we have 1 atom-weight of A combining with the given, constant, weight of B. In the second compound, 2 atom-weights of B combine with 1 atom-weight of A, therefore 1 atom-weight of B (the "constant" weight, or "reference" weight) would com-

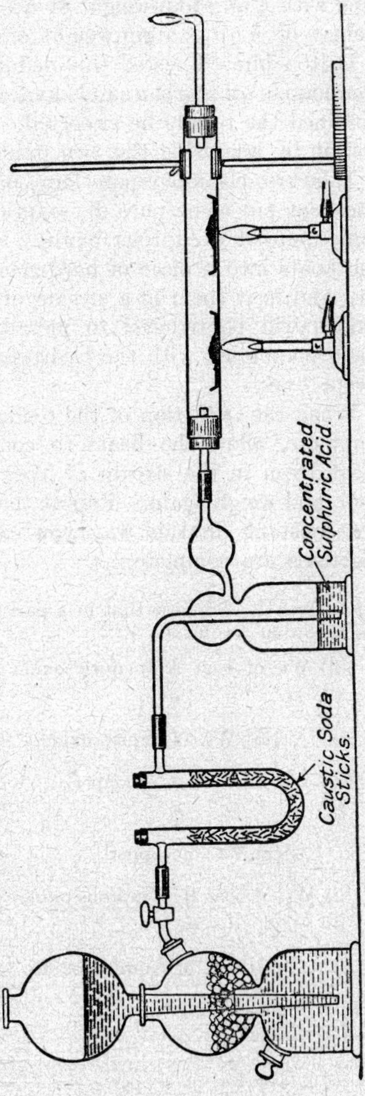

FIG. 24.

bine with $\frac{1}{2}$ an atom-weight of A. Now the ratio of 1 atom-weight of A to $\frac{1}{2}$ atom-weight of A is 2 : 1.

Dalton himself tested this deduction by analysing certain compounds of carbon and hydrogen, and found that he obtained the results he expected. In the laboratory we can test it by analysing the two oxides of copper :—

Take two clean dry porcelain boats and weigh them. Into one boat put some pure dry cupric oxide and into the other some pure dry cuprous oxide. Re-weigh. Now introduce the boats into a piece of hard-glass combustion tubing (Fig. 24), and heat them in a stream of pure dry hydrogen. The oxides will be reduced to metallic copper, the oxygen in them combining with the hydrogen to form steam, which is swept away.

When the reduction of the oxides to copper appears to be complete, allow the boats to cool, and then weigh them. Heat them in the stream of hydrogen again for 5 minutes, cool, and weigh again. Repeat this process until the weights are constant (in this way you can make certain that the reactions are complete).

EXAMPLE I.—Suppose that in a particular experiment we obtained the following results :

A.	(ii) Wt. of boat A + cupric oxide	= 5·16 grams.
	(i) ,, ,, ,,	= 3·52 grams.
	∴ (iii) Wt. of cupric oxide	= 1·64 grams.
	(iv) Wt. of boat A + copper	= 4·83 grams.
	(i) ,, ,, ,,	= 3·52 grams.
	∴ (v) Wt. of copper	= 1·31 grams.
B.	(ii) Wt. of boat B + cuprous oxide	= 5·20 grams.
	(i) ,, ,, ,,	= 3·67 grams.
	∴ (iii) Wt. of cuprous oxide	= 1·53 grams.
	(iv) Wt. of boat B + copper	= 5·03 grams.
	(i) ,, ,, ,,	= 3·67 grams.
	∴ (v) Wt. of copper	= 1·36 grams.

What we have to do to see if the Law is true (in this case, and within the limits of the accuracy to which we are working) is to calculate either (*a*) those weights of oxygen which have combined with a fixed weight of copper in the two oxides, or (*b*) those weights of copper which have combined with a fixed weight of oxygen. It does not matter which we choose. Let us choose alternative (*a*).

In the cupric oxide, we have found that 1·64 — 1·31, *i.e.* 0·33, grams of oxygen have combined with 1·31 grams of copper. We must therefore calculate how many grams of oxygen have combined with 1·31 grams of copper in the cuprous oxide.

Well, from our results,

1·36 grams of copper in the cuprous oxide combined with 0·17 gms. of oxygen.

$$\therefore\ 1{\cdot}31\ \text{,,}\quad\text{,,}\quad\text{,,}\quad\text{,,}\quad\text{,,}\quad\text{,,}\quad\text{,,}\quad \frac{0{\cdot}17 \times 1{\cdot}31}{1{\cdot}36}$$

$$= 0{\cdot}16 \text{ grams.}$$

If the law of Multiple Proportions is true, then 0·33 and 0·16 should be in a simple ratio to one another. We see that, allowing for inevitable experimental error, they are; the ratio $\frac{0{\cdot}33}{0{\cdot}16}$ is roughly equal to 2 : 1. Therefore the Law is true in this case.

Example II.—Two oxides of nitrogen were found to have the following percentage composition by weight:

	Nitrogen.	*Oxygen.*
A	63·7	36·3
B	25·9	74·1

Are these figures in accordance with the Law of Multiple Proportions? In oxide A, we have 36·3 grams of oxygen combined with 63·7 of nitrogen. Let us take 63·7 grams of nitrogen as our fixed weight of one element. We have then to find how many grams of oxygen would combine with 63·7 grams of nitrogen in oxide B.

25·9 grams of nitrogen combine with 74·1 grams of oxygen.

$$\therefore\ 63{\cdot}7\ \text{,,}\quad\text{,,}\quad\text{,,}\quad \frac{74{\cdot}1 \times 63{\cdot}7}{25{\cdot}9}\quad\text{,,}\quad\text{,,}$$

$$= 182{\cdot}2 \text{ grams.}$$

If the law of multiple proportions is true, then 36·3 and 182·2 should be in a simple ratio to one another. Well, 36·3 × 5 = 181·5, which is very close to 182·2. Hence 36·3 : 182·2 very nearly as 1 : 5, which is a simple ratio. Therefore the Law is true in this case.

Example III.—Phosphorus forms two chlorides. 15·00 grams of the first chloride were found to contain 11·62 grams of chlorine, while 12·00 grams of the second chloride contained 10·22 grams of chlorine. Are these figures in agreement with the Law of Multiple Proportions ?

Let us take 1 gram of phosphorus as our fixed weight of one element. In the FIRST chloride,

$$15{\cdot}00 - 11{\cdot}62 = 3{\cdot}38 \text{ grams} = \text{wt. of phosphorus.}$$

If 3·38 grams phosphorus combine with 11·62 grams chlorine,
then 1 gram „ combines „ $\frac{11{\cdot}62}{3{\cdot}38}$

= 3·44 grams chlorine.

In the SECOND chloride,

$$12{\cdot}00 - 10{\cdot}22 = 1{\cdot}78 \text{ grams} = \text{wt. of phosphorus.}$$

If 1·78 grams phosphorus combine with 10·22 grams chlorine,
then 1 gram „ combines „ $\frac{10{\cdot}22}{1{\cdot}78}$

= 5·74 grams chlorine.

But 3·44 and 5·74 are in the ratio of 3 : 5 ; therefore the law is true in this case.

QUESTIONS

1. Mention some Greek ideas about the structure of matter.

2. What were Aristotle's "four elements" ? Who was Aristotle, and when did he live ?

3. Why do chemists consider Dalton to be the founder of the Atomic Theory ?

4. What are the main points of Dalton's Atomic Theory ?

5. Explain and define the terms *atom* and *molecule*.

6. What do you mean by the *atomicity* of a molecule ?

7. What is the meaning of the term *law* in Science ? Give examples to illustrate your answer.

8. State the *Law of the Conservation of Matter*, and describe an experiment to illustrate its truth.

9. State the *Law of Multiple Proportions*, and describe an experiment to illustrate its truth.

10. How would you attempt to show that the *Law of Constant Composition* is true in a particular instance ?

11. Three oxides of nitrogen have the following compositions by weight :

(i) Nitrogen, 63·64 per cent. Oxygen, 36·36 per cent.
(ii) Nitrogen, 46·67 per cent. Oxygen, 53·33 per cent.
(iii) Nitrogen, 30·43 per cent. Oxygen, 69·57 per cent.

Show that these figures serve to illustrate the Law of Multiple Proportions.

12. The following compositions by weight were shown by the two chlorides of iron :

(i) Iron, 44·1 per cent. Chlorine, 55·9 per cent.

(ii) Iron, 34·46 per cent. Chlorine, 65·54 per cent.

Illustrate from these data the Law of Multiple Proportions.

13. Two oxides of sulphur have the following composition by weight :

(i) Sulphur, 50·0 per cent. Oxygen, 50·0 per cent.

(ii) Sulphur, 40·0 per cent. Oxygen, 60·0 per cent.

Show how this illustrates the Law of Multiple Proportions.

14. Water and hydrogen peroxide have the following composition by weight :

(i) *Water* : Hydrogen, 11·11 per cent. Oxygen, 88·89 per cent.

(ii) *Hydrogen peroxide* : Hydrogen, 5·88 per cent. Oxygen, 94·12 per cent.

Do these data support the Law of Multiple Proportions ?

15. Two manganese salts of potassium have the following composition by weight :

(i) Potassium, 39·6 per cent. MnO_4, 60·4 per cent.

(ii) Potassium, 24·7 per cent. MnO_4, 75·3 per cent.

Show how these figures illustrate the Law of Multiple Proportions.

16. Two oxides of carbon have the following composition by weight :

(i) Carbon, 28·44 per cent. Oxygen, 71·56 per cent.

(ii) Carbon, 44·28 per cent. Oxygen, 55·72 per cent.

Illustrate the Law of Multiple Proportions from these data.

17. A metal forms two oxides. 1·000 gram of one oxide on reduction in a current of hydrogen yielded 0·799 grams of metal. 1·000 gram of the second oxide, on similar treatment, yielded 0·888 grams of metal.

Calculate the equivalent of the metal in each case, and show that the results are in agreement with the Law of Multiple Proportions.

CHAPTER VIII

MOLECULAR AND ATOMIC WEIGHTS

We have seen in the last chapter that the conclusions drawn from Dalton's Atomic Theory are found to be true in practice. This is strong evidence that atoms and molecules really do exist. Recent work by SIR J. J. THOMSON, LORD RUTHERFORD and others has put the matter beyond doubt, and we can now measure the actual size of these minute particles. They are extraordinarily small—so small that we shall never be able to see them, even with a microscope—but by charging them with electricity we can follow their movements almost as well as if they were large enough to be seen by the naked eye. To get some idea of how small atoms are, imagine a glass globe about the size of an electric light bulb completely evacuated of all matter. Then suppose a tiny hole were made, big enough to allow 10,000,000 atoms to pass through into the globe every second. How long do you think it would take for the globe to fill ? Your guess will probably be very wide of the mark, for the true answer is 100,000 years ! A single atom of hydrogen weighs about 0·00000000000000000000000167 grams.

Small as these atoms are, they are not simple bodies, but consist of even smaller particles of negative electricity revolving around a central positively-charged nucleus, rather like planets revolving around a sun. Still, in chemistry we regard them as indivisible wholes, and indeed they behave as such in ordinary chemical reactions.

Since atoms and molecules are so extraordinarily minute, to know their actual weight is not very useful, although it is, of course, interesting. It is far more important for us to know how many times one kind of atom or molecule is heavier than another; that is, we want to know their *relative* weights. In order that these relative weights shall all be greater than 1, we choose as our standard the weight of the lightest known atom, namely, that of hydrogen, and take that as our unit. We then find how many times a given atom or molecule is heavier than the atom of hydrogen, and call the number so obtained the *atomic weight* of the element, or the *molecular weight* of the substance concerned.

DEFINITIONS:

Atomic Weight.—*The atomic weight of an element is a* number, *representing the number of times its atom is heavier than the atom of hydrogen.*

Molecular Weight.—*The molecular weight of an element or compound is a* number, *representing the number of times its molecule is heavier than the ATOM of hydrogen.*

Note carefully that (like equivalents) atomic and molecular weights are *numbers or ratios merely*, and tell us nothing of the actual weight in grams of the atom or molecule. All the information they give us is, that *if* the hydrogen atom weighs x grams, then the atom of oxygen for example (Atomic Weight 16), weighs $16x$ grams, and the molecule of marble (Molecular Weight 100) weighs $100x$ grams and so on. This conception is very useful in practice, for if we know the relative numbers of atoms or molecules taking part in a reaction, and also know their atomic or molecular weights, we shall know also the *relative weights in grams* (or in any other units) of the substances concerned. Thus, suppose we knew that one molecule of caustic potash is neutralized by one molecule of hydrochloric acid, and that the molecular weight of caustic potash is 56 while that of hydrochloric acid is 36·5; we could then say that when caustic potash and hydrochloric acid react they do so in the proportions by weight of 56 to 36·5 in any units we cared to choose, probably grams, but equally truly in pounds or ounces.

In 1811, AMEDEO AVOGADRO, Professor of Physics at Turin

University (see frontispiece), was struck by some remarkable results on the combination of gases obtained by the French chemist, GAY-LUSSAC. Gay-Lussac had found that *when gases react together, their volumes are in a simple ratio to one another and to the volumes of the products if these are gaseous.* This is known as **Gay-Lussac's Law** or the **Law of Gaseous Volumes**, and may be illustrated by the following examples :

(i) 1 vol. of hydrogen combines with 1 vol. of chlorine to form 2 vols. of hydrogen chloride.

(ii) 2 vols. of carbon monoxide combine with 1 vol. of oxygen to form 2 vols. of carbon dioxide.

(iii) 2 vols. of hydrogen combine with 1 vol. of oxygen to form 2 vols. of steam.

(iv) 1 vol. of nitrogen combines with 3 vols. of hydrogen to form 2 vols. of ammonia.

Avogadro saw that these very significant results could easily be explained by making a simple hypothesis, which can be expressed as follows.

Avogadro's Hypothesis.

Equal volumes of all gases under the same conditions of temperature and pressure contain equal numbers of molecules.

This famous hypothesis, which was not finally accepted by chemists until Avogadro's countryman, CANNIZZARO, explained its great value very clearly in 1858 (two years after Avogadro's death), is really the foundation-stone of modern chemistry. Practically all our theoretical views, if traced back to their ultimate basis, are found to rest on Avogadro's Hypothesis. It is not possible for a beginner at chemistry to understand its importance fully, but he will be able to get some idea of its great value by observing how it renders possible the *determination of molecular weights*, as described in the following pages.

(a) **Vapour Density.**—The density of a gaseous substance, that is, its mass per unit volume, is always very small, so chemists prefer to express the density of such substances in terms of the density of hydrogen taken as unity. This applies not only to substances which are normally gaseous, but to the vapours of all substances which can be vaporized. Hence the VAPOUR DENSITY of a substance is the relative density of its vapour in terms of that of hydrogen as unity, or *the number of times a certain volume of its vapour is heavier than the same volume of hydrogen under the same conditions of temperature and pressure.*

We shall arrive at an important conclusion if we consider this definition in the light of Avogadro's Hypothesis. We have, at constant temperature and pressure,

$$\text{Vapour Density} = \frac{\text{weight of a certain volume of vapour}}{\text{weight of the same volume of hydrogen}}$$

$$\therefore \text{ by Avogadro, V.D.} = \frac{\text{weight of } n \text{ molecules of the vapour}}{\text{weight of } n \text{ molecules of hydrogen}}$$

$$= \frac{\text{weight of 1 molecule of the substance}}{\text{weight of 1 molecule of hydrogen}}.$$

In other words, *the number which expresses the vapour density of a substance is also the number of times the molecule of the substance is heavier than the molecule of hydrogen.*

If we combine this with the definition of molecular weight, we shall make another important step, for

$$\text{M.W.} = \frac{\text{weight of 1 molecule of the substance}}{\text{weight of 1 } atom \text{ of hydrogen}}, \text{ and}$$

$$\text{V.D.} = \frac{\text{weight of 1 molecule of the substance}}{\text{weight of 1 } molecule \text{ of hydrogen}}.$$

Therefore the **molecular weight of a substance is as many times its vapour density as there are atoms in the molecule of hydrogen.**

Now we are beginning to see our way to the determination of molecular weights, and can realize the importance of Avogadro's Hypothesis. If only we can find how many atoms (" x ") there are in the molecule of hydrogen we shall be able to find the molecular weight of any gaseous or volatile substance simply by measuring how many times a certain volume of the gas or vapour is heavier than the same volume of hydrogen under the same conditions of temperature and pressure, and then multiplying this number by "x."

(b) **Atomicity of the Hydrogen Molecule.**—It has been found by experiment that any definite volume of hydrogen will combine with an equal volume of chlorine to form twice that volume of hydrochloric acid gas, or

1 volume of hydrogen combines with 1 volume of chlorine, forming 2 volumes of hydrochloric acid gas.

Hence, by Avogadro's Hypothesis,

1 molecule of hydrogen combines with **1 molecule** of chlorine, forming 2 **molecules** of hydrochloric acid gas.

Therefore, since all molecules of hydrochloric acid gas must be identical, each of them must contain **half a molecule** of hydrogen. But if the molecule of hydrogen consisted of one atom, or of any *odd* number of atoms, it could not be divided into halves, for atoms are indivisible. Hence *the molecule of hydrogen must contain at least* 2 *atoms.*

No facts have ever come to light which render it likely that the molecule of hydrogen contains *more* than 2 atoms, so we are justified in assuming that it is in reality *di-atomic*, *i.e.* it consists of 2 atoms.

We have already seen that the molecular weight of a substance is equal to its vapour density multiplied by the number of atoms in the molecule of hydrogen. We have now found that the molecule of hydrogen contains 2 atoms. Hence

The molecular weight of a substance is twice its vapour density.

To find the molecular weight of a substance, therefore, all we have to do is to determine its vapour density and multiply by 2. You are now able to see one of the reasons why chemists set so much store by Avogadro's Hypothesis.

Methods of Determining Vapour Density

1. **Gases.**—In the case of a gas, we take a glass globe, evacuate it with an air-pump, weigh it, fill it with the gas and then weigh it again. We then evacuate it once more,

fill it with hydrogen at the same temperature and pressure, and re-weigh. Then

$$\text{V.D. of gas} = \frac{(\text{Wt. of globe} + \text{gas}) - (\text{wt. of globe})}{(\text{Wt. of globe} + \text{hydrogen}) - (\text{wt. of globe})}$$

Of course, to get accurate results certain precautions have to be taken, but in principle the method is very simple.

2. **Volatile Liquids (and Solids).**—To determine the vapour density of a volatile substance we use a method invented by VICTOR MEYER. The apparatus (Fig. 25) consists of an inner tube A, the lower end of which is enlarged into a cylindrical bulb, while the upper end is enlarged to carry a rubber stopper H. Towards the upper end of the tube A there is a side-neck B communicating with a pneumatic trough C. The inner tube is surrounded by a wider outer tube or jacket G, at the bottom of which is a bulb F in which are placed 70–80 c.c. of a liquid whose boiling-point is at least 30° higher than that of the liquid whose vapour density is required. The apparatus is set up as shown, except that the graduated tube D is not yet placed over the end of the side-neck. The liquid in F is boiled and the heating continued until the temperature of the inner tube is constant, that is, when no more bubbles of air escape from the end of the side-neck, and no water is sucked back. When this is so, the graduated tube, filled with water, is placed in position (as is shown in the figure).

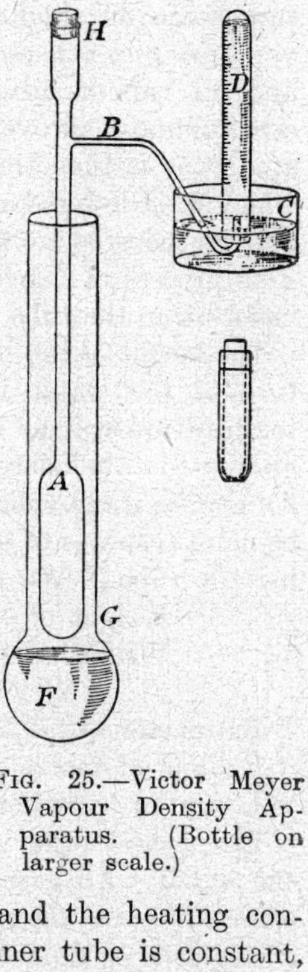

FIG. 25.—Victor Meyer Vapour Density Apparatus. (Bottle on larger scale.)

Meanwhile a small bottle, of such a size that it slips easily down the tube A, is weighed empty and is then filled with the liquid whose V.D. is required, and weighed again. Next, the cork is removed, the weighed bottle and contents dropped in, and the cork replaced—all as quickly as possible. The bottle falls to the bottom of the inner tube, where a little glass wool may be placed to break its fall. The liquid in the little bottle now finds itself in a place which is at a temperature some 30° higher than its boiling-point. It therefore vaporizes *very rapidly* and blows the stopper out of the bottle; and the vapour, advancing up the tube *en masse*, drives its own volume of air over into the graduated tube D. The graduated tube is then transferred to a deep jar full of water, in which it is lowered until the levels of the water inside and outside the tube are the same, and the volume of the air read. This process of "levelling" is necessary in order to get the moist air in the tube at atmospheric pressure.

The height of the barometer is then read, and the temperature of the water in the pneumatic trough taken. This temperature will be the temperature of the moist air in the graduated tube, since the air has passed through the water. (Of course, if the volume of air is not read off at once, it would be more accurate to take the temperature of the air surrounding the tube.) We now have the following data—

Weight of bottle + liquid $= x$ gms.
Weight of bottle $= y$ gms.
$\therefore$ Weight of liquid $= x - y$ gms.

Barometer = say 770 mm. Temperature = say 15° C.

Volume of moist air after levelling $= m$ c.c.

1 litre of hydrogen at N.T.P. weighs 0·09 gms.

From these data we can calculate the Vapour Density of the liquid. All gases obey the same gas-laws, therefore *the volume of air in the graduated tube is equal to the volume which $x - y$ gms. of the substance in the state of moist vapour would occupy if it could exist under the same conditions of temperature and pressure.* The whole point of the method is the ingenious way in which the vapour of the liquid is made to drive over its own volume of air, which remains gaseous under conditions in which the vapour itself could not. One reason for having the temperature of the outer jacket so much higher than the boiling-point of the liquid under experiment will now be clear: it is to ensure that the vapour of the liquid shall come off with a rush, and therefore drive the air over before diffusion of the vapour into the air can take place. If diffusion occurred, the gas driven through the side-neck would consist partly of air and partly of vapour, and as the latter would condense in the water of the trough, the experiment would be useless, since the volume of air collected would no longer be equal to the volume of vapour produced. The shape of the inner tube also helps to prevent diffusion. A second reason for the comparatively high temperature of the outer jacket is that, at temperatures only just above their condensation-points, vapours do not accurately obey Boyle and Charles's Laws. Hence if the temperature of the jacket were only just sufficient to vaporize the liquid, incorrect results would be obtained.

The result is calculated as follows:

Volume of moist air at 770 mm. 15° C. = m c.c.

Vapour pressure of water at 15° C. = 12·7 mm.

∴ true pressure of the air = 770 − 12·7 mm. = 757·3 mm.

Temperature = 15° C. = 288° Absolute.

$$\therefore \text{ Volume of air dry at N.T.P.} = \frac{m \times 757{\cdot}3 \times 273}{760 \times 288}$$

$$= n \text{ c.c.}$$

∴ n c.c. of the vapour at N.T.P. would weigh $x - y$ gms. But n c.c. of hydrogen at N.T.P. weigh $n \times 0{\cdot}00009$ gms.

$$\therefore \text{ Vapour density} = \frac{x - y}{n \times 0{\cdot}00009}$$

and the Molecular Weight of the substance will be twice this.

For liquids which boil up to 70° C., water may be used in the outer jacket. For those with higher boiling-points suitable substances to use in the outer jacket are aniline, B.P. 182°; nitrobenzene, B.P. 208°; sulphur, B.P. 444°, etc.

Alternative Method of finding Molecular Weights of Certain Liquids and Solids (Freezing-Point Method).—Every pure liquid has a perfectly definite freezing-point—pure water, for example, freezes at 0° C. If a substance is dissolved in a liquid, the freezing-point of the solution is lower than that of the pure liquid. Salt water, for instance, freezes at a lower temperature than pure water. The difference between the freezing-point of a pure liquid and that of a solution formed by dissolving a substance in the liquid is called the *depression of the freezing-point* for that particular solution.

When we dissolve a substance in a liquid, we call the latter the *solvent*, while the substance dissolved is called the *solute*. It was found by SIR CHARLES BLAGDEN in 1788 that, using the same solute and the same solvent, *the depression of the freezing-point* caused by dissolving different weights of the solute in the solvent *is directly proportional to the concentration of the solution* [**Blagden's Law**].

For example, suppose that we have a solute S, and that the solvent is water. Suppose also that we find that the depression of the freezing-point produced in a 1 per cent. solution of S in water is 3°. Then we should find (*a*) that a 2 per cent. solution of S in water showed a depression of the freezing-point of 6°, (*b*) that a 3 per cent. solution showed a depression of 9°, (*c*) that a 4 per cent. solution showed a depression of 12°, and so on.

Bearing this in mind, let us turn to some work of RAOULT (1883). If you look at the chapter on Electrolysis (p. 126), you will see that we can divide all substances into two classes, (*a*) those whose aqueous solutions conduct electricity, and (*b*) those whose aqueous solutions do not conduct electricity. The former substances are called *electrolytes* and the latter *non-electrolytes*. All acids, bases and salts are electrolytes, while substances like sugar, alcohol, and glycerol (glycerine) are non-electrolytes.

Now Raoult found that if he took the molecular weight in grams of any non-electrolyte and dissolved it in a fixed volume of water, *he always got the same depression of the freezing-point, whatever non-electrolyte he used.*

To make Raoult's discovery quite clear, let us consider the following example :

Suppose that in each of five beakers, i, ii, iii, iv and v, we place 1,000 c.c. of water. The freezing-point of this water will be 0° C. Let us now take the molecular weights in grams of the five following non-electrolytes—

Urea	(= 60 grams)	Alcohol	(= 46 grams)
Cane-sugar	(= 342 grams)	Resorcinol	(= 110 grams)
Grape-sugar	(= 180 grams)		

and place the urea in i, the cane-sugar in ii, the grape-sugar in iii, the alcohol in iv, and the resorcinol in v, and stir until they have completely dissolved. If we were now to determine the freezing-points of the five solutions, we should find that in every case the freezing-point was − 1·86° C. Evidently we have here another method for determining the molecular weight of a non-electrolyte. All that we need do is to take another beaker with 1,000 c.c. of water in it, and find out how many grams of the substance we have to dissolve in the water to get a solution which will freeze at − 1·86° C. This number of grams will be the molecular weight of the substance. A consideration of Blagden's Law, however, will show us that since the depression in solutions of the same substance is directly proportional to the concentration, we need in practice only to dissolve a known weight of the substance in a measured volume of solvent, and note the depression caused. We can then work out the result by proportion.

First Example.—Suppose that we dissolved 0·378 grams of a substance in 12·4 c.c. of water and found that the depression of the freezing-point produced was 0·32°. What is the Molecular Weight of the substance ?

What we have to do is to calculate, by proportion and Blagden's Law, how many grams of the substance we should have to dissolve in 1,000 c.c. of water to get a solution showing a depression of 1·86° C.

According to the above figures,

0·378 grams dissolved in 12·4 c.c. produced a depression of 0·32°

$$\therefore 0{\cdot}378 \text{ ,, ,, ,, } 1{,}000 \text{ c.c. would give ,, ,, } \frac{0{\cdot}32 \times 12{\cdot}4}{1{,}000}$$

$$= 0{\cdot}004° \text{ (by Blagden's Law).}$$

Now,

if a depression of 0·004° is caused by 0·378 grams in 1,000 c.c.

$$\therefore \text{ ,, ,, } 1{\cdot}86° \text{ ,, ,, } \frac{0{\cdot}378 \times 1{\cdot}86}{0{\cdot}004} \text{ grams}$$

$$= 175{\cdot}8 \text{ grams.}$$

This is the Molecular Weight.

Second Example.—0·3132 grams of fruit-sugar were dissolved in

14·5 c.c of water. The freezing-point of the solution was found to be 0·223° lower than that of pure water. What is the M.W. of fruit-sugar ?

0·3132 grams in 14·5 c.c. gave a depression of 0·223°

$\therefore$ 0·3132 „ „ 1,000 c.c. would give „ „ $\frac{0{\cdot}223 \times 14{\cdot}5}{1{,}000}$

= 0·0032° (by Blagden's Law).

If a depression of 0·003° is caused by 0·3132 grams in 1,000 c.c.

$\therefore$ „ „ 1·86° „ „ $\frac{0{\cdot}3132 \times 1{\cdot}86}{0{\cdot}0032}$ grams

= 182.

This is the Molecular Weight. [Fruit-sugar is $C_6H_{12}O_6$ $\therefore$ M.W. = 180.]

This method of determining the molecular weights of non-electrolytes (alternatively known as the *Cryoscopic Method*) is extremely useful in practice. In carrying it out experimentally, the temperatures have to be measured very accurately, since the depression produced is as a rule very small. For rough work, a thermometer reading to a tenth of a degree is sufficient, since with such an instrument the temperature may be read approximately to the hundredth part of a degree. For more accurate work, a thermometer graduated in hundredths of a degree is employed, enabling the temperature to be estimated to the thousandth part of a degree.

The apparatus used is shown diagrammatically in Fig. 26.

To carry out a determination proceed in the following way. Suppose that you are going to find the molecular weight of cane-sugar. Take a few grams of pure sugar and dry it on filter-paper in a desiccator overnight. Fit up the apparatus shown in the figure. See that the inner tube A is quite dry and then run into it exactly 10 c.c. of water from a burette. Replace the cork with thermometer and stirrer, and stir until ice begins to form in the inner tube. You will probably find (using an ordinary thermometer graduated in tenths of a degree) that the temperature falls considerably below 0° C. before the water freezes—the water becomes, in fact, *super-cooled*. Directly ice begins to form, however, the temperature jumps up to the true freezing-point, which should, of course, be exactly 0° C., but unless the thermometer is unusually accurate, you will probably find that it is slightly above or below 0°. Remove the inner tube from the apparatus, stir well, and note the constant temperature shown as long as there is any ice in the liquid. This is the freezing-point ($t°$) of the water as shown by your thermometer. Allow the remaining ice in the inner tube to melt.

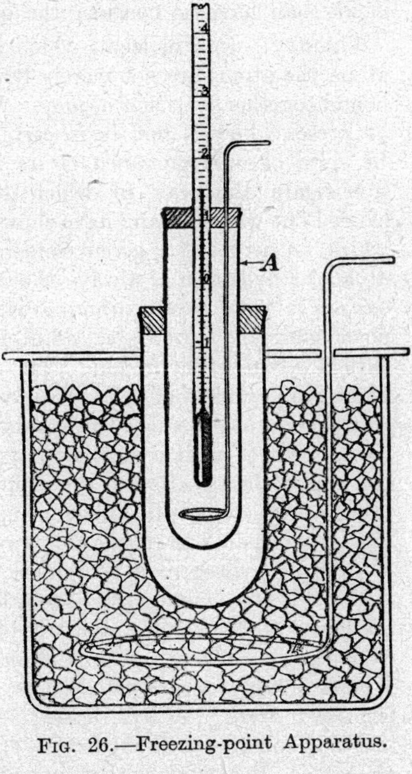

FIG. 26.—Freezing-point Apparatus.

Weigh accurately about 0·5 grams of the dry sugar on a watch-glass, remove the cork from the inner tube, and carefully introduce all the sugar. Shake gently until all is dissolved, taking care that none is left on the sides of the tube. Replace the cork with the thermometer and stirrer, put the inner tube back into the freezing-mixture, stir well, and determine the freezing-point of the solution (t' °) in the manner described above.

Then calculate the Molecular Weight of sugar — that is, find how many grams of it you would have to dissolve in 1,000 c.c. of water to get a depression of the freezing-point of 1·86°.

Besides those which have been described, there are other methods of finding molecular weights, but as they are used only in cases of special difficulty we shall not consider them here.

Methods of Determining Atomic Weights

The determination of atomic weights is not quite so easy as that of molecular weights, and before we can understand it we shall have to consider the question of *valency*.

Valency.—In a molecule which consists of more than one atom, the atoms are not merely lying side by side: they are bound together by *chemical force*. What this force is, nobody at present knows, but it is certainly electrical in nature. In spite of our ignorance of its nature, however, we can investigate the way in which it behaves. Experiments carried out with this aim have shown chemists that the power which an atom of a given element has of combining with atoms of hydrogen is always the same. Thus any atom of oxygen is capable of combining with 2 atoms of hydrogen—never more and never less; an atom of chlorine can combine with 1 atom of hydrogen; that of phosphorus with 3 of hydrogen; and that of carbon with 4 of hydrogen. No element is known which will combine with hydrogen in such a way that there is a smaller proportion of hydrogen in the compound than 1 atom of the element to 1 of hydrogen; in other words, there is no known element of such small combining power that 2 or more atoms of it are required to hold 1 atom of hydrogen in combination.

For this reason, chemists have taken as the unit of combining power of an atom the ability to hold in combination 1 atom of hydrogen. *The number of atoms of hydrogen with which 1 atom of an element will combine is called the VALENCY [i.e. the "worth"] of that element.* Some elements, however, will not combine with hydrogen, but will do so with other elements. It is evident that in such cases the valency of the element cannot be *directly* measured, but if we remember that ability to hold in combination 1 atom of hydrogen is merely the "unit of combining power," we shall be able to measure the valency in an indirect way. For example, lead will not combine with hydrogen, but it will do so with oxygen, in such a way that 1 atom of lead combines with 1 atom of oxygen. Now 1 atom of oxygen will combine with 2 atoms of hydrogen; we therefore assume that if lead and hydrogen could be made to combine they would do so in the proportion of 1 atom of lead to 2 of hydrogen, and therefore say that the valency of lead is *two*. Similarly, gold will not combine with hydrogen, but will with chlorine in such a way that 1 atom of gold combines with 3 of chlorine. Since 1 atom of chlorine will combine with 1 of hydrogen, we say that the valency of gold is 3.

Atoms are chemically indivisible, therefore *the valency of an element must always be a whole number.*

A table of the valencies of the common elements is given on p. 455. You will see that sometimes an element may have more than one valency. There is a reason for this, as chemists have found by an investigation of the structure of atoms, but it is too advanced for us to consider it here.

Relation between Atomic Weight and Equivalent.— Now that we have gained some idea of the nature of valency, we shall be able to see that there is a very close relationship between the three numbers which represent respectively the valency, the atomic weight, and the equivalent of an element. Suppose that 1 atom of an element, of atomic weight, say, 20, combines with 1 atom of hydrogen. We could represent the molecule of the compound as formed (Fig. 27) as—

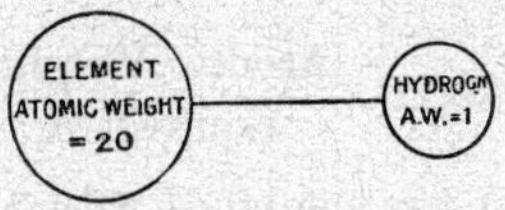

FIG. 27.

What is the equivalent of this element? We know that the equivalent of an element is the number of units of weight of it which will combine or otherwise react with 1 of the same units of weight of hydrogen. *Let the unit of weight chosen in this case be the weight of 1 atom of hydrogen.* Then since the atomic weight of the element is 20, 20 units of weight of it have combined with 1 unit of weight of hydrogen, $\therefore$ its equivalent is 20. But the atomic weight of the element is also 20, $\therefore$ in this case $\frac{\text{Atomic Weight}}{\text{Equivalent}} = 1$. But 1 atom of the element has combined with 1 atom of hydrogen, therefore the valency of the element = 1.

$$\therefore \text{Here, at any rate, } \frac{\text{Atomic Weight}}{\text{Equivalent}} = \text{Valency.}$$

Now let us suppose that 1 atom of the element combines with 2 atoms of hydrogen. The molecule will then be as in Fig. 28.

What is the equivalent of the element here? Choosing the same unit as before, namely, the weight of 1 atom of hydrogen, it is clear that 20 units by weight of the element

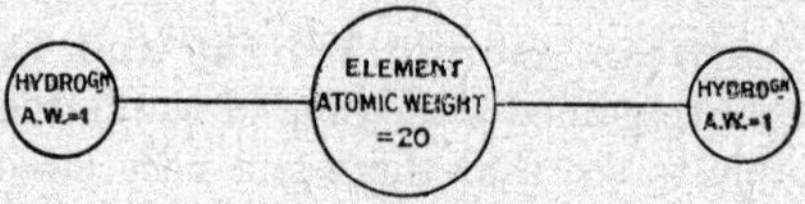

FIG. 28.

have combined with 2 units by weight of hydrogen, $\therefore$ the equivalent of the element $= \frac{20}{2} = 10$. The atomic weight of the element = 20, $\therefore$ $\frac{\text{Atomic Weight}}{\text{Equivalent}} = \frac{20}{10} = 2$. But 1 atom of the element has combined with 2 of hydrogen, therefore the valency is 2, and here again $\frac{\text{Atomic Weight}}{\text{Equivalent}} = \text{Valency}$

Similarly, if 1 atom of the element combines with n atoms of hydrogen, a figure will show that the equivalent $= \frac{\text{Atomic Weight}}{n}$, or $\frac{\text{Atomic Weight}}{\text{Equivalent}} = \text{Valency.}$

This conclusion, that **Atomic Weight = Equivalent × Valency,** is of the greatest importance, and should be very carefully noted. We shall see in the next section how it helps to determine Atomic Weights.

First Method of finding Atomic Weights.—You learnt in Chapter VI that the equivalent of an element can as a rule be determined not only with ease but also with great accuracy. Now, all we need to know, in order to get the atomic weight of an element when we have its equivalent weight, is its valency, for A.W. = E × V. And from the definition of valency, we know that the latter must be some small *whole number*, since it is a *number of atoms*, which are indivisible. Our chief requirement, therefore, is a method of finding the valency of an element. Unfortunately there is no direct method of doing this, but we can carry the position by a flank attack, thanks to a discovery of the French chemists Dulong and Petit.

Dulong and Petit's Law.—Dulong and Petit found that the atomic weight of a solid element multiplied by its specific heat [1] generally equals 6·4 approximately—

$$\text{A.W.} \times \text{S.H.} = 6{\cdot}4 \text{ (about).}$$

6·4 is called the atomic heat, and we could state Dulong and Petit's Law in this way: the atomic heats of all solid elements are the same. Now this is only a very rough rule, but it helps us in this way. If we had to discover the A.W. of a metal, we could first find its specific heat—a very easy thing to do—and then divide this into 6·4. The quotient would give us a rough value for the A.W.

If, next, we divided the rough A.W. by the exact equivalent, as determined by one of the ways described in Chapter VI, we should get the *approximate* valency. But we know that the valency, being a number of atoms (see definition, p. 102), must be a *whole number*. Hence we take the nearest

[1] Specific heat of a substance is the number of calories required to raise the temperature of 1 gram of it 1 Centigrade degree.

A calorie is the amount of heat required to raise the temperature of 1 gram of water 1 Centigrade degree.

whole number to the rough valency as being the *true* valency. Thus, if the valency came out to 2·9, we should know that it was really 3, and so on. Having thus obtained the exact equivalent and the true valency, all we have to do is to multiply them together to get the true Atomic Weight.

Second Method of Finding Atomic Weights.—A little reflection will show you that, since the smallest number of atoms of an element which can possibly exist in the molecule of any of its compounds is *one*, the smallest *weight* of that element which can possibly exist in the *molecular weight* of any of its compounds must be the *atomic weight* of the element. If you haven't grasped the idea yet, read the sentence through again, and continue until you have thoroughly understood it.

Suppose we took a large number of compounds of a given element. We should be very unfortunate if at least one of those compounds did not contain *one* atom of the element per molecule. Suppose now we (*a*) found the molecular weights of all those compounds, and (*b*) analysed them and calculated the weight of the given element in the molecular weight of each compound. Then the smallest weight of that element in the molecular weight of any of the compounds would give an upper limit for its atomic weight—that is, the A.W. could not be *greater* than this. If we could be *sure* that the compound in question contained only *one* atom of the element per molecule, we should know that the number obtained was the real atomic weight, but of course this is a point on which we unfortunately cannot be certain.

Anyhow, if we examine a large number of compounds of the element, we shall be justified in taking the smallest weight of that element which we find in the molecular weight of any of those compounds as the atomic weight, until some fact turns up which shows that we are wrong.

For an example, let us consider the case of carbon. This element forms many compounds whose molecular weights are easily determined, some of which give the following data on analysis :

Compound.	*Mol. Wt.*	*Parts by wt. of Carbon in Mol. Wt.*
Acetylene	26	24
Methane	16	12
Ethylene	28	24
Ethane	30	24
Carbon monoxide	28	12
Carbon dioxide	44	12
Benzene	78	72
Alcohol	46	24
Cane-sugar	342	144
Grape-sugar	180	72
Carbon disulphide	76	12

From these figures it is concluded that the atomic weight of carbon is 12. No carbon compound has ever been discovered the molecular weight of which contains less than 12 parts by weight of carbon. If such a compound were discovered, we should have to alter the atomic weight : an event which is unlikely to occur, as we can get additional evidence on atomic weights in ways which are too advanced to be discussed here. All agree in pointing to the value 12 for the atomic weight of carbon.

Questions

1. Define *Atomic Weight* and *Molecular Weight.*
2. State *Gay-Lussac's Law.*
3. State *Avogadro's Hypothesis* and explain its importance.
4. Define *vapour density.* What is the relation between the vapour density of a substance and its molecular weight ?
5. What evidence is there to show that the molecule of hydrogen contains an even number of atoms, at least two ?
6. Describe Victor Meyer's method of determining vapour densities.
7. Describe the cryoscopic method of determining molecular weights.
8. State *Blagden's Law.*
9. Define *valency.* What is the relation between the atomic weight, the equivalent, and the valency of an element ?
10. How would you proceed to find the atomic weight of a metal experimentally ?
11. State *Dulong and Petit's Law* and explain its use.
12. Define *atomic heat, specific heat* and *calorie.*
13. In a Victor Meyer's experiment 0·1185 grams of chloroform displaced 24·0 c.c. air measured over water at 12° and 760·5 mm. pres-

sure. Vapour tension of water at 12° = 10·5 mm. Find from these data the vapour density of chloroform.

14. A Victor Meyer determination of the vapour density of a liquid gives the following data:

Temperature	= 15° C.
Pressure of atmosphere	= 776·8 mm.
Weight of liquid taken	= 0·0789 grams.
Volume of air displaced collected over water	= 25·2 c.c.

Find the vapour density of the liquid.

15. A substance weighing 0·3370 grams displaced, in a Victor Meyer's apparatus, 31·6 c.c. of air measured over water at 18·5° C., the height of the barometer being 774·1 mm. What is the vapour density of the substance?

16. In a Victor Meyer determination 0·3130 grams of a liquid gave 38·6 c.c. of gas collected over water and measured at 16·9° C. and 769·3 mm. pressure. Calculate the vapour density of the liquid.

17. In a Victor Meyer determination of vapour density, 0·0967 grams of a substance displaced 22·4 c.c. of air, measured over water at 17·2° C. and 764·2 mm. pressure. What is the vapour density of the substance?

18. 1·8 grams of a substance dissolved in 25 grams of water gave a depression of the freezing-point of 0·4° C. Find the molecular weight of the substance.

19. When 0·936 grams of a substance were dissolved in 26·9 grams of water, the freezing-point was depressed by 1·078° C. Find the molecular weight of the substance.

20. 5·0 grams of a metal, on heating in the air, yielded 6·25 grams of its oxide. The specific heat of the metal is 0·096. What is its atomic weight?

CHAPTER IX

FORMULÆ AND EQUATIONS

Chemists are like other men—they are anxious to save themselves unnecessary work. As a means to this end they have invented formulæ and equations which enable them to remember, and to express, a great deal about chemicals and chemical actions with very little trouble. If, therefore, you are just beginning the study of chemistry, don't be alarmed when you come across mysterious symbols such as $2KClO_3 = 2KCl + 3O_2$! They are not at all terrible, and if you

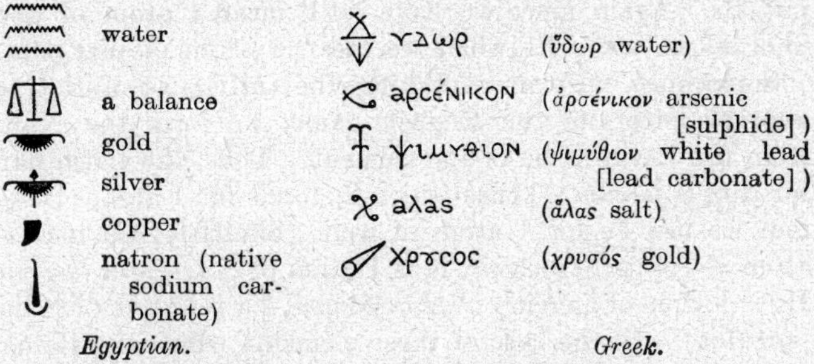

FIG. 29.—Ancient Chemical Symbols.

will give your mind seriously to the matter for an hour or two you will find that formulæ and equations, instead of being fearful obstacles to overcome, are just the very things you want to help you on your way. They are very different indeed from their ancestors—the cabbalistic signs which ancient chemists used to employ to keep their knowledge secret, and of which you will see a few illustrated in Fig. 29.

Dalton used a notation involving a system of circles, and

the opposite page is reproduced from Part II of his book, *A New System of Chemical Philosophy*.

Our present symbols and formulæ, introduced by BERZELIUS (1779–1848), are meant to make things plain rather than to shroud them in mystery, and they succeed admirably.

Atoms.—When a chemist wants to say "1 atom of nitrogen," as he does very often, he is too lazy to write it out in full every time, so he simply writes N. Similarly, for 1 atom of hydrogen he puts H, and for single atoms of carbon, oxygen, sulphur, phosphorus and iodine he puts C, O, S, P, and I respectively. There is nothing very difficult in that, is there? In exactly the same way, for 1 atom of any other element he uses just the initial letter of the name of the element. But what is he going to do when there are two or more elements whose names begin with the same letter? Well, in that case, instead of using the initial letter only, he uses the initial letter and another letter of the name, *e.g.* B means 1 atom of boron, so for 1 atom of bromine we put Br. Again, since we have let P mean 1 atom of phosphorus, we write Pt when we mean 1 atom of platinum.

Sometimes, instead of taking the initial, or initial and another letter, of the English name, we form the symbol from the Latin name of the element. Thus, the Latin name for iron is *ferrum*; hence (since F stands for 1 atom of fluorine) we use Fe for 1 atom of iron. Similarly, Cu means 1 atom of copper (*cuprum*), K is 1 atom of potassium (*kalium*), Hg is 1 atom of mercury (*hydrargyrum*), Na is 1 atom of sodium (*natrium*). In the case of those elements which the Romans did not know, we cannot use the true Latin name (because there isn't one), but chemists have concocted names which look as though they might be Latin—*e.g. kalium* and *natrium* (for potassium and sodium), just mentioned.

Remember, then, that *the symbol for an element stands for a perfectly definite quantity of that element, namely*, 1 ATOM. Whatever you do, don't write H, for example, for "hydrogen" in general. H is 1 *atom* of hydrogen, and if you use the symbol H as shorthand for "hydrogen," every chemist will cut you dead.

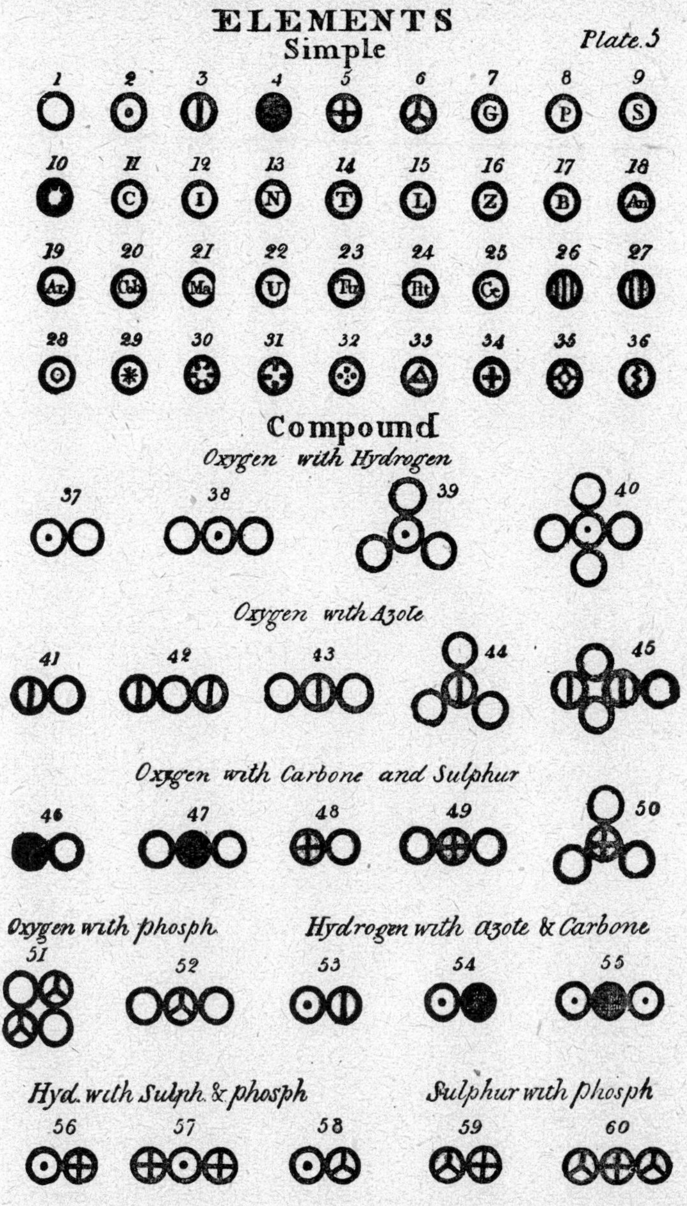
ELEMENTS
Simple
Plate 5
1 2 3 4 5 6 7 8 9
G P S
10 11 12 13 14 15 16 17 18
C I N T L Z B Au
19 20 21 22 23 24 25 26 27
Ar Cob Ma U Tu Tit Ce
28 29 30 31 32 33 34 35 36
Compound
Oxygen with Hydrogen
37 38 39 40
Oxygen with Azote
41 42 43 44 45
Oxygen with Carbone and Sulphur
46 47 48 49 50
Oxygen with phosph.
51 52
Hydrogen with azote & Carbone
53 54 55
Hyd. with Sulph. & phosph
56 57 58
Sulphur with Phosph
59 60

The table below should be learnt by heart. The names in brackets are the "Latin" names.

TABLE OF SYMBOLS FOR 1 ATOM OF COMMON ELEMENTS

Element.	Symbol.	Element.	Symbol.	Element.	Symbol.
Aluminium . .	Al	Iodine	I	Phosphorus . .	P
Barium . . .	Ba	Iron (*ferrum*) . .	Fe	Potassium (*kalium*)	K
Bromine . . .	Br	Lead (*plumbum*) .	Pb	Silicon	Si
Calcium . . .	Ca	Magnesium . .	Mg	Sulphur . . .	S
Carbon . . .	C	Manganese . . .	Mn	Silver (*argentum*) .	Ag
Chlorine . . .	Cl	Mercury (*hydrargyrum*) . . .	Hg	Sodium (*natrium*).	Na
Copper (*cuprum*)	Cu	Nitrogen . . .	N	Sulphur . . .	S
Gold (*aurum*) . .	Au	Oxygen . . .	O	Tin (*stannum*) .	Sn
Hydrogen . . .	H			Zinc	Zn

Suppose we wanted to say shortly "2 atoms of oxygen, not joined together"—well, we write 2O. Similarly, 10H and 5Na mean 10 atoms of hydrogen, all separate, and 5 atoms of sodium, all separate.

Molecules.—We know, however, that in ordinary hydrogen gas, the atoms are sociable and go about in pairs, and that the smallest particle of hydrogen which normally exists, that is, the *molecule*, is thus *diatomic* (consisting of *two* atoms). To express a molecule of hydrogen, therefore, we put H_2.

That is, "H_2" means "1 molecule of hydrogen, consisting of 2 atoms joined together," while "2H" means "2 atoms of hydrogen, not joined together," and "$2H_2$" means "2 molecules of hydrogen, each consisting of 2 atoms joined together."

Again, $3O_2$ means 3 molecules of oxygen each consisting of 2 atoms, while $2O_3$ means 2 molecules of ozone (p. 201) each containing 3 atoms of oxygen. For practice, say what the following formulæ stand for: (i) $3N_2$. (ii) P_4. (iii) $3S_8$. (iv) $10Cl_2$. (v) 18K. (vi) 2Ag. (vii) 3Al. (viii) $5I_2$.

The *formulæ of compounds* are written similarly. Thus H_2SO_4 stands for 1 *molecule* of sulphuric acid, consisting of 2 atoms of hydrogen, 1 of sulphur, and 4 of oxygen. $2H_2SO_4$

means 2 molecules of sulphuric acid—a figure in front of a formula refers to the *whole* of the formula.

EXAMPLES.

$2KNO_3$ = 2 molecules of potassium nitrate, each consisting of 1 atom of potassium (K), 1 of nitrogen and 3 of oxygen.

3NaCl = 3 molecules of common salt, sodium chloride, each consisting of 1 atom of sodium (Na) and 1 of chlorine.

$5KMnO_4$ = 5 molecules of potassium permanganate, each consisting of 1 atom of potassium, 1 of manganese, and 4 of oxygen.

EXERCISES.—Say what the following formulæ mean—

(i) $3HNO_3$ (HNO_3 = 1 molecule of nitric acid).
(ii) 5HCl (HCl = 1 ,, ,, hydrochloric acid).
(iii) $2NaNO_3$ ($NaNO_3$ = 1 ,, ,, sodium nitrate).
(iv) $6CaCO_3$ ($CaCO_3$ = 1 ,, ,, calcium carbonate).
(v) 2NaOH (NaOH = 1 ,, caustic soda or sodium hydroxide).

In copper nitrate, each copper atom is combined with two $—NO_3$ groups, and we write the formula for 1 molecule of this compound $Cu(NO_3)_2$. We could, of course, write CuN_2O_6 if we liked, but this would not show the relation between copper nitrate and nitric acid (HNO_3) so well as the formula $Cu(NO_3)_2$. $Cu(NO_3)_2$ is read "Cu, NO_3 *twice*," and *not* Cu, NO_3 *two*. Similarly, $Ca_3(PO_4)_2$, the formula for 1 molecule of calcium phosphate, is read "Ca three, PO_4 twice." In other words, a small figure after a bracket refers to all within the bracket.

EXAMPLES.

$Al_2(SO_4)_3$ is read Al *two*, SO_4 *three times*, and stands for 1 molecule of aluminium sulphate, consisting of 2 atoms of aluminium and three SO_4 groups (or 3 atoms of sulphur and 12 of oxygen).

$Ba(OH)_2$ is read Ba, OH *twice*, and stands for 1 molecule of barium hydroxide, consisting of 1 atom of barium and 2 —OH groups (or 2 atoms of oxygen and 2 of hydrogen).

$Ca(OCl)_2$ is read Ca, OCl *twice* (1 molecule of calcium hypochlorite), but $CaOCl_2$ is read Ca, O, Cl *two* (1 molecule of bleaching-powder).

EXERCISES.—Read the following formulæ and say what they tell you about the composition of the molecules of the substances—

(i) $Ca(ClO_3)_2$ —calcium chlorate.
(ii) $KClO_3$ —potassium chlorate.
(iii) $AlPO_4$ —aluminium phosphate.
(iv) $Ba_3(PO_4)_2$ —barium phosphate.
(v) $Al(NO_3)_3$ —aluminium nitrate.

(vi) K_2SO_4 —potassium sulphate.
(vii) $Al_2(SO_4)_3$ —aluminium sulphate.
(viii) H_3PO_3 —phosphorous acid.
(ix) $KHSO_4$ —potassium bisulphate.
(x) $C_{12}H_{22}O_{11}$ —cane sugar.

N.B.—*Remember that the formula of a compound stands for* 1 MOLECULE *of that compound,* and not for the compound in bulk.

Equations.—We have already seen that in a chemical reaction no matter is created and none is destroyed. Hence, the same numbers of the same atoms exist after the change as before it, but after the change they are not combined together in the same way as they were before the change took place. We can express this fact in a *chemical equation.* The left-hand side of the equation shows how the atoms are arranged originally, and the right-hand side shows their new grouping after the change has occurred. Since the same numbers of the same atoms occur on both sides, we can put the sign of equality between, *e.g.*

$$Zn + H_2SO_4 = ZnSO_4 + H_2.$$

If you examine this equation, you will see that on the left-hand side, *and on the right-hand side,* we have 1 atom of zinc, 2 of hydrogen, 1 of sulphur, and 4 of oxygen. And since, so far as we know, the Law of the Conservation of Matter (p. 34) is *always* obeyed by chemical compounds, it follows that our equations, if they are correct, must *always* have the same numbers of the same atoms on both sides. This equation, for example, is wrong :

$$Zn + H_2SO_4 = ZnSO_2 + H_2,$$

since on the left-hand side we have 4 atoms of oxygen and on the right only 2. You should therefore always check your equations by counting up the atoms.

Now, what does this equation, $Zn + H_2SO_4 = ZnSO_4 + H_2$, tell us ? It tells us :

(i) That, *under certain conditions which are not mentioned, and which we could not find out from the equation,* zinc and sulphuric acid will act upon one another in such a way that hydrogen is displaced from the acid and zinc takes its place.

(ii) That 1 atom of zinc will act upon 1 molecule of sul

phuric acid, containing 2 atoms of hydrogen, 1 of sulphur and 4 of oxygen, to give 1 molecule of zinc sulphate, containing 1 atom of zinc, 1 of sulphur, and 4 of oxygen; and 1 molecule of hydrogen, containing 2 atoms.

(iii) That the valency of zinc is 2 (since 1 atom of zinc has taken the place of 2 of hydrogen), and that the valency of the SO_4 group of atoms is also 2.

If we know the atomic weights of the elements concerned (Zn = 65; H = 1; S = 32; O = 16) it tells us:

(iv) That 65 units of weight of zinc will react with 98 of the same units of weight ($= 2 + 32 + 4 \times 16$) of sulphuric acid to give 161 ($65 + 32 + 4 \times 16$) units of weight of zinc sulphate and 2 units of weight of hydrogen. Hence, suppose we wanted to get 1 ton of hydrogen, how much zinc should we have to use, and how much zinc sulphate should we get? Well, the equation is true whatever units we employ, so long as we employ the same units throughout. We can therefore see from the equation that

65 tons of zinc yield 2 tons of hydrogen and 161 tons of zinc sulphate,

$\therefore$ 1 ton of hydrogen will be given by $\frac{65}{2}$ tons of zinc, and $\frac{161}{2}$ tons of zinc sulphate would be formed at the same time.

Ans.—32·5 tons of zinc; 80·5 tons of zinc sulphate.

Or, again, what weight of sulphuric acid should we require to dissolve 10 grams of zinc?

65 grams of zinc require 98 grams of sulphuric acid,

$$\therefore 10 \quad " \quad " \quad " \quad \frac{98 \times 10}{65} \quad " \quad " \quad "$$

$$= 15{\cdot}08 \text{ grams.}$$

EXERCISES.—Interpret the following equations:

(i) $KOH + HNO_3 = KNO_3 + H_2O$.
(ii) $KOH + HCl = KCl + H_2O$.
(iii) $Na_2CO_3 + 2HCl = 2NaCl + H_2O + CO_2$.
(iv) $NH_4Cl + NaOH = NaCl + H_2O + NH_3$.
(v) $2NH_4Cl + Ca(OH)_2 = CaCl_2 + 2H_2O + 2NH_3$.
(vi) $2KClO_3 = 2KCl + 3O_2$.

N.B.—KOH	= 1 molecule of	caustic potash or potassium hydroxide.
HNO_3	= 1 ,, ,,	nitric acid.
KNO_3	= 1 ,, ,,	potassium nitrate.
HCl	= 1 ,, ,,	hydrochloric acid.
KCl	= 1 ,, ,,	potassium chloride.
Na_2CO_3	= 1 ,, ,,	sodium carbonate.
$NaCl$	= 1 ,, ,,	salt or sodium chloride.
CO_2	= 1 ,, ,,	carbon dioxide.
NH_4Cl	= 1 ,, ,,	ammonium chloride.
$NaOH$	= 1 ,, ,,	caustic soda or sodium hydroxide.
NH_3	= 1 ,, ,,	ammonia.
H_2O	= 1 ,, ,,	water.
$Ca(OH)_2$	= 1 ,, ,,	slaked lime or calcium hydroxide.
$CaCl_2$	= 1 ,, ,,	calcium chloride.
$KClO_3$	= 1 ,, ,,	potassium chlorate.

What information about the reaction between zinc and sulphuric acid does the equation

$$Zn + H_2SO_4 = ZnSO_4 + H_2$$

not give us—information that perhaps we should like to have ?

(i) It does not tell us whether it is necessary to apply heat or not.

(ii) It does not tell us whether we can use the concentrated acid or whether we have to dilute it.

(iii) It tells us nothing of the physical states of the substances concerned, *i.e.* whether they are solids, liquids, or gases.

(iv) It does not tell us whether heat is given out or taken in during the reaction.

(v) It does not tell us how long the action takes.

(vi) It does not tell us whether anything is precipitated or not, or whether the action is explosive or not.

In other words, therefore, an equation gives us a good deal of information about the reaction it represents, but it leaves a great deal untold. A man who learnt chemistry by means of equations *only* would know very little. On the other hand, an equation is very useful, since the information which it does give is *definite*, and is also as a rule that which it is most important for us to know. Equations, in short, are more useful in enabling us to *remember* our chemical knowledge than in helping us to *acquire* it.

We have not yet, however, extracted all the assistance which an equation can give us. Equations are particularly valuable when we are dealing with gases, for they enable us to calculate the *volumes* of the gases concerned.

It is found by experiment that 2 grams of hydrogen at N.T.P. occupy 22·4 litres.[1] Let us suppose that the number of molecules in 22·4 litres of hydrogen at N.T.P. is *n*. Then, by Avogadro's Hypothesis, 22·4 litres of any other gas at N.T.P. would also contain *n* molecules. Hence the ratio

$$\frac{\text{weight of 22·4 litres of a gas at N.T.P.}}{\text{weight of 22·4 litres of hydrogen at N.T.P.}}$$

is equal to the ratio

$$\frac{\text{weight of } n \text{ molecules of the gas}}{\text{weight of } n \text{ molecules of hydrogen}},$$

or, in other words, the *vapour density* of the gas (p. 93). But we know that the vapour density is half the molecular weight of the gas (p. 94); therefore, if *n* molecules of hydrogen weigh 2 grams, *n* molecules of the gas must weigh the *molecular weight in grams* of the *gas*. It follows, therefore, that *the molecular weight in grams of any gas at N.T.P. occupies* 22·4 *litres.*

The molecular weight in grams of a substance is called its GRAM-MOLECULAR-WEIGHT, or G.M.W., and the volume occupied by the G.M.W. of a gas at N.T.P., *i.e.* 22·4 litres, is called its GRAM-MOLECULAR-VOLUME, or G.M.V.

Learn: **The molecular weight in grams (G.M.W.) of any substance in the state of gas occupies 22·4 litres at N.T.P.**

By means of the Gas Laws, we can easily calculate what volume the G.M.W. (and, by proportion, any other weight) of a gas would occupy at any other temperature and pressure.

EXAMPLES.—1. *What volume of hydrogen, measured dry at N.T.P., would be liberated by the action of* 13 *grams of zinc upon dilute sulphuric acid?*

---

[1] Strictly, 22·4 litres of hydrogen at N.T.P. weigh 2·016 gm. For elementary purposes the difference may be neglected.

The equation is

$$Zn + H_2SO_4 = ZnSO_4 + H_2.$$

∴ 65 grams of zinc give 2 grams of hydrogen.

∴ 13 „ „ „ $\frac{2 \times 13}{65} = 0{\cdot}4$ grams.

But 2 grams of hydrogen = G.M.W. of hydrogen.

∴ 2 „ „ occupy 22·4 litres at N.T.P.

∴ 0·4 „ „ „ $\frac{22{\cdot}4 \times 0{\cdot}4}{2}$ „ „

= 4·48 litres. *Answer.*

Or, in a shorter way,

65 grams of zinc yield 1 G.M.V. of hydrogen at N.T.P.

= 22·4 litres „ „

∴ 13 „ „ „ $\frac{22{\cdot}4 \times 13}{65}$ „ „ „

= 4·48 litres. *Answer.*

2. *What is the weight of 1 litre of nitrous oxide, N_2O, at N.T.P.?*

The M.W. of nitrous oxide = 14 × 2 + 16 = 44.

∴ „ G.M.W. „ „ „ = 44 grams.

Hence 44 grams „ „ „ occupy 22·4 litres at N.T.P.

If 22·4 litres „ „ „ weigh 44 grams at N.T.P.,

∴ 1 litre „ „ „ weighs $\frac{44 \times 1}{22{\cdot}4}$ „ „

= 1·96 grams. *Answer.*

3. *What weight of calcium carbonate, $CaCO_3$, must we use to give* 20 *litres of dry carbon dioxide at* 37° 700 *mm., when acted upon by dilute nitric acid?*

The equation is

$$CaCO_3 + 2HNO_3 = Ca(NO_3)_2 + H_2O + CO_2.$$

The M.W. of calcium carbonate is 40 + 12 + 3 × 16 = 100.

From the equation we see that 100 grams of calcium carbonate would yield 22·4 litres of carbon dioxide at N.T.P. This volume at 37° 700 mm. would become, by Boyle's and Charles's Laws,

$$\frac{22{\cdot}4 \times 310 \times 760}{273 \times 700} \text{ litres} = 27{\cdot}6 \text{ litres.}$$

Then, if 27·6 litres of carbon dioxide at 37° 700 mm. come from 100 grams calcium carbonate,

20 litres of carbon dioxide at 37° 700 mm. come from $\frac{100 \times 20}{27{\cdot}6}$ grams calcium carbonate.

= 72·5 grams. *Answer.*

4. *What volume of acetylene, C_2H_2, measured at* 15° 770 *mm., could be obtained by acting with water upon* 16 *grams of calcium carbide?*

The equation is

$$CaC_2 + 2H_2O = Ca(OH)_2 + C_2H_2.$$

Hence, 1 molecule of calcium carbide gives 1 molecule of acetylene.

∴ 1 G.M.W. „ „ „ 1 G.M.V. of acetylene at N.T.P.

i.e. 64 grams „ „ give 22·4 litres „ „

∴ 16 „ „ „ „ $\frac{22{\cdot}4 \times 16}{64}$ „ „

= 5·6 litres.

5·6 litres at N.T.P. become, at 15° 770 mm.,

$$\frac{5{\cdot}6 \times 288 \times 760}{273 \times 770} \text{ litres.}$$

= 5·73 litres. *Answer.*

EXERCISES. For exercises see end of chapter, p. 124.

Calculation of a Formula for a Compound from its Composition by Weight.—If you are given the formula of a compound, and you know the atomic weights of the elements of which it is composed, you can easily calculate its percentage composition by weight.

EXAMPLE.—*The formula for caustic potash is KOH. What is its percentage composition by weight?*

Its molecular weight is clearly 39 + 16 + 1 = 56.

56 parts by weight of caustic potash contain 39 parts by weight of potassium.

∴ 100 „ „ „ „ $\frac{39 \times 100}{56}$ „ „

= 69·64.

Similarly, 56 parts by weight of caustic potash contain 16 parts by weight of oxygen.

∴ 100 „ „ „ $\frac{16 \times 100}{56}$ „ „

= 28·57.

And 56 parts by weight of caustic potash contain 1 part by weight of hydrogen.

∴ 100 „ „ „ „ $\frac{1 \times 100}{56}$ parts „ „

= 1·79.

∴ Percentage composition by weight of caustic potash =

Potassium	69·64
Oxygen	28·57
Hydrogen	1·79
	100·00

In exactly the same way we could find what weight of oxygen is contained in 100, or 50, or 28, or any number of grams of potassium chlorate, if we knew the formula for potassium chlorate ($KClO_3$) and the atomic weights of potassium, chlorine, and oxygen.

Can we carry out the reverse process, that is, can we calculate the formula of a compound from its composition by weight, if we know the atomic weights of the elements in it? In order to answer this question, let us suppose that we knew that the sodium chloride molecule consisted of sodium and chlorine atoms in equal numbers, but that we did not know how many of each there were. That is, we know that the formula is NaCl, or Na_2Cl_2 or Na_3Cl_3 . . . Na_nCl_n, but we don't know which of these is right. Could we tell if we knew the composition of salt by weight? Well, suppose salt is NaCl. Then $23 + 35{\cdot}5$, *i.e.* 58·5 parts by weight of it contain 23 parts by weight of sodium and 35·5 parts by weight of chlorine. If, on the other hand, it is Na_2Cl_2, then 117 parts by weight of it contain 46 parts by weight of sodium and 71 parts by weight of chlorine. The ratio of weight of sodium to weight of chlorine in the first case is $\frac{23}{35{\cdot}5}$, and in the second $\frac{46}{71}$. But $\frac{46}{71}$ is the same as $\frac{23}{35{\cdot}5}$.

Hence, the proportion by weight of sodium to chlorine is the same in NaCl as in Na_2Cl_2, and, of course, in Na_3Cl_3 . . . Na_nCl_n. It is clear, therefore, that from the composition by weight *alone* of a substance, we cannot possibly calculate its true formula. All we can do is to get its *simplest* formula, or *empirical formula* as it is usually called. The true formula for grape-sugar, for example, is $C_6H_{12}O_6$, but if we were given merely its composition by weight, all we could say is that its formula must either be CH_2O or some multiple of this, *e.g.* CH_2O, $C_2H_4O_2$, $C_3H_6O_3$, $C_4H_8O_4$, $C_5H_{10}O_5$, $C_6H_{12}O_6$, $C_7H_{14}O_7$, etc.—in other words, $(CH_2O)_n$ where n is a whole number.

Let us see how it is possible to calculate the empirical formula of a substance from its composition by weight. The proportion by weight of an element in a given compound will obviously be greater (*a*) the more atoms of it there are in the molecule, and (*b*) the larger is its atomic weight. Hence, if we take the numbers representing the proportions by weight of the various elements in a compound, and divide each by the atomic weight of the element concerned, the numbers which we get as quotients will be *in the ratio of the numbers of atoms of those elements present in the molecule of the compound.*

EXAMPLE.—100 parts by weight of grape-sugar contain:

40·00	parts by weight of carbon.
6·67	,, ,, ,, hydrogen.
53·33	,, ,, ,, oxygen.

If we divide 40 by the atomic weight of carbon we get $\frac{40 \cdot 00}{12} = 3 \cdot 33$.

,, ,, 6·67 ,, ,, ,, hydrogen ,, $\frac{6 \cdot 67}{1} = 6 \cdot 67$.

,, ,, 53·33 ,, ,, ,, oxygen ,, $\frac{53 \cdot 33}{16} = 3 \cdot 33$.

Hence, in the molecule of grape-sugar, there are 6·67 atoms of hydrogen and 3·33 atoms of oxygen to every 3·33 atoms of carbon, so that we could write the formula $C_{3 \cdot 33}H_{6 \cdot 67}O_{3 \cdot 33}$. But it is clear that we cannot have 3·33 carbon atoms, since atoms are indivisible. What we have to do, therefore, is to find the *simplest whole number ratio* corresponding to 3·33 : 6·67 : 3·33. This, of course, is obvious —it is 1 : 2 : 1; therefore the empirical formula for grape-sugar is CH_2O. But the true formula might equally well be $C_2H_4O_2$ or $C_3H_6O_3$, etc., as pointed out above.

ANOTHER EXAMPLE.—In 250 parts by weight of sulphuric acid, there are 5·01 of hydrogen, 80·16 of sulphur, and 160·32 of oxygen. What is the empirical formula of sulphuric acid?

5·1 divided by the atomic weight of hydrogen = $\frac{5 \cdot 01}{1} = 5 \cdot 01$.

91·6 ,, ,, ,, ,, sulphur = $\frac{80 \cdot 16}{32} = 2 \cdot 51$.

160·32 ,, ,, ,, ,, oxygen = $\frac{160 \cdot 32}{16} = 10 \cdot 02$.

∴ atoms are in the ratio H : S : O as 5·01 : 2·51 : 10·02.

On simplification, this ratio is seen to be very close to 2 : 1 : 4,
∴ empirical formula for sulphuric acid is H_2SO_4.

The true formula is either H_2SO_4 or some whole number of times this.

EXERCISES.—For exercises see end of chapter, p. 124.

True Formulæ.—We know that the true formula for a compound must be the empirical formula multiplied by some whole number, but the problem still remains of finding this number. Sometimes this is easy, sometimes difficult, and sometimes impossible. It is easy if we can find the *molecular weight* of the compound, as you can see from the following considerations. We have found that the empirical formula for grape-sugar is CH_2O. Now, chemists have determined the molecular weight of grape-sugar, and it turns out to be 180. What would its molecular weight be if its *true* formula were CH_2O? Obviously, $12 + 2 + 16 = 30$. This, however, is only $\frac{1}{6}$ of the actually observed molecular weight, hence the true formula must be not CH_2O, but $(CH_2O)_6$ or $C_6H_{12}O_6$.

In other words, to determine the true formula for a compound we want to know two things:

(i) its composition by weight, which gives its *empirical* formula, and

(ii) its molecular weight, which enables us to find out which multiple of the empirical formula to choose.

If the molecular weight of a compound can be determined easily, then it is easy to get its true formula; if the molecular weight determination is difficult, it is correspondingly difficult to get the true formula, while if the molecular weight cannot be determined—as in the case of many solid compounds—we cannot tell what the true formula of the substance is, in which event we use the empirical formula until we get further evidence.

For methods of determining molecular weights, see Chapter VIII, pp. 90–102.

Questions

1. Write the symbols for 1 atom of the following elements: hydrogen, oxygen, sulphur, sodium, silicon, phosphorus, platinum, silver, gold, copper, iron, mercury.

2. Write the formulæ for 1 molecule of the following substances: hydrogen, oxygen, ozone, water, nitric acid, aluminium sulphate, sodium nitrate, ammonium chloride, calcium chloride, calcium hydroxide, grape-sugar, cane-sugar, sulphuric acid, caustic potash, caustic soda, calcium carbonate, calcium carbide, potassium chlorate.

3. State all the information which you can gather from the following equations :

(i) $CaCO_3 + 2HCl = CaCl_2 + H_2O + CO_2$.
(ii) $Ca(OH)_2 + H_2SO_4 = CaSO_4 + 2H_2O$.
(iii) $Zn + 2HCl = ZnCl_2 + H_2$.
(iv) $MnO_2 + 4HCl = MnCl_2 + 2H_2O + Cl_2$.
(v) $2H_2 + O_2 = 2H_2O$.

4. Explain the terms *gram-molecular-weight* and *gram-molecular-volume.*

5. Work out mentally and write down the volumes at N.T.P. of the given weights of the gases mentioned below :

8·5 grams of ammonia (NH_3).
4 ,, ,, methane (CH_4).
8 ,, ,, oxygen (O_2).
96 ,, ,, ozone (O_3).
3·55 ,, ,, chlorine (Cl_2).
5·5 ,, ,, nitrous oxide (N_2O).

6. What is the *empirical formula* of a substance ? How is it obtained ?

7. What do you want to know to get the *true* formula of a substance ?

8. Work out the percentage compositions by weight of the following substances :

(i) Calcium carbonate ($CaCO_3$).
(ii) Potassium bicarbonate ($KHCO_3$).
(iii) Copper nitrate ($Cu(NO_3)_2$).
(iv) Camphor ($C_{10}H_{16}O$).
(v) Naphthalene ($C_{10}H_8$).
(vi) Potassium permanganate ($KMnO_4$).
(vii) ,, dichromate ($K_2Cr_2O_7$).
(viii) Red lead (Pb_3O_4).
(ix) Potassium chlorate ($KClO_3$).
(x) Water (H_2O).

9. Calculate the weight of 10 litres of a mixture of 1 volume of nitrogen with 3 volumes of hydrogen, and compare it with the weight of 10 litres of ammonia (NH_3), measured under the same conditions of temperature and pressure.

10. Find the volume of dry hydrogen sulphide (H_2S), measured at 15° 740 mm., which could be obtained by dissolving 10 grams of ferrous sulphide (FeS) in (*a*) dilute hydrochloric acid, and (*b*) dilute sulphuric acid.

11. How many litres of ammonia (at N.T.P.) could be obtained by heating 100 grams of ammonium chloride with sufficient slaked lime ?

12. A compound was found to contain 39·3 per cent. sodium and 60·7 per cent. chlorine by weight. Find its empirical formula.

13. The composition by weight of a certain compound was found to be as follows:

Potassium	56·52 per cent.
Carbon	8·70 ,,
Oxygen	34·78 ,,

What is the empirical formula of the compound?

14. An organic compound gave on analysis the following composition by weight:

Carbon	32·0 per cent.
Hydrogen	4·0 ,,
Oxygen	64·0 ,,

Find its empirical formula. If its molecular weight is 150, what is its molecular formula?

15. 1·288 grams of a compound contained on analysis 0·520 grams zinc, 0·256 grams sulphur, and 0·512 grams oxygen. What is its empirical formula?

16. 1·52 grams of a compound were found to contain 0·439 grams potassium, 0·360 grams sulphur and 0·721 grams oxygen. What is its empirical formula? Further evidence gives its molecular weight as 270; what is its molecular formula?

17. A compound has the following composition by weight:

Sodium	29·11 per cent.
Sulphur	40·51 ,,
Oxygen	30·38 ,,

Find its empirical formula.

18. An organic compound gives the following results on analysis:

Carbon	26·67 per cent. by weight.
Hydrogen	2·22 ,, ,,
Oxygen	71·11 ,, ,,

Find its empirical formula. If its molecular weight is 90, what is its molecular formula?

19. 1·31 grams of a compound on analysis were found to contain 0·907 grams silver, 0·134 grams sulphur, and 0·269 grams oxygen. What is the empirical formula of the compound?

20. What is the empirical formula of a compound, which has the following composition by weight?

Potassium . .	42·39 per cent.	Iron . . .	15·22 per cent.
Carbon . . .	19·565 ,,	Nitrogen . .	22·825 ,,

CHAPTER X

ELECTROLYSIS

When the wires from an electric battery are immersed in water made slightly acid by the addition of a little sulphuric acid, the water is decomposed into hydrogen and oxygen. The hydrogen comes off from the wire attached to the negative pole of the battery, and the oxygen from that attached to the positive pole. This decomposition of a substance by the passage of electricity through it is called *electrolysis*. Pure water will not noticeably conduct electricity, but if a little acid or alkali is added conduction takes place and the water is *electrolysed*.

The two metallic plates or wires which are placed in the liquid to bring about electrolysis are called the *electrodes*. The electrode connected to the positive pole of the battery is called the *anode* or *positive electrode*, and that connected to the negative pole is called the *cathode* or *negative electrode*. Aqueous solutions (that is, solutions in water) of acids, bases and salts will conduct electricity, and the dissolved substances are decomposed in the process. Thus, if a current of electricity is passed through a solution of copper chloride, chlorine is evolved at the anode (if this is made of a substance such as carbon, not attacked by chlorine) and copper is deposited on the cathode. Substances which are liberated at the anode are said to be *electro-negative*, since they are attracted to the *positive* pole, and it is a general rule of electricity that a positively-charged body repels another positively-charged body, but attracts a negatively-charged one, and vice versa. In the same way, substances which make their appearance at the cathode are called *electro-positive*.

Substances whose solutions will conduct electricity are called *electrolytes*. *Non-electrolytes* are substances whose solutions do not conduct electricity (*e.g.* sugar, alcohol, glycerol).

The substances which appear at the electrodes during electrolysis were called *ions* by FARADAY (1791–1867), who first studied this phenomenon thoroughly. He gave them this name because they *wander* to the electrodes (from the Greek,

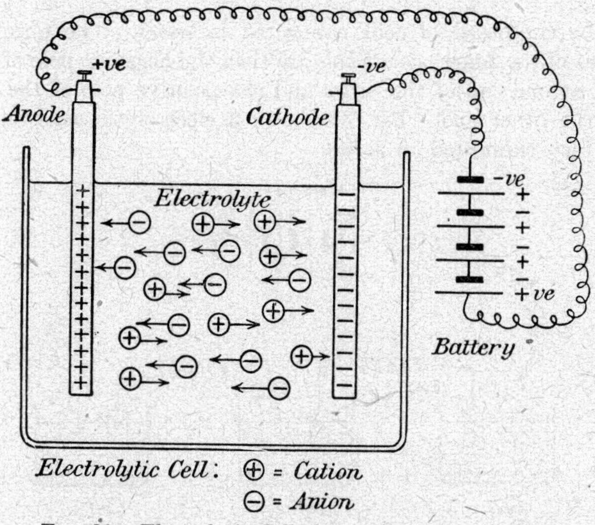

FIG. 30.—Electrolytic Cell shown diagrammatically.

to go or to wander). Those which go to the *anode* were called *anions*, and those which go to the *cathode* were called *cations*. Nowadays we use these words in a slightly different sense, about which you will learn later on.

Diagrammatically we can represent these ideas as in Fig. 30.

The sign we use for a single cell of a battery is ▮|, where the short, thick stroke represents the negative pole, and the long, thin one the positive pole. A battery of 5 such cells connected in series is shown in Fig. 31, or more simply in Fig. 32.

If the positive pole of one cell is connected to the negative of the next, and the positive of this to the negative of the third, and so on, as shown in the diagram, the battery is said

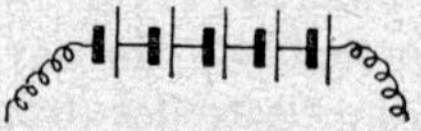

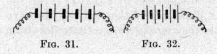

FIG. 31.

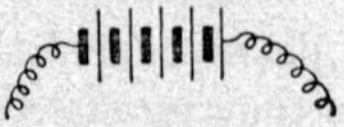

FIG. 32.

to be composed of cells connected *in series*. The terminal poles of the *battery as a whole* are then the negative pole of the cell at one end of the series and the positive pole of the cell at the other end. Fig. 33 shows 3 electrolytic cells and a battery connected in series.

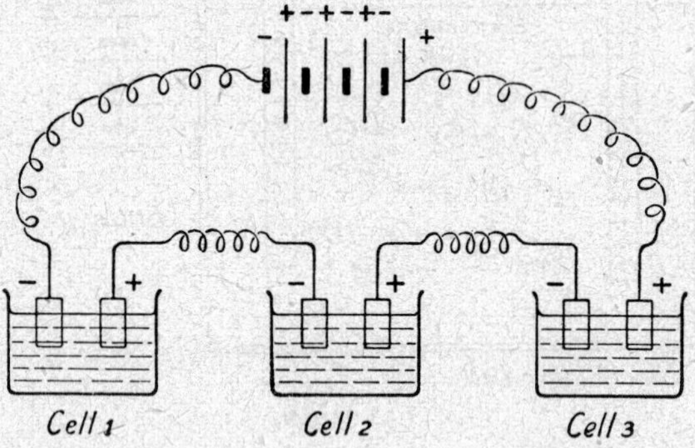

FIG. 33.

Note that the electrode in Cell 1 connected with the negative terminal pole of the battery is also negative—it is really an extension of the pole; similarly with the anode in Cell 3.

Faraday's Laws of Electrolysis.—Faraday showed that *the same quantity of electricity passed through solutions of electrolytes connected up in series will liberate in each cell weights of the products of electrolysis which are in the ratio of their chemical equivalents.* Thus the same quantity of electricity which liberates 1 gram of hydrogen will liberate 8 grams of oxygen, 35·5 grams of chlorine, 31·8 grams of copper, or 108 grams of silver, etc.

The unit of quantity of electricity is called the *coulomb*, which is the quantity of electricity conveyed by a current of 1 *ampère* flowing for 1 second. The number of coulombs required to liberate the gram-equivalent of any substance is found experimentally to be 96,000. A smaller or a greater number will liberate a proportionately smaller or greater weight. Faraday's Laws may therefore be expressed in modern terms as follows:

FIRST LAW. *The weight of an ion liberated in electrolysis is proportional to the quantity of electricity which has passed through the electrolyte* (*i.e.* to current × time).

SECOND LAW. *The quantity of electricity required to deposit the gram-equivalent of an ion is* 96,000 *coulombs* (or 1 "*faraday*").

The quantity of electricity which flows through the circuit is measured by noting the time in seconds and multiplying this by the number of ampères of the current as shown by an ampère-meter or *ammeter* connected up in series in the circuit. An electrolytic cell is often called a *voltameter*; this must not be confused with a voltmeter, which is an instrument used for measuring the *voltage* or "pressure" of a current.

In an electrolysis it often happens that the products first formed will act upon water or upon one another, so that the *final* products actually obtained may be *secondary*. Thus, when a solution of caustic soda is electrolysed, the *primary* (first-formed) products are *sodium* at the cathode and the *hydroxyl group* (OH) at the anode. The sodium, however, immediately acts upon the water so that the *actual* product at the cathode is hydrogen—

$$2Na + 2H_2O = 2NaOH + H_2.$$

At the anode, similarly, two hydroxyl groups react together, forming oxygen and water—

$$2OH = H_2O + \text{oxygen}.$$

Hence, the final result of electrolysing a solution of caustic soda is that hydrogen is liberated at the cathode and oxygen at the anode. In other words, it *appears* as though the *water* had been electrolysed, the weight of caustic soda remaining constant. The same sort of thing happens in the case of dilute sulphuric acid. Here the primary products of electrolysis are hydrogen and the "sulphate" group of atoms, SO_4. The latter groups, however, when liberated at the anode, act upon the water present to give sulphuric acid and oxygen—

$$2SO_4 + 2H_2O = 2H_2SO_4 + O_2,$$

hence the actual product at the anode is secondary, namely, oxygen.

To take a rather different case, suppose we electrolyse a solution of copper sulphate, using a platinum or copper cathode and a copper anode. Here the copper particles go to the cathode, where they are deposited, while the SO_4 groups at the anode dissolve the latter to form more copper:

$$Cu + SO_4 = CuSO_4.$$

The net result of electrolysis in this case is therefore *the transference of copper from the anode to the cathode.* This process is used in copper-plating, and similar ones in gold- and silver-plating, hence the term "electro-plate."

Details of the electrolysis of water are given on p. 161, and of concentrated hydrochloric acid on p. 231.

Arrhenius's Theory of Electrolytic Dissociation.—To explain Faraday's Laws and certain other facts about the behaviour of solutions, Arrhenius (1859–1927) in 1887 suggested that when electrolytes are dissolved in water they immediately split up, more or less completely, into electrically charged particles or ions. Thus, on dissolving salt in water, Arrhenius's theory supposes that the sodium chloride molecules each split up into a positively charged sodium atom and a negatively charged chlorine atom. These atoms, in their charged state, have different properties from the same atoms uncharged, and are known as *sodium ions* and *chlorine ions* respectively:

$$NaCl = Na^+ + Cl^-$$
$$\text{or } NaCl = Na^{\cdot} + Cl'$$

Arrhenius further supposed that the charge on each ion was numerically equal to its valency, so that if the charge on a sodium ion is 1, then that on a magnesium ion is 2, since the valency of magnesium is 2; and that on an aluminium ion is 3, since the valency of aluminium is 3. Again, a solution of sodium sulphate, Na_2SO_4, would contain two positively charged sodium ions, each carrying a charge of 1 unit, for every SO_4 or "sulphate ion" carrying a negative charge of 2 units:

$$Na_2SO_4 = Na^+ + Na^+ + SO_4^{--}.$$

In every case, the total charges carried by the positive ions would be exactly equal to the total charges carried by the negative ions, so that the solution as a whole would appear to be uncharged.

You will learn a good deal more about Arrhenius's theory in your more advanced work. Here, we will just spend a moment in seeing how it explains such a process as the electrolysis of copper sulphate solution. According to Arrhenius, as soon as copper sulphate is dissolved in water, it splits up as follows:

$$CuSO_4 = Cu^{++} + SO_4^{--}.$$

Suppose we now pour the solution into an electrolytic cell and electrolyse it, using copper electrodes. The copper ions, being positively charged, are attracted to the negative electrode or cathode. On arrival, their positive charge is neutralized and they then become ordinary copper atoms; the latter are deposited on the copper cathode, which therefore grows thicker.

For every copper ion discharged at the cathode, a sulphate ion, SO_4^{--}, is discharged at the anode. But the SO_4 group of atoms, *uncharged*, is very chemically active, and immediately attacks the copper of the anode, converting it into copper sulphate:

$$SO_4 + Cu = CuSO_4.$$

The anode therefore gets smaller. The copper sulphate formed round it, however, itself immediately *ionizes* (*i.e.* splits up into its ions), and the ions then behave in the same way as those of the original copper sulphate. You will see that the net result is that copper is transferred from the anode to the cathode, as we have learned already on p. 130.

What would happen if we used platinum electrodes instead of copper ones ? Well, the copper ions would still be discharged at the cathode, and the platinum would therefore become copper plated. At the anode, the discharged SO_4 ions would find the platinum too tough a proposition even for them, and in disappointed rage they would fiercely attack the water molecules in the neighbourhood, forming sulphuric acid and liberating oxygen :

$$2SO_4 + 2H_2O = 2H_2SO_4 + O_2.$$

Finally, all the copper would have been deposited on the platinum cathode, an equivalent weight of oxygen would have been set free at the anode, and for every molecule of copper sulphate that vanished a molecule of sulphuric acid would have been formed instead ! If we now stopped passing the current we should have a solution of sulphuric acid, *i.e.* a solution containing hydrogen ions and sulphate ions :

$$H_2SO_4 = H^+ + H^+ + SO_4^{--}.$$

In a solution of caustic soda, there are sodium ions, Na^+, and hydroxyl ions, $—OH^-$. If we were to electrolyse it, the sodium ions would be discharged at the cathode, and ordinary sodium atoms would be formed. These would immediately attack the surrounding water, liberating hydrogen :

$$2Na + 2H_2O = 2NaOH + H_2,$$

and the sodium hydroxide formed at the same time would itself immediately ionize :

$$NaOH = Na^+ + OH^-.$$

At the anode, the hydroxyl ions would be discharged and so converted into uncharged —OH groups. These would attack one another, with the formation of water and evolution of oxygen :

$$2OH = H_2O + \text{oxygen}.$$

You will see that, since every OH group corresponds to one sodium atom, and every sodium atom to one hydrogen atom at the cathode, the result of electrolysing sodium hydroxide solution is the liberation of hydrogen (cathode) and oxygen (anode) in the proportions by volume in which they occur in water. The sodium hydroxide itself is unchanged in weight, just as much being left at the end as at the beginning. We *say*, therefore, that "the water has been electrolysed": though you will understand now that the process is really an electrolysis of the sodium hydroxide followed by secondary actions of the discharged ions.

Try to interpret, in terms of ions, the electrolysis of water acidulated with sulphuric acid, using platinum electrodes.

Arrhenius's Theory and Faraday's Laws.—In electrolysis, for each positive charge neutralized at the cathode a negative charge is neutralized at the anode. Thus, in the electrolysis of concentrated hydrochlorine acid, for every hydrogen ion discharged at the cathode a chlorine ion is discharged at the anode. Hence, equal numbers of hydrogen and chlorine atoms are liberated in any given time, and the weights of hydrogen and chlorine are thus in the ratio of their chemical equivalents.

If we electrolyse copper sulphate solution between platinum electrodes, a sulphate ion is discharged at the anode for every copper ion discharged at the cathode. But, as we have seen, every sulphate group immediately liberates an atom of oxygen from a molecule of water; hence for every atom of copper set free an atom of oxygen is also set free, and the ratio by weight of copper to oxygen is thus the ratio of their chemical equivalents (63·6 to 16, or 31·8 to 8).

The same kind of thing is true of all other ions. The ratio by weight in which they are liberated is the ratio of the quotients of their atomic or "group" [*e.g.* in SO_4 this is 96: in —OH 17, etc.] weights divided by their corresponding valency. Thus the valency of nickel is 2 and its atomic weight 59, while the valency of chlorine is 1 and its atomic weight 35·5. Hence one nickel atom will be Ni^{++} and one chlorine atom Cl^-, and *one* nickel ion will be discharged for every *two* chlorine ions discharged. Therefore the ratio by weight in which these elements will be liberated is *Nickel:*

Chlorine $= \frac{59}{2} : \frac{35 \cdot 5}{1}$, *i.e.* the ratio of their chemical equivalents.

We see, in short, that if Arrhenius's theory is true, the weights of substances liberated in electrolysis *must* be in the ratio of their equivalents; for—

(*a*) the equivalent of a substance is equal to its atomic (or "group") weight divided by its valency;

(*b*) the valency of a substance is numerically equal to the number of charges it carries when it is in the form of an ion;

(*c*) substances are liberated in such a way that equal numbers of positive charges and negative charges are neutralized in the same time.

Hence, if we have x ions of a univalent element A discharged in the same time as $\frac{x}{2}$ ions of a bivalent element B, and if the atomic weights of A and B are m and n respectively, then weights of A and B liberated in the same time are in the ratio

$$\frac{mx}{\frac{nx}{2}} = \frac{2m}{n}.$$

But the ratio of the equivalents of these elements is $\frac{\frac{m}{1}}{\frac{n}{2}} = \frac{2m}{n}$.

Again, the same current flowing for the same time will clearly be able to discharge the same number of charges; hence the weight of a substance liberated in electrolysis will be proportional to the quantity of electricity that has passed. This is, of course, another of the facts discovered by Faraday.

Lastly, we saw on p. 129 that Faraday showed that the gram-equivalent of *any* substance was liberated by the passage of 96,000 coulombs. Arrhenius's theory explains this experimental fact in the following way:

96,000 coulombs liberate 1 gram of hydrogen. Let the number of atoms in 1 gram of hydrogen be x. Then since the valency of hydrogen is 1, the number of charges neutralized by 96,000 coulombs is $x \times 1$, *i.e.* x.

Suppose we have now an element A, of atomic weight 63·6 and valency 2. Then in 63·6 grams of A there will be x atoms of A, and in the gram *equivalent* of A $\left(\frac{63 \cdot 6}{2}\right)$ there will be $\frac{x}{2}$ atoms. But each atom will, as an ion, carry *two* charges, since its valency is 2. Therefore $\frac{x}{2}$ atoms will carry $\frac{x}{2} \times 2 = x$ charges. These can be neutralized by 96,000 coulombs, but as they are carried by the gram-equivalent of A, 96,000 coulombs will liberate this weight of A in electrolysis : which is what we set out to prove.

Questions

1. What is a *voltameter* ?
2. Explain the terms *electrolyte, non-electrolyte, anode, cathode, electrode, cation, anion, coulomb, faraday.*
3. State Faraday's Laws of Electrolysis.
4. The same quantity of electricity which deposits 3·53 grams of a metal in an electrolytic cell will liberate 453 c.c. of hydrogen, collected over water at 18° C. 763 mm. What is the equivalent weight of the metal ?
5. Explain the electrolysis of
   (*a*) copper sulphate solution between copper electrodes,
   (*b*) ,, ,, ,, ,, platinum ,,
   (*c*) acidulated water,
   (*d*) potassium sulphate solution between platinum electrodes,
   in terms of Arrhenius's theory of ions.
6. How are Faraday's Laws explained by Arrhenius's theory ?

CHAPTER XI

SOLUBILITY

If we add a pinch of salt to a cupful of water, the salt gradually disappears. We say that it has *dissolved* in the water, and the resulting liquid is called a *solution of salt.* In the same way we can make aqueous solutions (*i.e.* solutions in *water*) of many other substances, such as sugar, copper sulphate, saltpetre, and sal-ammoniac. If we took petrol instead of water, we should find that we could not dissolve salt or copper sulphate in it, but that we could easily make a petrol solution of, say, paraffin-wax. In other words, salt and copper sulphate are *soluble* in water but *insoluble* in petrol. Paraffin-wax, on the other hand, is *soluble* in petrol, but it is *insoluble* in water.

A solution, then, consists of two parts—a liquid to do the dissolving, and a substance which is dissolved. The former is called the *solvent* and the latter the *solute*—

$$\textbf{Solution}\begin{cases}\text{SOLVENT}\\ \text{SOLUTE}\end{cases}$$

Generally, the solute is a solid, but it may be a liquid or even a gas. Thus soda-water is a solution of carbon dioxide in water, while ordinary river-water and sea-water contain dissolved oxygen and nitrogen.

To go back to the solution of salt in water. If we have a definite volume of water, say, 100 c.c., we cannot dissolve in it an *unlimited* weight of salt. If we go on adding salt little by little, we shall find that after a time no more will dissolve. Further addition results merely in the excess of salt sinking to the bottom and remaining there as a solid.

When a solution will dissolve no more of the solute it is said to be saturated; weaker solutions, which have not yet reached this stage, are called *unsaturated*.

Further investigation would show us that 100 c.c. of hot water require rather more salt, before the solution is saturated, than do 100 c.c. of cold water. That is, salt is somewhat "more soluble" in hot water than in cold. When talking about the *solubility* of a substance in water, we therefore have to state the temperature at which the solubility is measured. In order to get a standard for comparison of the solubilities of different substances, we define solubility in the following way:

SOLUBILITY.—*The solubility of a substance in a given solvent at a particular temperature is the maximum weight in grams of the substance which* 100 *grams of the solvent will dissolve at that particular temperature.*[1]

The solubility of a substance in water is therefore the maximum number of grams of the substance which can be dissolved in 100 grams of pure water at the temperature concerned.

SOLUBILITY OF SALTPETRE (POTASSIUM NITRATE) IN WATER.—Experiments made on the solubility of saltpetre in water at different temperatures have given the following results:

Temperature in ° C. . . .	0	10	20	30	40	50	60	70
Solubility . . . . . (*i.e.* grams of saltpetre in 100 grams of water.)	13	20	32	45	63	85	110	140

In order to be able to see at a glance how the solubility of a substance varies with the temperature, it is convenient to plot the solubility against the temperature, on squared paper, and so construct a *solubility curve*. Thus, taking the figures

[1] Strictly speaking, we ought to add to this definition the phrase "*in presence of excess of the solid substance.*" This is because, under special conditions, "supersaturated" solutions of certain substances may be formed (cf. p. 140). These contain more of the dissolved solute than corresponds to true saturation, but the excess of solute is at once deposited if a crystal of the solid is added. A supersaturated solution *cannot* be formed as long as any of the solid solute is present.

given in the table above, we can make the solubility curve for potassium nitrate (Fig. 34).

This curve shows us that the solubility of potassium nitrate (saltpetre) increases rapidly and regularly with rise of temperature. It also enables us to estimate the solubility at temperatures intermediate between those at which it was actually determined: thus, at 48° we see that the solubility is 80.

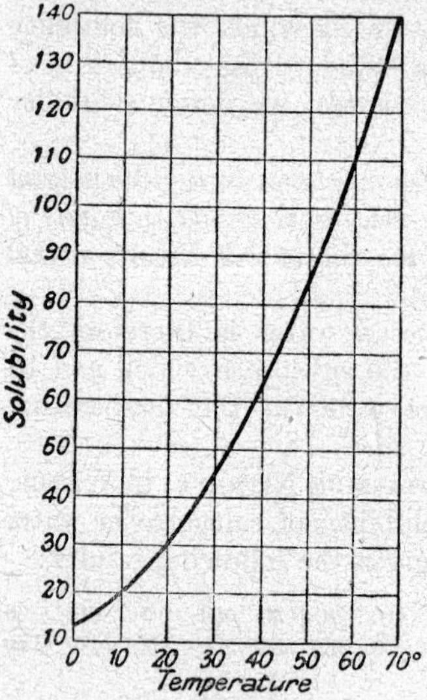

FIG. 34.—**Solubility Curve of Saltpetre.**

Other solubility curves are given in books of reference, whence you will see that the solubility of salt does not increase much with rise of temperature. All the substances you are likely to meet are more soluble in hot water than in cold, and this is true of the vast majority of compounds. A few, however, are *less* soluble in hot water than in cold; if we take a cold saturated solution of such a substance (*e.g.* calcium butyrate) and heat it, we shall find that solid separates out, as would be expected.

Determination of the Solubility of a Solid in Water.—Accurate determination of the solubility of a substance in water is a matter of some difficulty. A rough method for finding it in the case of salt at ordinary temperatures is described below:—

Take a clean beaker and in it put about 50 c c of distilled water. Add pure salt, a little at a time, and stir well after each addition. Continue adding salt until there is a level teaspoonful or so which will not dissolve but sinks to the bottom and remains there. Stir well again for 5 minutes, then allow the excess of salt to settle until the solution above is perfectly clear. Meanwhile, carefully weigh a clean dry porcelain dish, and clean and dry a 20 c.c. pipette.

Now fill the pipette with the clear saturated solution, taking care not to suck up any of the solid salt at the bottom. Run the solution from the pipette into the weighed dish, and weigh again. Take the temperature of the rest of the solution in the beaker.

Set the dish with the solution on asbestos gauze on a tripod, and evaporate gently so as to avoid spirting. When all the water appears to have been driven off, allow the basin and salt to cool in a desiccator and then weigh. Heat again for a few minutes, cool, and re-weigh. Continue this process until the weight is constant. You will then have the following weights:

(ii) Weight of basin + solution	=	y	grams
(i) " "	=	x	"
∴ (iii) Weight of solution	=	$y - x$	grams
(iv) Weight of basin and salt	=	z	grams
(i) " "	=	x	"
∴ (iv) Weight of salt	=	$z - x$	grams.

Therefore weight of water which has dissolved this weight of salt $= (y - x) - (z - x) = y - z$ grams.

Then, if

$y - z$ grams of water dissolve $z - x$ grams of salt,

100 " " " $\dfrac{(z - x) \times 100}{(y - z)}$ " "

and this is the solubility of salt at the temperature, $t°$ C., of your experiment.

(*Note* that it is not necessary to run out *exactly* 20 c.c. or any other definite volume of the solution, since the weight of water is found by direct weighing.)

To determine solubilities at temperatures considerably above room-temperature, it is necessary to take precautions in transferring the solution to the basin, since solid may begin to separate. For details you should refer to your practical textbooks.

Supersaturation.—If a hot saturated solution of a substance which is more soluble in hot water than in cold is allowed to cool, as a rule the excess of solid crystallizes out and is deposited. Occasionally, however, if the solution is kept quite still and free from dust, etc., while it is cooling, crystallization of the excess of solute does not occur. The cold solution, then, contains more of the solid than it is properly entitled to. Such a solution is said to be *supersaturated.* A supersaturated solution is generally unstable, and will deposit its excess of solid if it is shaken, or—better still, if a tiny crystal of the solid is introduced. Supersaturation, indeed, cannot exist if the solution is in contact with the solid solute, so that in making determinations of solubility we always take care to use excess of the solute and thus avoid the possibility of supersaturation.

The phenomenon of supersaturation and the deposition of the excess of solute on addition of a crystal of the solute to the supersaturated solution, can easily be studied in the case of sodium thiosulphate (photographers' "*hypo*").

Fractional Crystallization.—If two solutes have very different solubilities in a given solvent, they may be more or less completely separated from one another by the process of *fractional crystallization.*

Suppose we consider the case of a mixture of equal weights of common salt and potassium nitrate, and assume (what is not actually the case) that the solubility of one salt in water is not affected by the presence of another. Solubility curves show that, while salt is not much more soluble in hot water than in cold, the solubility of potassium nitrate increases very rapidly with rise of temperature. Suppose we took 100 grams of the mixture and added 50 c.c. of boiling water. Now 50 c.c. of boiling water dissolve more than 50 grams of saltpetre, for 100 c.c. dissolve 170 grams even at 80°. Hence *all* the saltpetre will dissolve.

The curves show us that 100 c.c. of boiling water dissolve

practically 40 grams of salt, ∴ 50 c.c. will dissolve 20 grams of salt. Hence, since there are 50 grams of salt in the 100 grams of mixture, we shall have 30 grams of salt left undissolved. The solution will contain all the potassium nitrate and 20 grams of the salt. If we pour it off and allow it to cool to 20° C., what will happen?

At 20° the solubility of saltpetre is 32, and that of salt is 36. Hence, at this temperature 50 c.c. of water can hold 16 grams of saltpetre and 18 of salt. Therefore 34 grams of saltpetre and 2 grams of salt will be deposited. To free this saltpetre from its slight admixture with salt we could wash it with a little ice-cold water, for salt is much more soluble than saltpetre at 0°.

In this way we should have been able to effect a separation of salt from saltpetre. The process is known as *fractional crystallization*, since the solute is crystallized out, not all at once, but in fractions. Fractional crystallization, of a more elaborate kind than that described here, is a very useful method of purifying various compounds, and is extensively used both in the laboratory and in commercial chemistry.

Crystals

Solid substances formed by solidification from the liquid (or gaseous) state, or by evaporation of their solutions, almost always take up perfectly definite shapes which are characterized by having plane faces and generally by being symmetrical. We say that a thing is *symmetrical* when it can be divided into halves by one or more planes in such a way that one-half is related to the other as an object is to its image in a mirror.

These regularly-shaped and usually symmetrical bodies are called *crystals*. A few solid substances, such as glass and charcoal, form fragments with no definite shape; such substances are said to be *amorphous* (Greek, *without form*). It should be noted that substances may sometimes be crystalline without exhibiting regular external shape, *e.g.* native diamond. Although "crystallography" has developed into an independent science, yet every chemist ought to know something about those wonderful structures which he handles every day.

Let us first examine a little more closely the difference between crystalline and amorphous substances. The latter, such as glass, are irregular in shape, and, when broken, form pieces with *curved* faces. Crystals, on the other hand, are regular in shape, and, when broken, form pieces with *plane* faces which meet in sharp edges. A further point of great importance is that the different crystals of a given substance are all similar to one another in a very striking feature, *viz.* the angles between corresponding faces of the crystals are always the same.

A crystal may therefore be defined as *a solid substance bounded by plane faces at definite angles to each other, and splitting, when struck, along definite planes.* It has a "crystalline" fracture, and is therefore unlike an amorphous substance, which has a "conchoidal fracture," *i.e.* gives fragments with curved surfaces.

The smallest crystal of a substance has essentially the same form as the largest. The latter is, indeed, formed by the *growth* of a smaller one. The molecules in a crystal are arranged in a definite pattern, which differs in different crystals, but is the same in all crystals of the same substance. Since crystals grow by the deposition of more and more layers of molecules on their faces, it is easy to understand why they always have a definite shape.

Although there are very many different crystalline forms, they can all be grouped into six systems, which are called the *regular*, *tetragonal*, *hexagonal*, *rhombic*, *monoclinic* and *triclinic*. These names may prove a little forbidding, but you should make a special effort to learn them, and the chief characteristics of the groups they denote, for you will find this knowledge of great value.

In order to describe a crystal geometrically, three, or sometimes four, lines or *axes* (singular, *axis*) are imagined within it. These axes intersect at a point inside the crystal, and the form of the crystal can be worked out if the relative lengths of the axes, and the angles at which they cut one another, are known. The various classes of crystals, then, are characterized by the number, relative lengths, and mutual inclination of these crystallographic axes.

Systems of Crystals.

1. **Regular.**—In this system the crystal has three axes equal in length and at right angles to one another (Fig. 35).

EXAMPLES.—Cube (*e.g.* common salt). Octahedron (*e.g.* alum).

FIG. 35.
(Axes in thick lines.)

2. **Tetragonal.**—Here the crystals have three axes all meeting at right angles, but one is longer or shorter than the other two.

EXAMPLE.—Bi-pyramid or tetragonal prism (Fig. 36).

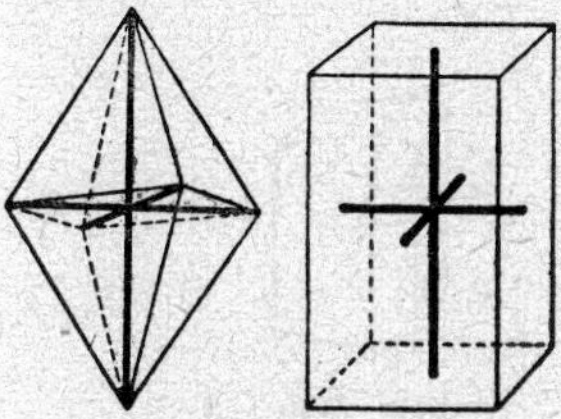

FIG. 36.

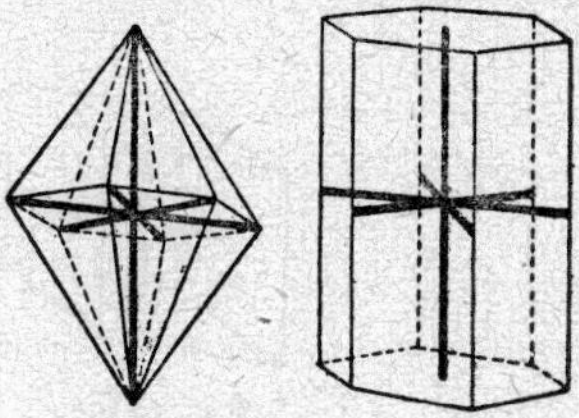

FIG. 37.

3. **Hexagonal.**—Here the crystals have **four** axes, three of which are equal, in the same plane, and intersect at an angle of 60 degrees, while the fourth is longer or shorter than the other three, which it meets at right angles.

EXAMPLES.—Hexagonal bi-pyramids (such as calcite, $CaCO_3$), hexagonal prisms (such as quartz, SiO_2) (Fig. 37).

4. **Rhombic.**—The crystals of this system have three unequal axes all at right angles. Many forms of crystals are included in the rhombic system. For an example, see the drawing of a rhombic sulphur crystal on p. 293. Another form is shown here (Fig. 38).

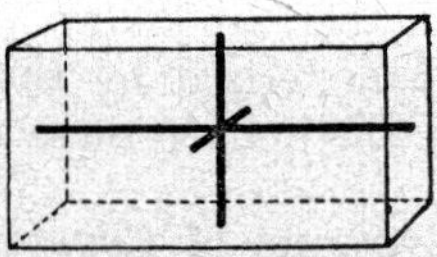

FIG. 38.

5. **Monoclinic.**—Monoclinic crystals have three axes all of different lengths. Two of them cut at an oblique angle, while the third is at right angles to the plane of the first two.

FIG. 39.—Crystal of Gypsum ($CaSO_4.2H_2O$).

EXAMPLES.—Washing-soda, cane-sugar, oxalic acid, monoclinic sulphur (p. 293), gypsum (Fig. 39).

6. **Triclinic.**—Here the crystals have three axes, which are all unequal in length and cut one another obliquely (Fig. 40A).

EXAMPLES.—Potassium dichromate (Fig. 40B), copper sulphate.

In the laboratory you will carry out experiments on the growth of crystals, and you will be shown how to measure

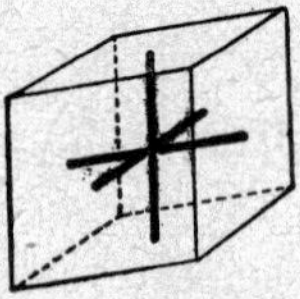

FIG. 40A.

FIG. 40B.
Crystal of Potassium dichromate.

the angles between their faces. Meanwhile, you should learn HAÜY'S LAW (1801)—*Every crystalline element or compound has a definite form characteristic of that substance,* and GUGLIELMINI'S statement (1688), that *the angles between similar faces of crystals of the same substance are exactly the same, and are characteristic of that substance.*

Isomorphism.—Very often we find that different, but chemically similar, substances crystallize in the same form; they are then said to be *isomorphous.* For example, calcite ($CaCO_3$), siderite ($FeCO_3$) and calamine ($ZnCO_3$) all form trigonal crystals of the same shape; these three minerals are therefore isomorphous with one another. The existence of isomorphism may seem to contradict the generalizations of Haüy and Guglielmini given above, but, as a matter of fact, the crystals of isomorphous substances are never *exactly* alike except in the regular system. Thus, in the case mentioned, the angles between corresponding faces in calcite, siderite, and calamine, are as follows:

Substance.	*Angle.*
Calcite, $CaCO_3$	105° 5′
Siderite, $FeCO_3$	107° 0′
Calamine, $ZnCO_3$	107° 40′

Mitscherlich's Law of Isomorphism.—The chief facts about isomorphism were summed up by Mitscherlich in 1819, who said that *compounds of the same class which have similar constitutions crystallize in the same form* (Mitscherlich's Law). By "compounds of the same class" we mean, for example, nitrates, or chlorides, or sulphates, or (as in the example above) carbonates, etc.

Applied in the reverse way, this law is useful in the determination of atomic weights, for it is assumed that compounds of the same class which crystallize in the same form have analogous constitutions. For example, suppose we were investigating the atomic weight of chromium, and that we had already determined its equivalent. We should then be trying to find its valency. Now when potassium sulphate and aluminium sulphate, in the proportion of 1 molecule of one to 1 of the other, are dissolved in water together, and the solution evaporated to crystallization, they combine together and crystallize out as a compound called *alum,* which forms beautiful crystals whose form can be very easily measured. If potassium sulphate and chromium sulphate are mixed in solution and the solution then evaporated to crystallization, it is possible to get crystals of a "chrome alum" which are isomorphous with those of ordinary alum. According to Mitscherlich's Law, we are able to conclude that since chromium has replaced aluminium in alum, giving rise to an isomorphous chrome alum, chromium and aluminium have the same valency, otherwise the constitutions of these two isomorphous compounds of the same class would not be analogous. Hence, if we know that the valency of aluminium is 3, we may justifiably conclude that the valency of chromium is 3, and from this and the equivalent we can get the atomic weight.

Questions

1. Define the terms *solubility, solvent, solute, saturated, supersaturated.*

2. Why is it important to state the *temperature* when giving the solubility of a substance in water?

3. Construct solubility curves for the following substances from the data given below:

Temperature.	0°	10	20	30	40	50	60	70	80	90	100°
Solubility of substance—											
Sodium nitrate	72·5	80	86	94	102	111·5	122	134	150	162	180
Potassium chlorate . .	4	5	7	10	12	20	26	32	39	47	56
Alum	4	9	15	22	32	45	62	96	136	—	—
Copper sulphate crystals .	32	36	42	49	57	66	78	95	117	150	—

4. Describe a method of determining the solubility of potassium chlorate in water at room temperature.

5. What do you mean by *fractional crystallization*? Of what use is this operation?

6. Refer to the solubility curves you have made in answer to Q. 3, and say how you would attempt to separate potassium chlorate from sodium nitrate, given a mixture of the two.

7. What is a *crystal*? How does it differ from an *amorphous* substance?

8. Define the terms *conchoïdal fracture, crystallographic axis, isomorphism.*

9. State Haüy's Law.

10. What use can be made of the phenomenon of isomorphism in the determination of atomic weights?

11. Mention the main characteristics of the six groups of crystal structure.

CHAPTER XII

CATALYSIS AND CHEMICAL CHANGE

Catalysis.—In the laboratory preparation of oxygen, it is customary to use potassium chlorate as a source of the gas—

$$2KClO_3 = 2KCl + 3O_2.$$

In order to get potassium chlorate to split up into potassium chloride and oxygen, a high temperature has to be employed. If, however, a little manganese dioxide is mixed with the potassium chlorate, the decomposition occurs much more readily. The manganese dioxide, which has brought about this remarkable change in the speed of the reaction, is left unchanged at the end. To prove this, you could start with a known weight of manganese dioxide, and recover and weigh it afterwards. When the action is over, the residue consists of a mixture of potassium chloride and manganese dioxide; now the former substance is soluble in water, while the dioxide is insoluble. Hence by stirring the residue with water and filtering, the manganese dioxide will be left on the filter-paper. If it is washed, dried and weighed, it will be found to weigh exactly the same as it did originally, except, of course, for the small error due to experimental inaccuracy.

The action of manganese dioxide on the decomposition of potassium chlorate is not an isolated phenomenon. Many chemical reactions can be hastened, and many can be retarded, by the addition of small quantities of substances which are left unchanged in mass and in chemical composition at the end of the reaction. This phenomenon is called *catalysis*, and the substances which bring it about are called *catalysts* or *catalytic agents.* Catalysts which increase the speed of a reaction are called positive catalysts; those which retard an action are called negative catalysts. Positive catalysts are much more common than negative catalysts, hence "catalyst" generally means *positive* catalyst, just as we write a for $+a$.

OSTWALD compared the action of a catalyst upon a chemical reaction to that of oil upon a machine. The similarity is, in fact, very great as we can see from the following points:

(i) The catalyst is left unchanged in weight and in chemical composition after the reaction: lubricating oil is not *consumed* by lubrication although it may be scattered and lost in this and other ways.

(ii) The addition of a catalyst affects the *speed* of the reaction only, not the products; similarly, if oil be added to a machine making paper bags, the machine will continue to make paper bags and not packets of cigarettes.

(iii) Within certain limits, the more catalyst is added, the greater its effect: the same is true of oil.

(iv) A catalyst will not start a reaction as a rule, and in no case unless the action is potentially possible: it is of no use adding oil to a machine if the necessary driving force is absent.

(v) A catalyst may be either positive or negative: axle-grease will increase the speed of a railway-truck, but would probably retard the action of a watch.

(vi) A substance which is a catalyst in one reaction may not be a catalyst in another reaction in which it is used (*e.g.* manganese dioxide in (*a*) decomposition of potassium chlorate and (*b*) oxidation of hydrochloric acid to chlorine); similarly, the same oil which is a "catalyst" when used for lubrication may be converted into margarine and used for food.

Many examples of catalysis are known, and it is interesting to learn that the idea is extremely ancient. We find it in a great number of the early chemical books, even as far back as the third and fourth centuries of our era. The alchemists believed that a minute portion of a wonderful substance called *Elixir* would convert an unlimited quantity of mercury or lead into gold. Thus the (probably legendary) Jewish woman-chemist, Mary—said to have been the sister of Moses

—hopefully declares "*one dram of it is sufficient for all [the lead] which lies between the East and the West.*" Mary has a further claim to our respect, for it is she who is supposed to have invented that essential piece of chemical apparatus, the water-bath, which to this day the French call *bain-marie*. The earliest recorded authentic example of catalysis is that of yeast upon dough.

Up to the present no completely satisfactory explanation of catalysis has been suggested. It is probable that the mechanism of the process may differ in different cases. The first scientific investigation of catalysis was made by KIRCHHOF in 1811, while the actual word (from *kata*, down, and *luo*, I unloose) was introduced by BERZELIUS in 1845. The well-known catalytic action of platinum upon a mixture of sulphur dioxide and oxygen, which is the basis of the contact process for the manufacture of sulphuric acid, was patented in 1831 by PEREGRINE PHILLIPS, a vinegar manufacturer of Bristol. Of late years, catalysis has increased in importance extremely rapidly, not only in the laboratory, but also in the large chemical factories.

Examples of catalysis discussed in this book are:

(i) The action of manganese dioxide on the decomposition of potassium chlorate by heat (see above, and p. 172).

(ii) The use of copper chloride in Deacon's process for the manufacture of chlorine, p. 220.

(iii) The use of oxides of nitrogen in the lead-chamber process for the manufacture of sulphuric acid, p. 305.

(iv) Catalytic combination of sulphur dioxide and oxygen by means of platinized asbestos, p. 308.

(v) Catalytic decomposition of hydrogen peroxide by means of finely divided metals, p. 204.

(vi) Catalytic combination of hydrogen and bromine by means of a white-hot platinum spiral, p. 236.

(vii) Catalytic oxidation of ammonia by means of a hot platinum spiral, p. 271.

(viii) Catalytic union of nitrogen and hydrogen by means of iron containing molybdenum, p. 258.

Note also (*a*) that the *enzymes* mentioned on p. 343 act

catalytically; and (*b*) that many substances when *absolutely dry* will not react together, whereas in the presence of even a trace of moisture reaction takes place at once. Thus dry ammonia has no action on dry hydrogen chloride. In these reactions water may be said to act as a catalyst.

Rate of a Chemical Change.—Although many chemical reactions are instantaneous (*e.g.* neutralization of an acid by a base), a great number of them require a considerable time and do not go to completion immediately. Thus, when zinc is placed in dilute sulphuric acid, it dissolves *gradually*—it does not all vanish at once. If we heated the acid we should find that the zinc dissolved more rapidly, while if we cooled it the solution would take place more slowly. It is clear, then, that the rate at which a chemical change takes place is a subject worth investigating, and it has, in fact, been investigated by a great number of different chemists during the last 150 years. The main facts which have emerged from their researches are discussed in what follows, but we must first settle exactly what we mean by the *rate* of a chemical reaction.

In order to measure the rate at which a chocolate packer is working, we count the number of boxes she fills in a given time. In the same way, we can measure the rate of a chemical change by finding what weight of the product or products of the reaction is produced in a given time, or, alternatively, by finding what weight of the original substance or substances is changed in a given time. For instance, suppose we took some zinc and added it to dilute sulphuric acid. We might find that, say, 150 c.c. of hydrogen were given off per minute. If we heated the mixture, the volume of hydrogen given off in a minute might increase to 450 c.c., in which event we should say that the rate of the change had been trebled. This method is quite satisfactory, but if you think about it, you will see that it is not yet definite enough. If we got 150 c.c. of hydrogen per minute, at a given temperature, by adding x grams of zinc to an excess of dilute sulphuric acid, we should get 300 c.c. per unit, at the same temperature, if we started with $2x$ grams of zinc instead of x grams.

Hence it is better to measure the rate of a chemical change in terms of the *proportion of the total* weight of the original substance or substances changed in a given time.

Factors which affect the Rate of a Chemical Change.

(i) *Rise of Temperature.*—The rate of every chemical reaction is increased on rise of temperature and decreased on fall of temperature. The extent of the change varies somewhat in different reactions, but it is roughly true to say that the rate of a chemical change is approximately doubled by a rise in temperature of 10° C.

(ii) *Alterations of Pressure.*—Where no gases are concerned in the reaction, the rate of the latter is scarcely affected by change of pressure, but in actions between, or resulting in the formation of, gases, the pressure may play a very important part. Increase of pressure, by bringing the molecules closer together, increases the rate of the reaction. This is what would be expected.

(iii) *Concentration of the Substances Concerned.*—Concentration and dilution in the case of gases correspond to high pressure and low pressure. We have seen that increased pressure increases the rate of a gaseous reaction; in exactly the same way, the rate of reactions between or in liquids is directly proportional to the *concentration* of each of the substances concerned. This fact, and that mentioned under (ii), may be summed up in what is known as the **Law of Mass Action,** or GULDBERG AND WAAGE'S Law after its discoverers:

The rate of a chemical change at a given moment is directly proportional to the concentrations at that moment of the substances taking part in the change. The concentration for this purpose is usually expressed in gram-molecules per litre, and is then called the *active mass* of the substance.

(iv) *Presence or Absence of a Catalyst.*—This has been discussed above.

(v) *Presence or Absence of Moisture.*—This may be included under (iv).

(vi) *Presence or Absence of Light.*—In a few cases, reactions take place much more quickly in the light than they do in the dark. Thus a mixture of hydrogen and chlorine combines only very slowly in the dark, but in bright sunlight it may explode. Similarly, white silver chloride remains unchanged in the dark, but on exposure to light it gradually turns purple and is finally changed into metallic silver, partly, at any rate.

Reversible Reactions.—If steam be passed over heated iron, iron oxide (magnetic oxide, Fe_3O_4) and hydrogen are formed—

$$\text{(i)}\ 3Fe + 4H_2O = Fe_3O_4 + 4H_2.$$

But if we pass hydrogen over heated iron oxide, we shall find that steam is formed and iron left—

$$\text{(ii)}\ Fe_3O_4 + 4H_2 = 3Fe + 4H_2O.$$

The reaction between iron and steam, or between iron oxide and hydrogen, is therefore said to be *reversible*, and to indicate this reversibility we usually write the equation with the sign $\rightleftharpoons$ instead of the sign of equality—

$$3Fe + 4H_2O \rightleftharpoons Fe_3O_4 + 4H_2.$$

The puzzle of the above reactions may be explained by the fact that in the first case the hydrogen is swept away, by the current of steam, as soon as it is formed, while in the second case the steam is swept away by the current of hydrogen. The reverse actions, therefore, have no opportunity to take place. What will happen if some iron and steam are heated together in a closed vessel? Experiments made to test this showed that at first iron oxide and hydrogen were formed, but that after a time no further change could be detected, although some of the iron and some of the steam were still left. However long the vessel is kept, at the same temperature, the composition of the mixture inside remains unaltered; in other words, a *state of equilibrium* has been reached. As, however, steam and iron, and iron oxide and hydrogen are present, chemical reactions must still be going on, and the equilibrium is therefore explained by assuming that as much steam is formed in a given time as is decomposed in that time; that is, the speed of the one reaction is equal to the speed of the other, and the equilibrium is a *kinetic* equilibrium.

When, in a reversible reaction, the conditions are so arranged that both the forward and the backward reactions are proceeding at the same speed, and equilibrium is thus established, the action is called a *balanced action*.

Many reactions are reversible, and it is possible that if we could produce the right conditions, all would be so ; but, in the present state of our knowledge, to reverse the majority of chemical actions is not within our power. Hence it is convenient to distinguish between reversible and irreversible reactions.

Examples of reversible reactions.

(i) If concentrated hydrochloric acid is poured on antimony sulphide, hydrogen sulphide and antimony chloride are formed—

$$Sb_2S_3 + 6HCl = 2SbCl_3 + 3H_2S.$$

If, however, hydrogen sulphide is passed through a solution of antimony chloride, the reverse reaction takes place, and antimony sulphide is precipitated.

(ii) If a mixture of 2 volumes of hydrogen and 1 volume oxygen is ignited, an explosion occurs and steam is formed—

$$2H_2 + O_2 = 2H_2O.$$

But if a stream of steam is passed over a white-hot platinum wire, some of the steam is split up again into hydrogen and oxygen.

(iii) "Dissociation" is a reversible reaction (see pp. 244 and 268).

(iv) The decomposition of calcium carbonate by heat. When calcium carbonate (limestone, chalk or marble) is heated, it splits up into quicklime and carbon dioxide—

$$CaCO_3 = CaO + CO_2.$$

If the carbon dioxide is allowed to escape, the reaction goes to completion.

When carbon dioxide is passed over quicklime, calcium carbonate is formed, $CaO + CO_2 = CaCO_3$.

The reaction is therefore reversible, and may be written—

$$CaCO_3 \rightleftharpoons CaO + CO_2.$$

When calcium carbonate is heated in a *closed vessel*, the rates of the two opposing reactions finally become equal, and equilibrium is attained. It has been found that, at a constant temperature, the pressure of the carbon dioxide in this experiment (as shown by a manometer attached to the vessel) is constant.

Very often in practice the fact that a reaction is reversible is somewhat of a nuisance, as we may desire to get the products of the forward change free from the substances we started with. Well, we can often alter the conditions so as to favour the one reaction at the expense of the other. Thus, in (iv) above, if we heat the limestone in the open air, the carbon dioxide goes off as fast as it is formed, so that the reverse change cannot take place. Similarly, in getting iron oxide from steam and iron we should take care to have a good current of steam so as to drive away all the hydrogen as soon as it was formed. In short, in order to get one action of the two, in a reversible change, to proceed to completion, we may—

(i) Remove one of the products of the change from the sphere of action as soon as it is formed; or

(ii) In the case of a reaction such as $A + B \rightleftharpoons C + D$, in which we want to get all the B converted, we could greatly increase the concentration of A. This would leave no opportunity for B to avoid meeting A, and so it would all be changed.

As an example of the second method, we may consider the synthesis of sulphur trioxide from sulphur dioxide and oxygen in the presence of heated platinized asbestos as a catalyst (p. 308)—

$$2SO_2 + O_2 \rightleftharpoons 2SO_3.$$

On the commercial scale, the valuable substance started with is the sulphur dioxide, since the oxygen is atmospheric and therefore costs no more than the expense of the labour used in dealing with it. Now, what the manufacturer wants to do is to get *all* his sulphur dioxide converted into the trioxide. It is not convenient to remove the trioxide as soon as it is formed, so he has to adopt another method. If the rate of the forward reaction, $2SO_2 + O_2 \rightarrow 2SO_3$, can be greatly increased, without increasing the rate of the backward reaction, this would increase the proportion of trioxide at equilibrium, but would not necessarily ensure the conversion of all the dioxide. To bring about the latter, the manufacturer takes care to mix his sulphur dioxide with far more than the calculated volume of oxygen. This means that every sulphur dioxide molecule has swarms of oxygen molecules around it, and simply cannot help changing into the trioxide.

Questions

1. Define *catalysis*.

2. The action of a catalyst upon a chemical reaction has been compared to that of oil upon a machine. How far do you think this comparison is justified ?

3. Mention *six* chemical reactions in which a catalyst is commonly employed, giving the name of the catalyst in each instance.

4. What does the *word* catalysis mean, by derivation ?

5. What are the main factors which affect the rate and extent of a chemical change ?

6. What do you mean by a *reversible* action ? Give examples.

7. What is the *Law of Mass Action* ?

8. How would you define *rate of a chemical reaction* ?

9. The action of steam upon iron is said to be reversible. What is meant by this statement ? What would happen if some iron and steam were heated in a closed vessel ?

10. How may one reaction, in a reversible change, be made to go practically to completion ?

CHAPTER XIII

HYDROGEN

Note.—When you are beginning the study of chemistry you—very naturally—often do not know which things are really important and which are only secondary. It is, of course, over this matter that a teacher's help is of greatest value, but in your private reading you will find the following points of assistance:

(i) When you meet with an element for the first time, learn by heart its *symbol, atomic weight, valency* (and atomicity in the case of a gas).

(ii) Next learn—

(*a*) How to prepare it in the laboratory;

(*b*) ,, ,, *pure,* if the method in (*a*) gives only an impure product;

(*c*) Its chief physical properties;

(*d*) ,, ,, chemical ,,

Commit to memory the *equations* in (*a*) and (*b*).

(iii) If early work on the element had a great influence upon the development of chemistry, you must learn the chief facts about its history (*e.g.* hydrogen and oxygen).

(iv) In the case of a compound, learn—

(*a*) Its formula;

(*b*) Its *equivalent* (after a time you can omit to do this, as you will be able to calculate it from the formula);

(*c*) How to prepare it in the laboratory;

(*d*) How to purify it if necessary;

(*e*) Its appearance and any striking physical properties;

(*f*) Its chief chemical properties.

Equations *must* be learnt in (*c*), and as many as possible in (*f*).

(v) Methods of settling the formulæ of compound gases should always be committed to memory.

(vi) If the substance—element or compound—is important commercially, you must know an *outline* of the commercial method of obtaining it.

HYDROGEN

Symbol: H; *Valency:* 1; *Atomicity* (number of atoms in molecule): 2, hence formula is H_2; *Atomic Weight:* 1.

History and Occurrence.—Hydrogen was discovered by CAVENDISH in 1766. He made it by the action of dilute sulphuric acid upon iron or zinc. The first to call it "hydrogen" was LAVOISIER, who gave it this name because it is a constituent of water.[1] Hydrogen occurs in large quantities on the earth in the form of its compound with oxygen, namely, water, of which it forms one-ninth by weight. Petroleum consists of compounds of carbon and hydrogen. Hydrogen is a necessary constituent of the bodies of all plants and animals. Free hydrogen is found in enormous quantities in the sun and other stars.

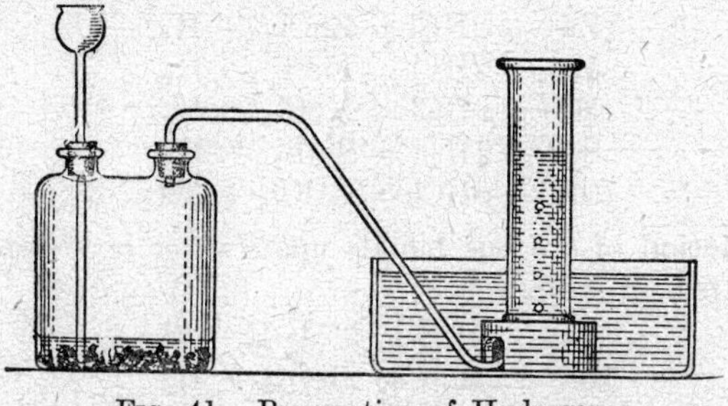

FIG. 41.—Preparation of Hydrogen.

Preparation.—In the laboratory, hydrogen is commonly prepared by the action of dilute sulphuric acid upon zinc. The apparatus is shown in Fig. 41. The granulated zinc is

[1] Hydrogen = *water-producer* (Greek).

placed in a Woulfe bottle and covered with a layer of water. Sulphuric acid is poured down through the thistle-funnel, when hydrogen at once comes off. It may be collected over water, or, since it is much lighter than air, by upward displacement (see p. 209). If required dry it can be bubbled through concentrated sulphuric acid and collected over mercury or by displacement of air.

The equation for the reaction is—

$$Zn + H_2SO_4 = \underset{\text{(Zinc sulphate)}}{ZnSO_4} + H_2.$$

A solution of zinc sulphate is left in the bottle. If it is filtered and then concentrated by evaporation, crystals of zinc sulphate heptahydrate ("white vitriol"), $ZnSO_4.7H_2O$, separate out on cooling.

Formation.—Hydrogen may be obtained in many other ways, some of which are given below:

(i) Action of magnesium or iron upon dilute sulphuric acid—

$$Mg + H_2SO_4 = MgSO_4 + H_2.$$
$$Fe + H_2SO_4 = FeSO_4 + H_2.$$

(ii) Action of zinc, iron, magnesium, tin or aluminium upon hydrochloric acid—

$$Zn + 2HCl = ZnCl_2 + H_2.$$
$$Fe + 2HCl = FeCl_2 + H_2.$$
$$Mg + 2HCl = MgCl_2 + H_2.$$
$$Sn + 2HCl = SnCl_2 + H_2.$$
$$2Al + 6HCl = 2AlCl_3 + 3H_2.$$

(iii) Action of various metals upon water or steam—

With cold water—

$$2Na + 2H_2O = 2NaOH + H_2.$$
$$2K + 2H_2O = 2KOH + H_2.$$
$$Ca + 2H_2O = Ca(OH)_2 + H_2.$$

With steam—

$$Mg + H_2O = MgO + H_2.$$
$$3Fe + 4H_2O = Fe_3O_4 + 4H_2.$$

For details of these actions, see p. 365.

HENRY CAVENDISH.
(*From the drawing by* W. ALEXANDER.)

Pure hydrogen may be obtained by the electrolysis of water made slightly alkaline by dissolving a little barium hydroxide, $Ba(OH)_2$, in it. The hydrogen is evolved at the cathode and pure oxygen at the anode. The action may be carried out in a voltameter (Fig. 42).

If the hydrogen is not required specially pure, the water may be made to conduct the electric current by adding a little sulphuric acid instead of barium hydroxide.

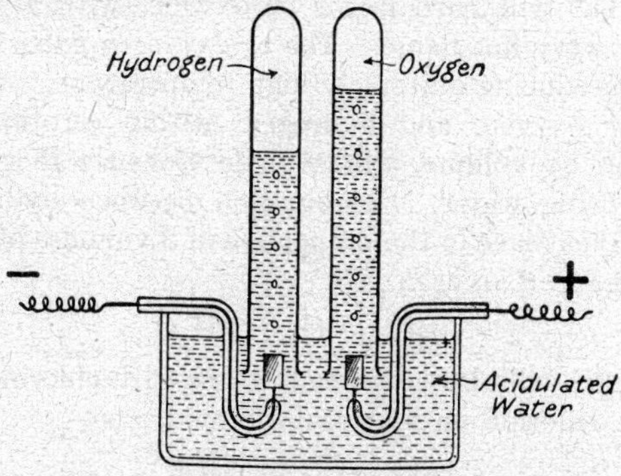

FIG. 42.—Preparation of Hydrogen by Electrolysis of Water.

Commercially, hydrogen is obtained as a by-product in the manufacture of sodium and caustic soda (see pp. 377, 379).

It is, however, principally obtained by the Bosch process. Steam is blown over white-hot coke, when the following action occurs :

$$C + H_2O = CO + H_2.$$

The mixture of carbon monoxide (CO) and hydrogen is known as water-gas (p. 348). It is mixed with a further quantity of steam and passed through red-hot tubes containing a suitable catalyst, *e.g.* iron oxide. Under these conditions, the carbon monoxide is converted into carbon dioxide, and more hydrogen is formed :

$$\underbrace{CO + H_2}_{\text{Water-gas}} + \underset{\text{Steam}}{H_2O} = \underset{\text{Carbon dioxide}}{CO_2} + 2H_2.$$

The carbon dioxide is dissolved out of the mixture by shaking with water under high pressure, and the hydrogen is thus isolated.

Properties.—Hydrogen is a colourless gas with no taste or smell. It is the lightest substance known (1 litre weighs 0·09 grams at N.T.P.), and is therefore used for filling balloons and airships, although it is rather dangerous for this purpose, since it is so inflammable. It will not support combustion, but will burn in air or oxygen, with a blue, non-luminous, very hot flame. The *oxyhydrogen flame* is, indeed, used for producing extremely high temperatures. A mixture of air, or oxygen, and hydrogen, within certain limits of proportion by volume, will explode violently if ignited, the product being water. Combination between hydrogen and oxygen takes place in the proportion of 2 volumes of hydrogen to 1 volume of oxygen.

$$2H_2 + O_2 = 2H_2O.$$

Hydrogen will also combine directly with chlorine, forming hydrogen chloride or hydrochloric acid gas—

$$H_2 + Cl_2 = 2HCl.$$

If the two gases are mixed, the mixture will explode when exposed to bright sunlight. In ordinary daylight the action takes place slowly, but the explosion can be brought about by applying a flame.

Owing to its great affinity for oxygen, hydrogen will often remove that element from oxides and other oxygen compounds, under suitable conditions. Thus if a metallic oxide is heated in a current of hydrogen, it is common to find that water is formed and the metal set free—

Metallic oxide + hydrogen = metal + water,

e.g. $CuO + H_2 = Cu + H_2O$
(Copper oxide)

$PbO + H_2 = Pb + H_2O$
(Lead oxide)

The conversion of a metallic oxide into the metal is called *reduction*. The word reduction has, however, been extended in meaning to include all cases of removal of oxygen from a substance, whether a metallic oxide or not. Further details about oxidation and reduction are found on p. 181. It is sufficient to notice here that hydrogen is a powerful *reducing agent, i.e.* a substance able to effect reduction.

Commercial Uses of Hydrogen.—(i) For filling balloons and airships. (ii) Mixed with carbon monoxide it forms "*water-gas*," used as a fuel (p. 348). (iii) In the oxyhydrogen flame. (iv) It forms about 50 per cent. of coal-gas (p. 317). (v) In the manufacture of ammonia by the Haber process (p. 258). (vi) In the conversion of oils into fats ("hardening" or "hydrogenation" of oils). (vii) In the hydrogenation of coal.

Diffusion of Gases.—Gases will pass through the wall of a porous earthenware pot, the rate of passage differing with different gases. GRAHAM, who was Master of the Mint in Queen Victoria's reign, found (*Graham's Law*) that the rates at which two gases passed through a porous partition are inversely proportional to the square roots of the densities of the gases, or

$$\frac{R'}{R} \propto \frac{\sqrt{D}}{\sqrt{D'}}$$

By comparing the rates of diffusion of two gases we can therefore find the ratio of their densities, and if we know the density of one of them we can calculate that of the other.

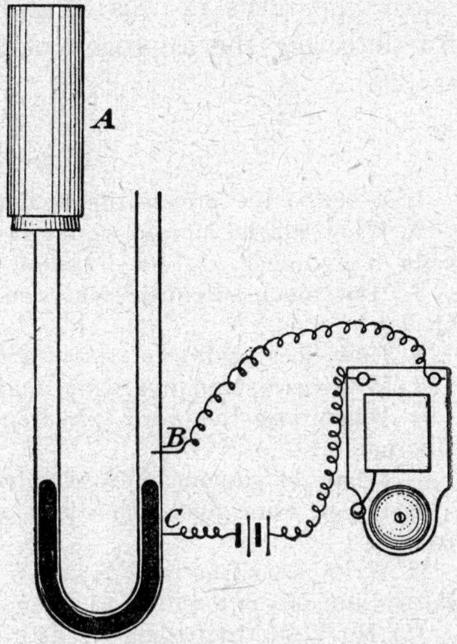

FIG. 43.—Apparatus to show Diffusion of a Gas.

That a light gas can pass through a porous partition more quickly than a heavier one is delightfully illustrated by the apparatus shown in Fig. 43.

A is a porous pot, fitted with a cork through which passes one limb of a U-tube containing mercury. Through the wall of the other limb two platinum wires are fused. These are connected in series to an electric bell and battery. The mercury level is so arranged that it is above C and just below B. If a gas-jar is filled with hydrogen or coal-gas and then inverted over A, the bell will ring. This is because the light hydrogen molecules (or hydrogen and methane molecules in the case of coal-gas) pass into the pot more quickly than the heavier air molecules can pass out. The pressure in the pot therefore increases, and pushes down the mercury in one limb and up in the other. Connection is thus made, by the mercury, between B and C; the current passes and the bell rings.

An apparatus of this kind has been used in coal-mines for detecting the approach of fire-damp (methane, CH_4, see p. 333).

Questions

1. Describe the preparation and properties of hydrogen.
2. What weight of zinc would you have to take to obtain (*a*) 100 tons of hydrogen, (*b*) 100 litres of hydrogen at N.T.P.?
3. How much sulphuric acid would you require for (*a*) and (*b*) in Q. 2?
4. How does hydrogen occur in nature?
5. Who discovered hydrogen, and when?
6. What does the word "hydrogen" mean? Who gave the gas this name?
7. What do you mean by a *reducing agent*?
8. If you were given some lead oxide, how could you obtain lead from it?
9. Write equations for the action upon water or steam of (*a*) iron, (*b*) sodium, (*c*) potassium, (*d*) magnesium, (*e*) calcium.
10. How can hydrogen be dried? How would you collect dry hydrogen?
11. How is hydrogen obtained commercially? What are its chief uses?

CHAPTER XIV

OXYGEN. AIR AND WATER. OZONE HYDROGEN PEROXIDE

Oxygen

The Theory of Phlogiston.—In the eighteenth century chemists explained what happens when things burn in terms of a theory called the Phlogiston Theory, which had been suggested by the German chemists Becher (1669) and Stahl (1723). The chief idea of this theory was as follows—all combustible substances were supposed to contain a "fire-stuff," *phlogiston*, which they lost when they were burnt. Combustible metals, for example, were regarded not as elements but as compounds of two things:

(*a*) *Phlogiston*, which was common to them all, and

(*b*) A *calx* or residue, which was different in different metals.

When metals were burnt, they were considered to lose their phlogiston, their calces being left—

Metal = *calx* + *phlogiston*

or, of course,

Calx = *metal* minus *phlogiston*.

Substances like carbon which, when burnt, yield only a little ash, were considered to consist almost entirely of phlogiston. Now, suppose we burn zinc in air. We get a white powder which, according to Becher and Stahl, is zinc calx, or zinc *minus* phlogiston. What will happen when zinc calx is heated with carbon? Well, since carbon is so rich in phlogiston, we might expect it to give up some to the zinc calx which should therefore be converted back again into metallic zinc. In point of fact, when zinc calx is heated with carbon, this is exactly what does happen, so that the theory was satisfactory so far.

Another fact which the Phlogiston Theory explained was that if a lighted candle is placed under a bell-jar, the flame is soon extinguished. This was thought to be due to the air in the jar becoming saturated with phlogiston, just as a sponge becomes saturated with water. When a sponge is saturated, it can take up no more. Similarly, when air becomes saturated with phlogiston it can take up no more and hence nothing can burn in it any longer.

Since thousands of tons of combustible substances are burnt every day, it follows that the atmosphere must always contain a certain amount of phlogiston.

Such was the state of affairs when an important discovery was made by the REV. JOSEPH PRIESTLEY (1733–1804). (See p. 452.)

Discovery of Oxygen.—On August 1, 1774, Priestley (who was a warm supporter of the Phlogiston Theory) heated *red calx of mercury* by means of a fine burning-glass which had just come into his possession. You will see his apparatus in Fig. 44. He obtained mercury and a gas which allowed things to burn in it with great brilliancy; a glowing splint, for example, at once burst into flame when plunged into the gas. Now, let us put ourselves into Priestley's place and see how we should have explained these results.

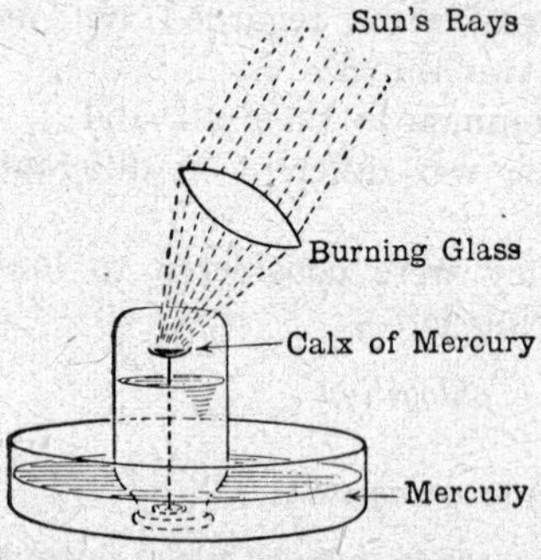

FIG. 44.—Priestley's Apparatus.

Calx of mercury we assume to be mercury *minus* phlogiston. We have heated this in a glass cylinder containing air, and have obtained mercury. This means that phlogiston must have been taken up by the calx; where can this phlogiston have come from? Obviously from the air in the cylinder. But the air in the cylinder is ordinary atmospheric air—does this contain phlogiston? Certainly, for fires all over the world are constantly liberating phlogiston and turning it into the air. Admitting this, what should be the properties of the residual air in the cylinder? Clearly this air has lost phlogiston, and is therefore *dephlogisticated air*; it should therefore be able to take up more phlogiston than the same volume of ordinary air—in other words, (*a*) things should burn in it more brightly, since they can give up their phlogiston more readily, and (*b*) it should support life longer. Both of these results were actually obtained by Priestley, and we can therefore see that his name for the gas, *dephlogisticated air*, was a good one.

Priestley gave an account of his discovery of "dephlogisticated air" to the great French chemist LAVOISIER (1743–1794). Lavoisier (p. 451) had himself been carrying out experiments on the calcination or burning of metals, and had found that in every case the calx weighed more than the metal from which it was made. This is contrary to what would be expected on the Phlogiston Theory, for if, when a metal is burnt, it *loses* something, the residue ought to weigh *less*. The fact that it weighs *more* convinced Lavoisier that a metal on burning combines with something in the air. He knew that a substance, when burnt in air enclosed in a bell-jar over water, did not combine with *all* the air, for about $\frac{4}{5}$ of the air was always left afterwards. This residual "air" would not support combustion and was fatal to the life of animals. Lavoisier therefore thought that the air consists of two gases, (*a*) active air, which is concerned in combustion and in breathing, and (*b*) inactive air, which takes no part in these changes.

When he heard of Priestley's discovery, he at once realized that "dephlogisticated air" was probably nothing else than "active air," or that part of the air which combined with metals during combustion. To test this idea he devised an experiment which has now become famous (Fig. 45). He confined mercury in a glass retort provided with a long neck communicating with air in a bell-jar placed in a trough of mercury. The level of the mercury in the bell-jar was noted by means of a strip of gummed paper. The mercury in the retort was heated for several days to a temperature just below its boiling-point. Lavoisier found that the mercury in the retort became covered with a red powder and that the level of the mercury in the bell-jar rose. After some time, no more red powder seemed to be forming and the mercury in the bell-jar stopped rising. At this stage Lavoisier noted the decrease in volume of the air in the bell-jar and found that it was not far short of one-fifth. The residual air would not support combustion or life, so he called it *azote*. On heating the red calx or powder formed in the retort, he obtained a volume of gas *equal to the diminution in volume of the air in the bell-jar*; this gas was of course Priestley's dephlogisticated air, and supported combustion extremely well. Lavoisier showed further that the increase in weight of the mercury in the retort during the above experiment was exactly equal to the loss in weight of the air in the bell-jar, and that a gas exactly like ordinary air could be produced artificially by mixing 1 volume of "dephlogisticated air" with 4 volumes of azote (the gas we now call *nitrogen*).

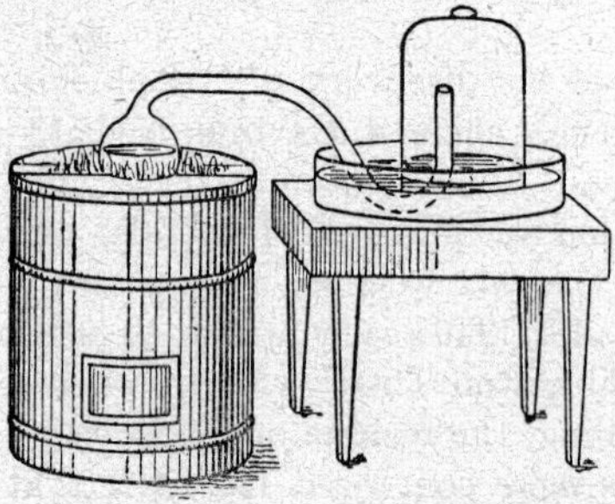

FIG. 45.—Lavoisier's Apparatus.

His chief conclusion was that *air consists of two gases, azote and dephlogisticated air, in the proportion by volume of* 4 *to* 1; *in combustion, only the latter gas is concerned, and this combines with the burning substance, hence the increase in weight.* The difference between the two theories of combustion is therefore as follows:

Phlogiston Theory: Metal = Calx + Phlogiston.

Lavoisier's Theory: Metal + Dephlogisticated Air = Calx.

To mark the difference, Lavoisier re-named dephlogisticated air, calling it at first *eminently breathable air*, but afterwards

Antoine Laurent Lavoisier.

oxygen (acid-producer), since he found that when non-metals were burnt in the gas and the products of combustion dissolved in water the resulting solutions were *acid*. He concluded further that oxygen was an essential constituent of all acids, in which he was not quite right.

Lavoisier's work forms the foundation of modern chemistry. On it Dalton was able to build his atomic theory, and from that time chemistry has never looked back. In 1869 WURTZ expressed the feeling of many chemists when he said, "*Chemistry is a French science. It was founded by Lavoisier of immortal memory.*" Lavoisier, however, had managed to make enemies of some of the French Revolutionists, who in 1794 guillotined him, remarking that the Republic had no need of men of science.

The Phlogiston Theory, which was overthrown by Lavoisier's brilliant work, had performed good service for chemistry in its early days, but of course it had to be abandoned when facts were discovered with which it would not fit. All chemical theories, even to-day, are held on the same understanding, namely, that if facts are discovered which are not in accordance with them, then the theories must be thrown over and new ones substituted. Who knows? A century hence some one may be writing a text-book in which he says, "The chemists of the first half of the twentieth century still believed in the oxygen theory of combustion. This theory, which was comparatively satisfactory for many years, was overthrown by the brilliant discoveries of Charles Nomdeguerre of Czecho-Slovakia. We find it hard to understand why the oxygen theory was accepted for so long, but we must remember that it is always very difficult to change the habits of mind in which we have been brought up"!

To his death, Priestley was a confirmed phlogistian, but all the younger chemists adopted Lavoisier's scheme, and before his death in 1794 Lavoisier had the joy of knowing that his views were winning all along the line. He perished in a revolution, it is true, but not before he had himself started a revolution in chemical thought, in comparison with which the French Revolution was merely a storm in a tea-cup. It is sad to think that his fellow-chemists, some of whom had much influence in the Revolutionary councils, made scarcely any attempt to save him.

Occurrence of Oxygen.—Oxygen forms 21 per cent. by volume and 23 per cent. by weight of the air. In water it is combined with hydrogen in the proportion by weight of 88·9 per cent. oxygen to 11·1 per cent. hydrogen. About 50 per cent. of the earth's crust is composed of oxygen, and it is an essential constituent of all living matter. It is probably present in the sun and in other stars.

Preparation.—Priestley's method of obtaining oxygen is still sometimes used—

$$2HgO = 2Hg + O_2.$$

We see, however, from the above equation, that 432 grams [*i.e.* 2 × (200 + 16)] of mercuric oxide would give only 32 grams (22·4 litres at N.T.P.) of oxygen, which is a very low yield. Moreover, mercuric oxide is very expensive. We therefore choose a substance which (*a*) is cheaper, and (*b*) will give a better yield of oxygen. Such a substance is potassium chlorate, a white crystalline solid of the formula $KClO_3$. When this is heated, it splits up into potassium chlor*ide*, KCl, and oxygen—

$$2KClO_3 = 2KCl + 3O_2$$

*potassium chlor*ATE = *potassium chlor*IDE + *oxygen.*

From this equation, we see that 2 [39 + 35·5 + 48] grams of the chlorate yield 96 grams of oxygen, or 3 × 22·4 litres at N.T.P., or 245 grams pot. chlorate = 67·2 litres of oxygen at N.T.P.

[*Exercise.*—Calculate the weight of potassium chlorate required to give 10 litres of oxygen, measured at 15° C. 740 mm.]

It has been found that if a little *manganese dioxide*, MnO_2, a black powder, is mixed with the potassium chlorate, the oxygen comes off at a much lower temperature (or—what amounts to the same—much faster at the same temperature). The manganese dioxide is left unchanged in weight and in chemical composition at the end of the reaction, and is there-

Lavoisier defends himself before the Revolutionary Tribunal.

fore not put into the equation. Substances, like manganese dioxide in this case, which will alter the rate of a chemical change without themselves being changed in weight or in chemical composition, are called *catalysts* (see p. 147). [*N.B.*—Learn NOW how to *spell* catalyst.] *You should note that,* though a substance may be a catalyst in one reaction, it does not follow that it is a catalyst in *all* the reactions in which it is used. Thus, when you prepare chlorine, you will employ manganese dioxide, but here it is *not* a catalyst, as it is used up and changed into manganese chloride (p. 210).

If you are asked how to show experimentally that manganese dioxide *does* act as a catalyst upon the decomposition of potassium chlorate by heat, remember that the three following points must be made:

(i) The products of the action (*viz.* potassium chloride and oxygen) are the same whether the manganese dioxide is present or absent. The potassium chloride may be identified (*a*) by the lilac colour it imparts to the Bunsen flame, indicative of *potassium*, (*b*) by the fact that its solution gives a white precipitate of silver chloride with silver nitrate solution, indicative of a *chloride*.

(ii) The rate of the reaction is altered by the addition of the manganese dioxide. This can be shown by just melting some potassium chlorate, when little or no oxygen is evolved. On dropping in a pinch of manganese dioxide a vigorous evolution of oxygen occurs.

(iii) The manganese dioxide is left unchanged in weight and in chemical composition at the end of the reaction. This can be shown by dissolving out the potassium chloride in water, and washing, drying and weighing the residue; there is no change in weight. Show that the black powder *is* manganese dioxide, *e.g.* by finding its action with hot-concentrated hydrochloric acid, when chlorine is evolved.

The apparatus used for the preparation of oxygen is shown in Fig. 46.

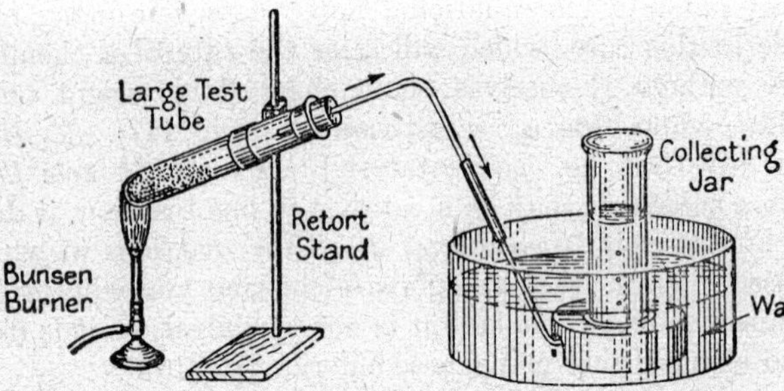

FIG. 46.—Preparation of Oxygen.

The gas is collected over water. If it is required dry it can be passed through concentrated sulphuric acid and collected over mercury.

Another way of obtaining oxygen in the laboratory is to drop water on to *sodium peroxide*, Na_2O_2 (Fig. 47)—

$$2Na_2O_2 + 2H_2O = 4NaOH + O_2.$$

The action takes place in the cold. Caustic soda (NaOH) is formed as well as oxygen.

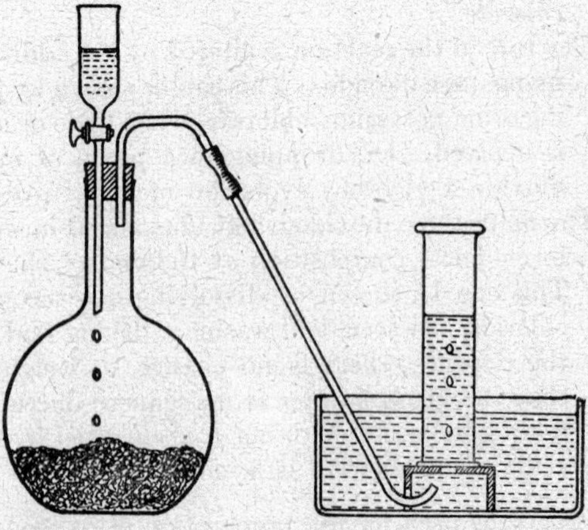

FIG. 47.—Preparation of Oxygen from Sodium Peroxide.

Commercially, oxygen is prepared by the fractional distillation of liquid air. Since oxygen boils at −182° and nitrogen at −194°, when liquid air is allowed to boil the nitrogen boils off first and can therefore be separated from the oxygen. Oxygen is put on the market compressed in steel cylinders at a pressure of about 120 atmospheres.

Properties.—Oxygen is a colourless gas with no taste or smell. It is slightly heavier than air (V.D. = 16, V.D. of air = 14·4), and has a molecular weight of 32 (formula O_2, atomic weight 16). It is only slightly soluble in water, but sufficient dissolves to enable fish and other aquatic animals to breathe. You must be careful not to imagine that fish breathe the *combined* oxygen in water: if they are placed in water which contains no dissolved oxygen they drown.

Oxygen boils at −182°. Liquid oxygen is a pale blue liquid which is attracted by a magnet.

Oxygen will not burn, but it supports combustion very readily. Thus it relights a glowing splint (test for oxygen), while red-hot iron, when plunged into oxygen, burns brilliantly—a delightful experiment which we owe to the eighteenth-century scientist Ingen-Housz—

$$3Fe + 2O_2 = Fe_3O_4 \text{ (magnetic oxide of iron).}$$

The products obtained when substances are burnt in oxygen are called *oxides*. Thus, when the following elements are burnt the oxides are obtained in each case:

Carbon.—Burns brightly, forming *carbon dioxide*, CO_2, a gas which turns lime-water milky—

$$C + O_2 = CO_2.$$

We see from the equation that every molecule of oxygen yields a molecule of carbon dioxide. Hence, by Avogadro's Hypothesis, 1 volume—whatever it may be—yields the *same* volume of carbon dioxide.

Sulphur.—Burns with a blue flame, forming the gas *sulphur dioxide*, SO_2—

$$S + O_2 = SO_2.$$

PHOSPHORUS.—Burns brilliantly, forming the light white solid *phosphorus pentoxide*, P_2O_5—

$$4P + 5O_2 = 2P_2O_5.$$

SODIUM.—Burns brilliantly, forming the yellow solid *sodium peroxide*, Na_2O_2—

$$2Na + O_2 = Na_2O_2.$$

MAGNESIUM.—Burns brilliantly, forming the white solid *magnesium oxide*, MgO—

$$2Mg + O_2 = 2MgO.$$

Classification of Oxides.—Oxides are classified as follows:

(i) Acidic oxides. (ii) Basic oxides. (iii) Peroxides and suboxides. (iv) Neutral oxides.

(i) ACIDIC OXIDES.—When non-metals combine with oxygen, the oxides obtained will generally unite with water to form acids—

$SO_2 + H_2O = H_2SO_3$, sulphurous acid.
$SO_3 + H_2O = H_2SO_4$, sulphuric acid.
$P_2O_5 + H_2O$ (cold) $= 2HPO_3$, metaphosphoric acid.
$P_2O_5 + 3H_2O$ (hot) $= 2H_3PO_4$, orthophosphoric acid.
$N_2O_5 + H_2O = 2HNO_3$, nitric acid.
$CO_2 + H_2O = H_2CO_3$, carbonic acid (p. 326).

They are therefore called *acidic oxides*. Note that they are *not acids*—they form acids *when they unite with water*. They are therefore sometimes called *acid anhydrides*; thus SO_3 is sulphur trioxide or *sulphuric anhydride*.

(ii) BASIC OXIDES.—Oxides of metals will usually react with acids to yield salts and water. They are therefore *bases*, and are called *basic oxides*. Examples are *calcium oxide*, CaO, *copper oxide*, CuO, *zinc oxide*, ZnO. All these will react with hydrochloric acid, for example, to give water + the chloride of the metal—

$$CaO + 2HCl = CaCl_2 + H_2O.$$
$$CuO + 2HCl = CuCl_2 + H_2O.$$
$$ZnO + 2HCl = ZnCl_2 + H_2O.$$

Some metallic oxides will combine with water to form *hydroxides*, which are still bases, *e.g.*:

$CaO + H_2O = Ca(OH)_2$, calcium hydroxide or *slaked lime*.

Note that hydroxides are not the same as *hydrates*. A hydroxide contains the hydroxyl group —OH, while a hydrate is merely a loose compound of a substance with water, *e.g.* copper sulphate crystals, $CuSO_4.5H_2O$, are copper sulphate *penta-hydrate*; $BaCl_2.2H_2O$ is barium chloride *dihydrate*. In a solid hydrate, the water is generally present as water of crystallization.

Basic oxides may be prepared—

(*a*) By heating the metal in air or in oxygen.

(*b*) By strongly heating the carbonate of the metal—

$$ZnCO_3 = ZnO + CO_2.$$

(*c*) By heating the hydroxide of the metal—

$$Cu(OH)_2 = CuO + H_2O.$$

(*d*) By heating the nitrate of the metal—

$$Pb(NO_3)_2 = PbO + 2NO_2 + \text{oxygen}.$$

(*e*) By heating a peroxide of the metal, when the excess of oxygen is sometimes lost—

$$Pb_3O_4 = 3PbO + \text{oxygen}.$$

Not all these methods are applicable in every case; sometimes one method is more convenient and sometimes another.

(iii) PEROXIDES AND SUBOXIDES contain respectively more and less oxygen than would be expected from the normal valency of the other element present. Peroxides are formed by both metals and non-metals. The commonest are—

	Normal oxide.
Sodium peroxide, Na_2O_2	Na_2O.
Hydrogen peroxide, H_2O_2	H_2O.
Manganese dioxide, MnO_2	MnO.
Lead peroxide, PbO_2	PbO.
Barium peroxide, BaO_2	BaO.
Nitrogen peroxide, N_2O_4	N_2O_3.
Chlorine peroxide, ClO_2	Cl_2O.

Peroxides often yield oxygen on heating alone or when heated with concentrated sulphuric acid. With hydrochloric acid, they sometimes give hydrogen peroxide in the cold (*e.g.* Na_2O_2, BaO_2), and on heating give oxygen (*e.g.* H_2O_2) or chlorine (*e.g.* $PbO_2 + 4HCl = PbCl_2 + 2H_2O + Cl_2$).

Suboxides contain less oxygen than the normal oxide, *e.g.* carbon suboxide, C_3O_2. They are as a rule unstable.

It often happens that an element has two normal valencies, in which case it may form two normal oxides, *e.g.* FeO and Fe_2O_3, both normal basic oxides. In this case, the oxide containing the higher percentage of the element other than oxygen is called the *-ous* oxide (from the Latin *osus*, richness), and the other the *-ic* oxide; thus FeO is ferr*ous* oxide and Fe_2O_3 ferr*ic* oxide.

(iv) Neutral Oxides.—Certain oxides cannot be placed in any of the above classes. Such are nitric oxide, NO, carbon monoxide, CO, and water, H_2O. These are called *neutral oxides.*

N.B. The classification of oxides is only provisional, and certain oxides can be classified under more than one head.

Oxidation and Reduction

When a substance combines with oxygen, it is said to be *oxidized*; *reduction* takes place when oxygen is removed from a substance. Thus—

$$2Cu + O_2 = 2CuO$$

represents an *oxidation* of copper to copper oxide, while

$$PbO + C = Pb + CO$$

represents the *reduction* of lead oxide to lead (and, of course, the *oxidation* of carbon to carbon monoxide).

Hydrogen is often used for bringing about reduction, and this term was soon extended to cases in which the hydrogen merely added itself on to the substance concerned and did not actually remove oxygen. Thus, the combination of hydrogen with sulphur is considered to be a *reduction* of the sulphur to hydrogen sulphide, H_2S—

$$S + H_2 = H_2S.$$

In the same way, the term oxidation has been extended to include cases of *removal of hydrogen* as well as those of addition of oxygen. Thus, the conversion of hydrogen sulphide into sulphur is an *oxidation*—

$$H_2S = S + H_2.$$

Hydrogen is a typical electropositive element, and oxygen a typical electronegative element. The terms oxidation and reduction have therefore been still further extended in meaning, to include *an increase in proportion of electronegative constituent in a substance* (OXIDATION), *and an increase in proportion of electropositive constituent* (REDUCTION).

EXAMPLES—

(*a*) $2FeCl_2 + Cl_2 = 2FeCl_3$ (*oxidation* of ferrous chloride to ferric chloride).

(*b*) K_2MnO_4 + chlorine = $KCl + KMnO_4$ (*oxidation* of potassium manganate to potassium permanganate).

(*c*) $2Cu + S = Cu_2S$ (*oxidation* of copper to copper sulphide).

(*d*) $S + H_2 = H_2S$ (*reduction* of sulphur to hydrogen sulphide).

(*e*) $MnCl_4 = MnCl_2 + Cl_2$ (*reduction* of manganic chloride to manganous chloride).

Oxidation and reduction may therefore take place, even when no oxygen or hydrogen is present. Note that every oxidation is necessarily accompanied by a corresponding reduction, and *vice versâ*. Thus, in (*c*) above, the sulphur is reduced by the copper, and in (*d*) the hydrogen is oxidized by the sulphur.

Oxidizing and Reducing Agents.—A substance which will bring about oxidation is an *oxidizing agent*, while one which causes reduction is a *reducing agent*. Common oxidizing agents are oxygen, ozone, hydrogen peroxide, chlorine, bromine, nitric acid, chlorates, nitrates, peroxides, potassium permanganate ($KMnO_4$) and potassium dichromate ($K_2Cr_2O_7$).

Common reducing agents are hydrogen, hydrogen sulphide, mixtures producing " nascent " hydrogen, hydriodic acid (HI), sulphur dioxide, carbon, zinc dust, aluminium powder, stannous chloride ($SnCl_2$), carbon monoxide.

Tests for Oxidizing Agents

(i) Heat in a hard-glass test-tube. Oxygen may be evolved (glowing splint test).

(ii) Heat with concentrated hydrochloric acid, and see whether chlorine is evolved.

(iii) Add a solution of the substance to a solution of potassium iodide acidified with dilute sulphuric acid. If an oxidizing agent is present, iodine will probably be liberated. This may be recognized by the blue coloration it gives with starch solution.

(iv) Heat with ferrous sulphate solution acidified with dilute sulphuric acid. Test the resulting liquid for ferric iron by potassium ferrocyanide (blue precipitate) or potassium thiocyanate (red coloration). (Do a blank test with the original solution of ferrous sulphate, as this often contains a little ferric salt. Ferrous ammonium sulphate is preferable.)

(v) Pass hydrogen sulphide through the hot solution. Oxidizing agents often cause precipitation of sulphur.

Tests for Reducing Agents

(i) Heat the substance with potassium permanganate solution acidified with sulphuric acid. Reducing agents often decolorize the permanganate.

(ii) Heat the substance with potassium dichromate solution acidified with sulphuric acid. Reducing agents often reduce the yellow dichromate to green chromium sulphate.

(iii) Heat with ferric chloride solution and a little hydrochloric acid. Test for reduction of the ferric iron to the ferrous state by addition of potassium thiocyanate (no red coloration with ferrous salt).

Acids, Bases and Salts

Three important groups of chemical compounds are *acids*, *bases* and *salts*. The connection between these three classes of substances is summed up in the equation—

$$\text{acid} + \text{base} = \text{salt} + \text{water}.$$

which means that when an acid and a base react together, they form two products, one being water and the other a salt. It is clear that if we can settle upon definitions of "acid" and "base," we shall then be able to define a "salt" as "that substance, other than water, which is produced by the action of an acid upon a base." Investigation of acids, bases and salts formed part of your preliminary science work, and will form also an important part of your practical course, so that here we shall consider the subject only in outline.

ACIDS.—From your investigation of the three common mineral acids—nitric, hydrochloric, and sulphuric, you will be in a position to recognize several properties possessed by each of them. These properties are:

(i) Characteristic "acid taste."
(ii) Reaction with indicators, *e.g.* blue litmus is turned red.
(iii) Action of the dilute acid upon a carbonate, yielding carbon dioxide with effervescence.
(iv) Corrosive action upon metals. Dilute sulphuric and hydrochloric acids with many metals yield hydrogen; we shall see, however, that hydrogen cannot be expected from *nitric acid,* since this substance, in addition to being an acid, is also an *oxidizing agent* (p. 272).

The above properties, then, are characteristic of acids; any substance which possesses these properties is considered to be an acid. Acids, however, differ very much in constitution, and therefore in properties, and sometimes we may find that the "acid" properties are interfered with, as in the case of nitric acid.

The evolution of hydrogen which occurs when dilute hydrochloric or sulphuric acid is added to zinc, for example, or magnesium, gives us a clue to a very important characteristic of all acids. Long investigation has shown that acids *invariably contain hydrogen,* some or all of which can be *replaced by a metal.* Occasionally this replacement can be brought about *directly* by the action of the dilute acid upon the metal itself, *e.g.* with zinc and dilute sulphuric acid—

$$Zn + H_2SO_4 = ZnSO_4 + H_2,$$

and with magnesium and dilute hydrochloric acid—

$$Mg + 2HCl = MgCl_2 + H_2.$$

In the majority of cases, however, the replacement has to be effected *indirectly*. The compounds formed from an acid by substituting metals for its *replaceable* hydrogen are called *salts*, the name of the salts of a particular acid being derived from the name of the acid. Thus, the salts of sulphuric acid are called *sulphates*, those of nitric acid *nitrates*, and those of hydrochloric acid *chlorides*. If the name of the acid ends in *-ous*, that of its salts ends in *-ite*; thus nitr*ous* acid yields nitr*ites* and sulphur*ous* acid sulph*ites*.

You will notice that the word "replaceable," mentioned a few lines above, was put in italics. This is for the reason that certain acids are known, a *part only* of whose hydrogen can be replaced by a metal. Acetic acid, for example, $C_2H_4O_2$, contains 4 atoms of hydrogen per molecule, but only one of these can be replaced by a metal. The number of atoms of hydrogen, *replaceable by a metal*, that the molecule of an acid contains, is called the *basicity* of the acid. Thus hydrochloric acid, HCl, and nitric acid, HNO_3, are *monobasic*; so is acetic acid, $C_2H_4O_2$. Sulphuric acid, H_2SO_4, is *dibasic*, and phosphoric acid, H_3PO_4, is *tribasic*.

The usual device for replacing the hydrogen in an acid by a metal is to act upon the acid with the *oxide* or *hydroxide* of the metal. The oxygen or hydroxyl group (—OH) of the compound selected then combines with the replaceable hydrogen of the acid, forming water, and the metal takes the place of this hydrogen. When sulphuric acid, for example, is treated with copper oxide, water and copper sulphate, $CuSO_4$, are formed—

$$CuO + H_2SO_4 = CuSO_4 + H_2O.$$

Similarly, with calcium hydroxide or slaked lime, $Ca(OH)_2$, the following action occurs—

$$Ca(OH)_2 + H_2SO_4 = CaSO_4 + 2H_2O.$$

With caustic soda or sodium hydroxide, NaOH, and hydrochloric acid, we get sodium chloride, NaCl, and water—

$$NaOH + HCl = NaCl + H_2O.$$

Bases.—The hydroxides and normal oxides of metals are called *bases.* They will react with acids to form compounds, usually neutral to litmus, called salts (see above).

Examples of bases are :

Calcium oxide or quicklime, CaO.

Lead oxide or litharge, PbO.

Zinc oxide, ZnO.

Magnesium oxide, MgO.

Sodium hydroxide or caustic soda, NaOH.

Potassium hydroxide or caustic potash, KOH.

Slaked lime or calcium hydroxide, $Ca(OH)_2$.

Copper hydroxide, $Cu(OH)_2$.

As we saw on pp. 178–9, only the *normal* oxides of metals have basic properties ; however, *all* metallic *hydroxides* are bases.

Bases which are soluble in water produce solutions which turn red litmus blue ; such bases are called *alkalis.* They are all hydroxides or substances which, when dissolved in water, yield hydroxides. Ammonia, NH_3 (p. 256), is a peculiar substance which combines directly with acids to form salts *but no water, e.g.*—

$$NH_3 + HCl = NH_4Cl, \text{ ammonium chloride.}$$

It cannot, therefore, be regarded as a true base, for bases, as we have seen, with an acid yield a salt *and water.* When dissolved in water, however, ammonia gives a solution containing the substance NH_4OH, ammonium hydroxide ($NH_3 + H_2O = NH_4OH$). This is a true base, since it will react with an acid to form a salt and water—

$$HCl + NH_4OH = NH_4Cl + H_2O.$$

Ammonia is therefore said to be a *basic anhydride*, the base itself being ammonium hydroxide.

Comparison of actions of Acids and Alkalis on indicators.

Indicator.	Acid.	Soluble Base. (Alkali.)
Litmus . . .	Blue litmus changed to red.	Red litmus changed to blue.
Methyl orange.	Yellow methyl orange changed to pink.	Pink methyl orange changed to yellow.
Phenol-phthalein	Red phenolphthalein changed to colourless.	Colourless phenolphthalein changed to red.

Insoluble bases naturally have no action on indicators.

General properties of bases—

(i) Action on indicators, if the base is soluble (see above).

(ii) When heated with an ammonium salt, a base will generally liberate ammonia, *e.g.*—

$$NaOH + NH_4Cl = NaCl + NH_3 + H_2O.$$

(iii) Solutions of alkalis will often precipitate metallic hydroxides from solutions of metallic salts, *e.g.*—

$$2KOH + CuSO_4 = Cu(OH)_2 \downarrow + K_2SO_4.$$

(iv) Bases neutralize acids, forming salts and water.

Salts.—We have seen (p. 183) that all acids contain hydrogen, the whole or part of which can be replaced by metals. The substances formed in this way are called *salts*, since common salt, *sodium chloride*, NaCl, is typical of the class. Having defined an acid as a substance which has the properties given on p. 183, and a base as a normal metallic oxide or hydroxide, we can now define a salt as *that substance other than water, which is formed when an acid neutralizes a base*, or, again—

acid + base = salt + water.

What Calais was to Queen Mary, this expression should be to the young student of chemistry!

Sometimes the molecule of an acid contains only *one* atom of hydrogen replaceable by a metal, *e.g.* nitric acid, HNO_3, and hydrochloric acid, HCl. It is clear that such an acid (*i.e.* a *monobasic* acid, p. 184) can form salts of one class only, namely, those in which *all* the replaceable hydrogen has been replaced by a metal, *e.g.* NaCl, sodium chloride, and KNO_3, potassium nitrate. Salts which may be regarded as formed from an acid (either directly or indirectly) by the substitution of *all* the replaceable hydrogen of the acid by a metal are called *normal salts, e.g.* the two examples just given, and copper sulphate, $CuSO_4$, lead nitrate, $Pb(NO_3)_2$, mercuric chloride, $HgCl_2$, and so on.

Suppose we have an acid containing *two* replaceable atoms of hydrogen per molecule (*i.e.* a *dibasic* acid, p. 184). When we form salts from an acid of this type, we can do so in two stages, replacing first one hydrogen atom by the metal, and then the other. Sulphuric acid is a dibasic acid, H_2SO_4. If we replace its hydrogen atoms by sodium we get first of all $NaHSO_4$ and then Na_2SO_4. The latter compound is *normal* sodium sulphate, as explained above. The compound represented by the formula $NaHSO_4$ still contains a replaceable hydrogen; it is therefore *acid.* But it has been formed from sulphuric acid by the replacement of hydrogen of the acid by a metal, sodium. It is therefore a salt. To express this peculiarity we call it an *acid salt—acid sodium sulphate.* Acid sodium sulphate is typical of the whole class of acid salts, which we may define as compounds formed from acids (either directly or indirectly) by the replacement of *part only* of the replaceable hydrogen of the acid by a metal. Any acid which has a basicity greater than 1 can form acid salts; thus, phosphoric acid, H_3PO_4, the basicity of which is 3, can form two acid salts and one normal salt with sodium—

$$NaH_2PO_4,\ Na_2HPO_4 \text{ and } Na_3PO_4.$$

Other examples of acid salts are—

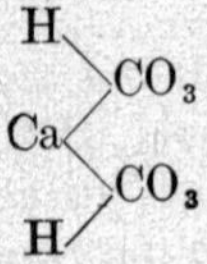

$$\text{Ca} \begin{cases} \text{H—CO}_3 \\ \text{H—CO}_3 \end{cases} \text{ or Ca(HCO}_3)_2, \text{ calcium bicarbonate, from carbonic}$$

$$\text{acid, } \begin{array}{c} \text{H} \\ \text{H} \end{array}\text{CO}_3 \text{ or } H_2CO_3.$$

$$\begin{array}{c} \text{Na} \\ \text{NH}_4\text{—PO}_4 \\ \text{H} \end{array} \text{ or } NaNH_4HPO_4, \text{ which is commonly known as "microcosmic salt."}$$

$$\begin{array}{c} \text{COOH} \\ | \\ \text{COOK} \end{array} \text{ or } KHC_2O_4, \text{ acid potassium oxalate, from oxalic}$$

$$\text{acid } \begin{array}{c} \text{COOH} \\ | \\ \text{COOH} \end{array} \text{ or } H_2C_2O_4.$$

It is, however, a peculiar fact that many " acid salts " do not show an acid reaction to litmus ; they may even be alkaline in solution. You will see, therefore, that the term *acid salt* is in these cases not very suitable, and alternative names are in use, *e.g.* we may call acid salts " *metal hydrogen salts* "—thus acid sodium sulphate, $NaHSO_4$, would be sodium *hydrogen* sulphate, NaH_2PO_4 would be sodium *dihydrogen* phosphate, and $NaNH_4HPO_4$ sodium ammonium *hydrogen* phosphate.

The acid salts of *dibasic* acids are occasionally called *bi-*salts, so that for $NaHSO_4$ we have the three names, *acid sodium sulphate, sodium hydrogen sulphate,* and *sodium bisulphate.* This reminds those of us who are old enough to remember the Boer War of the song which said that " the baby's name is Kitchener, Carrington, Methuen, Kekewich, White, Cronje, Plumer, Powell, Majuba, . . ." but you will soon get used to it. As long as you remember that *acid salts are salts which still contain hydrogen replaceable by a metal,* and do not necessarily turn blue litmus red, you will have no difficulty.

Corresponding to acid salts there are *basic* salts. It is perhaps simplest to regard these as normal salts which have combined with excess of the oxide or hydroxide of the metal

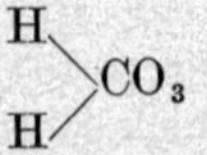

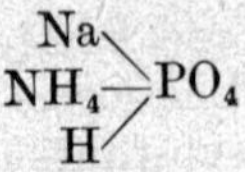

present. Thus, $CuCO_3.Cu(OH)_2$ is *basic copper carbonate*, and $BiCl_3.Bi_2O_3$ is *basic bismuth chloride.*

General Methods of Preparing Acids, Bases and Salts

1. Acids. See Appendix, p. 441.
2. Bases. See Appendix, p. 442.
3. Salts. See Appendix, p. 442.

Air

To discover the composition of the atmosphere took chemists about 2,000 years. Elementary students are now expected to know all about it in two weeks, but modern youth does not always appreciate the great compliment which is thus paid it. In the same way, we know very little about the composition of water, but "water" is an essential constituent of the syllabuses of all elementary examinations in chemistry.

Air is a mixture of various gases, with more or less solid matter—dust, soot, germs, etc.—floating about in it. The chief constituents are oxygen, nitrogen, argon, carbon dioxide and water-vapour; other gases occur in small proportions but appear to be of little importance. The percentages of argon and carbon dioxide are very small (1 per cent. argon, 0·03 per cent. carbon dioxide). Argon is an inert, unreactive gas which was overlooked for many years. Carbon dioxide, on the other hand, although there is only about $\frac{1}{30}$th as much of it as there is of argon, is of the utmost importance since, as described on p. 353, it is the chief *food* of green plants.

The proportion of water-vapour in the atmosphere varies considerably. At times it is high, and at other times the air is very dry. If you take a definite volume of dry air and let it stand in contact with water, you will find that some of the water is taken up, as water-vapour, by the air. At a definite temperature, the weight of water which can thus be taken up by a given volume of air is constant at constant pressure. Air which has taken up as much water-vapour as it can possibly do at a given temperature and pressure is said to be *saturated*. Ordinary air is generally not saturated, and the ratio of the weight of water-vapour which a certain volume of it *could* hold to the weight which it actually *does* hold at the temperature and pressure concerned is called the *relative humidity* of the air.

Hot air can take up more water-vapour than cold air. Hence, when hot moist air is cooled its relative humidity becomes greater and greater until it reaches 1; further cooling then results in the deposition of *liquid* water or *dew*. The temperature at which this occurs for a given sample of air is called the *dew-point*; it is determined by means of an instrument called the *hygrometer*.

Since the amount of water-vapour in the air is constantly changing, we usually neglect it when talking about the composition of the atmosphere. This, after all, is very reasonable, although it is a habit for which chemists have been criticized. We do not really forget that there *is* water-vapour in air, but from the present point of view it does not concern us very much.

Composition of the Atmosphere.—Nearly 99 per cent. of dry air is made up of two gases, oxygen and nitrogen, approximately in the proportion by volume of 1 to 4. This proportion is remarkably constant, and hence the question (beloved by all examiners) arises: Is air a *mixture* of oxygen and nitrogen or is it a *compound* of the two? Well, there is an easy way of deciding. If air is a compound, we can work out its formula from its composition by weight; this is 23 per cent. oxygen and 77 per cent. nitrogen. Now A.W. of oxygen = 16 and A.W. of nitrogen = 14.

$$\frac{23}{16} = 1{\cdot}44\,; \quad \frac{77}{14} = 5{\cdot}5.$$

The ratio 1·44 : 5·5 is—very roughly—1 : 4, so that if air is a compound its formula must be N_4O or some multiple of it. The inaccuracy shown by the figures (4 × 1·44 = 5·76, not 5·5) is, however, greater than would be expected in view of the careful analyses that have been made, so that this alone would arouse our suspicions. We can go a step farther. If air is a compound of the formula N_4O, its vapour density (*i.e.* half its M.W.) ought to be $\frac{56 + 16}{2} = 36$. As a matter of fact, the vapour density of air is not 36 but 14·4; hence air cannot be a compound.

If, on the other hand, air is a mixture of oxygen and nitrogen in the proportion by volume of 1 : 4, its vapour density ought to be between that of oxygen $\left(\frac{32}{2}\right)$ and nitrogen $\left(\frac{28}{2}\right)$ — it should, in fact, be $\frac{(4 \times 14) + 16}{5}$ $= \frac{72}{5} = 14{\cdot}4$, which is the experimentally observed figure.

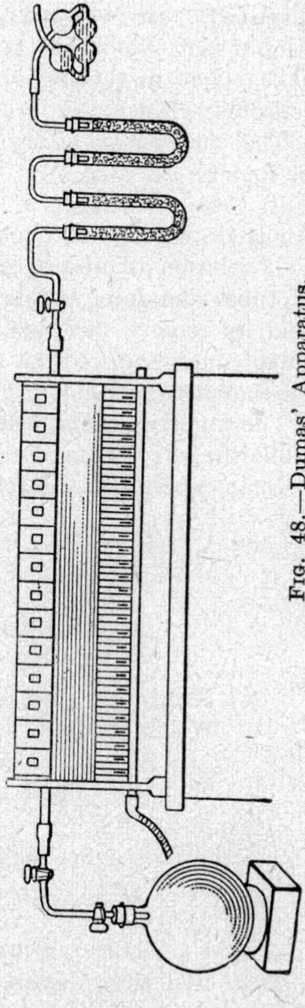

FIG. 48.—Dumas' Apparatus.

Other points which show that *air is a mixture* and not a compound are:

(i) Its composition, although fairly constant, does show *slight* variations, too large to be put down to experimental errors.

(ii) The chemical and physical properties of air are those which would be expected of a mixture of nitrogen and oxygen in the proportions in which they occur in air.

(iii) A gas closely resembling ordinary air may be made by mixing 4 volumes of nitrogen with 1 volume of oxygen. No heat is evolved or absorbed during the mixing.

(iv) The oxygen may be separated more or less completely by purely *mechanical* means. Such are, for example, the fractional distillation of liquid air (see p. 177), and shaking air up with freshly-boiled water; oxygen having a greater solubility than nitrogen, the percentage of oxygen in the dissolved "air" is greater than that in atmospheric air. Air, in fact, which has been dissolved in water in this way will relight a glowing splint when boiled out again and collected.

The composition of dry air, free from carbon dioxide, may be found:

(i) *Gravimetrically* (*i.e.* by weight), by DUMAS' method. Air is drawn first through a set of bulbs containing caustic soda solution to absorb carbon dioxide, then through a series of tubes containing pumice soaked in concentrated sulphuric acid, to remove moisture, and finally through a weighed tube containing red-hot copper turnings, into a weighed evacuated copper globe (Fig. 48).

The copper combines with the oxygen to form copper oxide, while the nitrogen (and argon) pass on into the globe.

In an experiment, the following weights would be obtained:

(*a*) Weight of tube + copper $= y$ gms.
Weight of tube + copper oxide $= x$ „

$\therefore$ Weight of oxygen $= x - y$ gms.

(*b*) Weight of globe empty $= m$ gms.
Weight of globe + nitrogen $= n$ „

$\therefore$ Weight of nitrogen $= n - m$ gms.

Hence the proportion by weight of nitrogen to oxygen in air is $\frac{(n - m)}{(x - y)}$. This ratio is found to be 77 : 23.

(*N.B.*—A modern furnace is shown in the figure. Dumas himself used spirit lamps, since in his time—1843—Bunsen burners were not invented.)

(ii) *Volumetrically*, by enclosing the air over mercury in a graduated tube containing a copper wire which may be electrically heated to redness. The volume of air taken is noted, the wire heated to redness for a few minutes, and the apparatus allowed to cool. A decrease in volume will be observed, since the copper will have combined with the oxygen to form copper oxide, the volume of which is practically the same as that of the copper wire itself and therefore may be neglected. After any necessary corrections for temperature and pressure, the volumetric composition of the air may therefore be calculated directly. The residual gas is nitrogen.

The Rare Gases of the Air.—Of the "rare gases" of the air, *viz.* helium, neon, argon, krypton and xenon, the first three find considerable application in industry. *Helium* is used instead of hydrogen in lighter-than-air craft, though for this purpose it is not obtained from the air but from certain gas-wells in America. *Neon* is the gas used to fill electric advertisement tubes; it gives a fine orange-red glow when an electric discharge is passed through it at low pressures. It is also used at the air-ports in the beacons for directing aircraft in fogs. *Argon* is used in ordinary "gas-filled" electric lamps.

Water

Natural Waters.

(i) *Rain-water* is the purest form of natural water. In country districts it contains only gaseous impurities such as carbon dioxide, oxygen and nitrogen, which it has absorbed from the air, together with a little salt from the sea. Naturally, rain-water in and near towns contains all sorts of impurities—soot, sulphur, hydrogen sulphide, sulphuric acid, and so on.

(ii) *River* and *spring water* contains varying amounts of solid matter in solution, according to the ground in which it occurs or over which it flows. Salts of calcium (or magnesium) render the water hard (see p. 198).

(iii) *Mineral waters* are naturally occurring waters which contain unusual impurities known or supposed to be beneficial in the treatment of various diseases. Thus, the waters at Bath are radio-active, and helium is given off from the King's

Well there. The water of a certain spring at Epsom contains magnesium sulphate or "Epsom salt."

(iv) *Sea-water* contains about 3·6 per cent. by weight of salts in solution, chiefly the chlorides and sulphates of sodium, potassium, calcium, and magnesium. Common salt (NaCl) forms about $\frac{2}{3}$ of the total solid matter present.

Composition of Water.—Water is assigned the formula H_2O. The evidence for this formula is as follows :

(i) In 1781 Cavendish showed that when oxygen and hydrogen are exploded together water is formed.

(ii) On electrolysis of slightly acidulated water, hydrogen is given off from the cathode and oxygen from the anode (see Fig. 42, p. 161). The volume of hydrogen is roughly twice that of the oxygen, hence, by Avogadro's Hypothesis, the composition of water must be such that there are two molecules of hydrogen to every molecule of oxygen.

Now we know that the molecules of both hydrogen and oxygen are di-atomic (*i.e.* contain 2 atoms). Hence the *simplest* formula for water is H_2O. It may be more complex, however, so we shall require further evidence.

(iii) When 2 volumes of hydrogen and 1 volume of oxygen are exploded in a eudiometer tube (Fig. 49) kept at such a temperature that the steam formed does not condense (*i.e.* above 100° C.), the volume of the steam is found to be equal to that of the hydrogen taken. Or—

2 volumes of hydrogen + 1 volume of oxygen give 2 volumes of steam.

∴ by Avogadro's Hypothesis—

2 molecules of hydrogen + 1 molecule of oxygen give 2 molecules of steam.

∴ 1 molecule of hydrogen + $\frac{1}{2}$ molecule of oxygen give 1 molecule of steam.

1 molecule of hydrogen = H_2 ; $\frac{1}{2}$ a molecule of oxygen = O.

∴ Formula for water is H_2O.

In order to keep the tube at the required temperature, the vapour of amyl alcohol ($C_5H_{11}.OH$, B.P. 130°) is passed through the outer jacket shown in Fig. 49.

(iv) The above evidence is really quite sufficient, but in the case of an important substance like water we prefer to make assurance doubly sure, so that there can be

> "*No possible, probable, shadow of doubt,*
> *No shadow of doubt whatever!*"

For this purpose, we may find the vapour density of water by weighing a known volume of steam at known temperature and pressure. Experiment shows the V.D. to be 9, ∴ M.W. = 18. But the atomic weight of oxygen is 16, hence

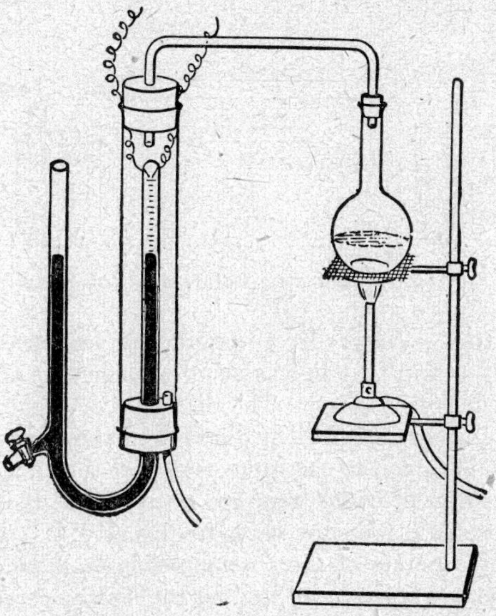

FIG. 49.—Composition of Steam.

there *cannot* be more than 1 atom of oxygen in the molecule of water. The remaining two parts by weight must be due to the hydrogen, of which there are therefore 2 atoms per molecule.

(v) *Gravimetrically* the composition of water may be found by passing pure hydrogen over heated copper oxide previously weighed, and measuring the weight of the water formed and the loss in weight of the copper oxide—

Copper oxide + hydrogen = water + copper.

A suitable apparatus is shown in Fig. 50.

The most accurate results so far obtained for the composition of water by weight are those of MORLEY (1895). He found that the proportion by weight of oxygen to hydrogen in water was 7·9396 : 1.

This gravimetric composition of water is of additional importance, since it gives, of course, the *equivalent of oxygen.*

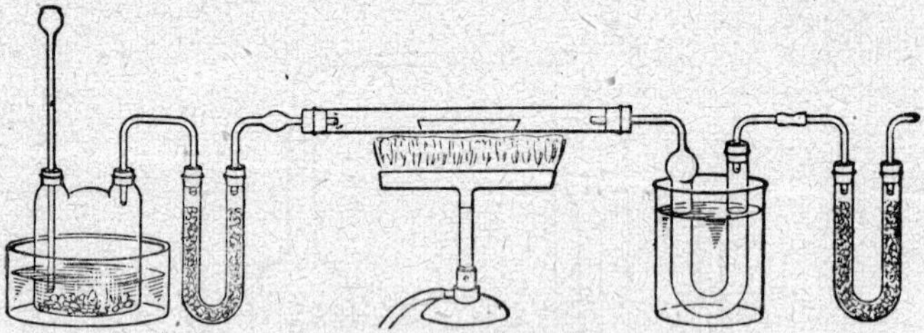

FIG. 50.—Gravimetric Composition of Water.

Properties.—Water is a practically colourless liquid, although it is said that in a layer of considerable thickness it has a bluish green colour. The difficulty of obtaining absolutely pure water in sufficient quantity makes any statement as to its colour open to question; the fact that impure water is blue or green of course requires no proof, as it is obvious.

At atmospheric pressure water freezes at 0° C. and boils at 100° C., these points of the thermometric scale being in fact fixed as the *melting-point of ice* and the *boiling-point of water.*

The *density* of water is taken as unity, *i.e.* the weight of 1 c.c. of water at its point of maximum density (4° C.) is taken as the *unit of weight,* 1 gram. In the same way the capacity of water for heat is used in fixing the *unit of heat*; thus the calorie is the amount of heat required to raise the temperature of 1 gram of water through one Centigrade degree.

Water is an excellent *solvent,* and will dissolve practically every substance, at least in traces. It is, therefore, very difficult to obtain pure. Pure water is usually prepared by distillation in apparatus made of block tin or of silver, with addition of a little potassium permanganate to oxidize any volatile organic matter. Owing to the labour of purification, pure water is an expensive liquid, costing about £1 per litre.

Heavy Water.—A very fascinating discovery has recently been made about water. Various scientists have shown that a few hydrogen atoms in a jar of the gas are different from the rest; they are, in fact, twice as heavy and so have an atomic weight of 2. It has been possible to isolate a quantity of this heavy hydrogen or "diplogen" and to make it combine with oxygen to form "heavy water," of molecular weight $2 + 2 + 16 = 20$. Heavy water has a different specific gravity from that of ordinary water, and does not boil at 100° C. or freeze at 0° C. Moreover, it is apparently poisonous to plants if undiluted by ordinary water.

Water of Crystallization.—Many substances have the power of combining directly with water, to form compounds in which the water is more or less loosely held. These compounds are called *hydrates*, and will generally give up their "water of hydration" on heating. In many cases hydrates are crystalline compounds which lose their crystalline form when the water is driven off: these are called crystalline hydrates, and the water in them is called "*water of crystallization*." Copper sulphate crystals, for example, are copper sulphate *pentahydrate*, $CuSO_4.5H_2O$, while barium chloride crystals have the constitution $BaCl_2.2H_2O$.

Many crystalline hydrates *effloresce* on exposure to air; that is, they lose some or all of their water of crystallization and fall to a powder. Experiment has shown that hydrates will effloresce if the vapour-pressure of the water of crystallization they contain is greater than the partial pressure of water-vapour in the atmosphere. It sometimes happens, therefore, that a salt which is not efflorescent when the relative humidity of the air is high will effloresce when the air is drier.

Deliquescence is a related phenomenon, but is not confined to hydrates; it may be shown by any substance which is very soluble in water. A deliquescent substance absorbs moisture from the air and gradually turns to a solution; common examples are calcium chloride, caustic potash, and caustic soda.

Hygroscopic substances are those which absorb moisture from the air; they may or may not deliquesce. All deliquescent substances are hygroscopic, of course, but not all hygroscopic substances are deliquescent. A hygroscopic substance which is not deliquescent is quicklime; another is black copper oxide (CuO).

Hardness of Water.—Water that will not readily lather with soap is said to be *hard*. Soap consists mainly of *sodium stearate*, and is made by boiling mutton-fat with caustic soda solution. Mutton-fat is a compound of *glycerol* ("glycerine") with an acid called *stearic acid*; when it is heated with caustic soda solution the glycerol is liberated and sodium stearate is formed—

glyceryl stearate + *caustic soda* = *glycerol* + *sodium stearate*
(Mutton fat) (Soap)

Soap is soluble in water, the solution having a "soapy" feel and lathering readily. If, however, soap is added to hard water, a curdy precipitate is formed, and much more soap is needed in order to produce a lather. Analysis of the curdy precipitate shows that it consists chiefly of calcium stearate. We may therefore conclude that hardness in water is due to the presence of soluble calcium compounds which decompose the soap and thus prevent the formation of a lather until sufficient soap has been added to precipitate all the calcium as calcium stearate—

sodium stearate + calcium compound = calcium stearate ↓
+ sodium compound.

It is clear from this equation that the hardness of water will depend on the weight of *calcium* per stated volume, and will not be affected by the nature of the acid radical with which the calcium is combined. The hardness of water is, however, usually expressed in terms of grains of calcium carbonate per gallon.

The chief salts which cause hardness are the bicarbonates

and sulphates. The former are present in water which has trickled through limestone rocks. Although calcium carbonate is insoluble in pure water, it dissolves in water containing carbon dioxide, owing to the formation of the bicarbonate, which is soluble—

$$CaCO_3 + H_2O + CO_2 = Ca(HCO_3)_2.$$

Natural water always contains carbon dioxide, which it has acquired in its passage, as rain, through the air, or which it has absorbed from the soil, where carbon dioxide is constantly present. Hence if natural water flows over calcium carbonate rocks it becomes hard.

Hardness due to calcium sulphate occurs only in those districts in which this compound is present in the soil ; it is, however, fairly widely distributed, and hence is a common cause of hardness.

Hardness may be estimated by titrating a measured volume of the water with a standard soap-solution until a " permanent " lather is obtained on shaking. (Permanency here means a duration of two minutes.) The soap-solution is standardized against a standard solution of calcium chloride.

" Softening " of Hard Water.—Water may be softened (that is, its hardness may be removed) by removal of the calcium salts which it contains. In the case of hardness due to bicarbonates, merely boiling the water is sufficient, since the bicarbonate decomposes on heating and the normal carbonate is precipitated—

$$Ca(HCO_3)_2 = CaCO_3 \downarrow + CO_2 + H_2O.$$

Such hardness is therefore said to be *temporary*, as opposed to that caused by the sulphate. This cannot be removed by boiling the water, and the hardness caused by it is called *permanent.*

The softening of the water used in large towns is an important problem, since very hard water is in many ways objectionable not only for domestic use but also in industry. It is obviously impossible to soften the whole of a town's water supply by the process of boiling. Other methods are therefore employed. CLARK's method for removing temporary hardness consists in adding to the water just sufficient *lime* to convert all the bicarbonate into normal carbonate—

$$Ca(HCO_3)_2 + CaO = 2CaCO_3 \downarrow + H_2O.$$

Care must be taken, of course, not to add too much lime, or the last state of that water will be worse than the first.

Permanent hardness is removed by the addition of the calculated quantity of sodium carbonate to bring about the reaction—

$$CaSO_4 + Na_2CO_3 = Na_2SO_4 + CaCO_3 \downarrow .$$

A modern method of completely softening hard water is the zeolite or *permutite* process. "Permutite" consists of a sodium aluminium silicate. When hard water is allowed to flow through a tube containing this substance the calcium is retained as calcium aluminium silicate; the spent permutite can be regenerated by pouring on to it a strong solution of salt and washing out the calcium chloride so formed.

Softening: NaAl silicate + Ca salt
= CaAl silicate + Na salt.
(insoluble) (soluble)

Regenerating: CaAl silicate + Na chloride
= Ca chloride + NaAl silicate.
(washed out) (regenerated)

Very soft water is unsuitable for a general water-supply, since not only does it taste "flat" (owing to absence of carbon dioxide), but it also dissolves lead from the lead pipes through which it almost always flows at one part or another of its course. The action of the water on the lead in the presence of air results in the formation of lead hydroxide, $Pb(OH)_2$, which is appreciably soluble. Lead salts are distinctly poisonous, and, as they do not pass out of the body, continued use of drinking-water containing lead would finally produce symptoms of lead-poisoning. With hard water, however, a coherent lining of a carbonate of lead is formed on the pipes and further solution of lead is therefore prevented.

The "furring" of kettles is caused by the precipitation of calcium carbonate on boiling temporarily hard water. The formation of stalactites and stalagmites in caves in limestone districts (Cheddar, etc.) is due to the slow decomposition of calcium bicarbonate in the water which drips from the roof of the caves, with consequent deposition of calcium carbonate —part being deposited on the roof (stalactite) and part on the floor when the drops fall (stalagmite). "Boiler-scale" consists of a hard mass of calcium carbonate and calcium sulphate.

Tests for Water.

(i) [Absence of] Taste. (ii) [Absence of] Smell.

(iii) Freezing-point 0° C.

(iv) Boiling-point 100° C. at 760 mm. pressure.

(v) When added to calcium carbide yields acetylene—

$$CaC_2 + 2H_2O = Ca(OH)_2 + C_2H_2.$$

(vi) When added to *anhydrous* copper sulphate, $CuSO_4$ which is white, the *blue* hydrated salt, $CuSO_4.5H_2O$, is formed

Ozone, O_3

When the silent electric charge is passed through oxygen, the latter is partially transformed into a peculiar modifica-

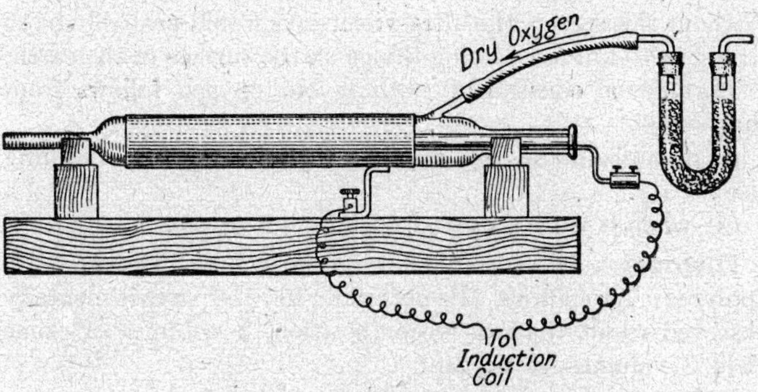

Fig. 51.—Ozone Apparatus.

tion, known as *ozone* on account of its smell (from the Greek *ozo*, I smell). A suitable apparatus is shown in Fig. 51.

It consists of two co-axial tubes, the outside of the outer

one and the inside of the inner one being coated with tin-foil. The oxygen is passed through the space between the tubes, and the two coats of tin-foil are connected one to one terminal of an induction coil and the other to the other terminal. On passing the discharge, part of the oxygen is converted into ozone.

Ozone is a powerful germicide, and for this reason is used to purify the air in underground railways, etc.

Properties.—Ozone is a pale blue gas, and has strong oxidizing powers. Thus it liberates iodine from potassium iodide—

$$2KI + H_2O + O_3 = 2KOH + I_2 + O_2,$$

and will convert black lead sulphide into white lead sulphate—

$$PbS + 4O_3 = PbSO_4 + 4O_2.$$

One of its most characteristic properties is that it will make mercury "tail," *i.e.* stick to glass. It is said to occur in small traces in the lower atmosphere, where it may be formed during thunderstorms. It certainly exists in large quantities in the upper atmosphere, where it plays an important part in absorbing much of the ultra-violet radiation from the sun. Without this screen, the ultra-violet rays would probably be so strong as to kill most living things on the surface of the earth.

That ozone consists of nothing but oxygen follows from the facts :

(i) it can be made from absolutely pure oxygen and nothing else ;

(ii) when it is decomposed nothing but oxygen is obtained.

Formula.—The formula for ozone can be discovered by applying Avogadro's Hypothesis to the experimentally observed result that, on decomposition, 2 volumes of ozone yield 3 volumes of oxygen.

∴ 2 molecules of ozone yield 3 molecules of oxygen.

∴ the ozone molecule must consist of $1\frac{1}{2}$ molecules, or 3 atoms, of oxygen.

Allotropy.—We have here met with our first example of what is a quite common phenomenon, *viz. allotropy*. *When* *an element exists in more than one form (in the same physical state), those forms being physically and often chemically distinct, it is said to exhibit allotropy, and the different forms are called allotropes or allotropic forms.* Ozone is therefore an *allotrope* of oxygen. In this case, the allotropy is accompanied by a different molecular structure, so that it has been suggested, as a reasonable idea, that allotropy is always to be accounted for (*a*) by variations in the *number* of atoms in the molecule, or (*b*) by variations in the *arrangement* of the atoms in the molecule, or (*c*) by both (*a*) and (*b*).

Other elements that exhibit allotropy are sulphur, carbon. phosphorus, and tin.

Hydrogen Peroxide, H_2O_2

In addition to its normal oxide, water, H_2O, hydrogen forms a second oxide containing a further atom of oxygen. This oxide, which is a colourless syrupy liquid, is called *hydrogen peroxide*, and has the formula H_2O_2. It was discovered in 1818 by Thénard, but was first obtained pure by Wolffenstein in 1894.

Preparation.—Hydrogen peroxide is prepared by acting upon barium peroxide with the quantity of cold dilute sulphuric acid required by the equation—

$$BaO_2 + H_2SO_4 = BaSO_4 \downarrow + H_2O_2.$$

The barium sulphate, which is precipitated, is filtered off, and the aqueous filtrate of hydrogen peroxide is then concentrated by evaporation under reduced pressure.

Barium peroxide, BaO_2, is a white powder made by heating barium oxide, BaO, a substance closely resembling quicklime, in air or oxygen—

$$2BaO + O_2 = 2BaO_2.$$

Properties.—Pure hydrogen peroxide is difficult to obtain, since it so easily decomposes into water and oxygen—

$$2H_2O_2 = 2H_2O + O_2.$$

It is therefore usually met with only in comparatively

dilute solution. On a bottle of the solution you will see the words "10 volume" or "20 volume." These indicate the number of c.c. of oxygen which can be obtained, at ordinary temperature and pressure, by decomposing the hydrogen peroxide in 1 c.c. of the solution into water and oxygen, according to the above equation.

EXERCISE.—What is the strength, in grams per litre, of a 20-volume solution of hydrogen peroxide?

Hydrogen peroxide is a powerful oxidizing agent, owing to the ease with which it loses its extra atom of oxygen and is converted into water. Thus it will liberate iodine from acidified potassium iodide solution,

$$H_2SO_4 + 2KI + H_2O_2 = K_2SO_4 + I_2 + 2H_2O,$$

and converts lead sulphide into lead sulphate—

$$PbS + 4H_2O_2 = PbSO_4 + 4H_2O,$$

just as ozone does. To distinguish between ozone and hydrogen peroxide we may make use of the fact that hydrogen peroxide will turn a solution of potassium dichromate, acidified with dilute sulphuric acid, a fine deep-blue colour, whereas ozone will not. The blue substance is called *perchromic acid*. It is unstable in aqueous solution, but if ether is added the perchromic acid dissolves and the blue ethereal solution floats on the top.

Hydrogen peroxide is used for bleaching delicate fabrics, such as silk and wool. It is also used as a disinfectant, since it readily kills germs.

When manganese dioxide, or a finely-divided metal, is added to a solution of hydrogen peroxide, decomposition occurs, and oxygen and water are formed. The action is catalytic.

Formula.—(i) On decomposition, hydrogen peroxide yields water and oxygen and nothing else, ∴ it consists of hydrogen and oxygen.

(ii) 34 parts by weight of hydrogen peroxide yield 18 parts by weight of water and 16 of oxygen, ∴ its empirical formula must be HO.

(iii) Its molecular weight, determined by the cryoscopic method (p. 100), is 34.

Hence the true formula must be $(HO)_2$ or H_2O_2.

Questions

1. What do you know of the phlogiston theory ?
2. Who were the men who suggested the phlogiston theory ?
3. When litharge is heated with carbon, lead is formed. How was this fact explained by the phlogistonists ?
4. Who discovered oxygen, and when ?
5. How was oxygen first prepared ?
6. Why was the name *dephlogisticated air* given to oxygen by its discoverer ?
7. What reasons led Lavoisier to disbelieve in the phlogiston theory ?
8. Describe Lavoisier's famous experiment with mercuric oxide, and state what conclusions he drew from it.
9. What happened to Lavoisier ?
10. Do you think the Revolutionist who said "The Republic has no need of men of science" was right ?
11. How would you prepare and collect a specimen of dry oxygen ?
12. What is a catalyst ? Give an example.
13. What are the chief properties of oxygen ?
14. Write equations for the changes which take place when the following elements are burnt in oxygen—sulphur, carbon, phosphorus, iron, sodium, magnesium.
15. Define the terms *oxidation* and *reduction*.
16. Give *six* examples of oxidation and *six* of reduction.
17. Name six oxidizing agents and six reducing agents.
18. How are oxides classified ?
19. If you were given an oxide, what experiments would you make in order to decide to which class it belonged ?
20. What are the principal properties of (*a*) acids and (*b*) bases ?
21. Give two general methods for preparing (*a*) acids, (*b*) bases, and (*c*) salts.
22. If you were given metallic zinc, state how you would prepare from it (*a*) zinc sulphate, (*b*) zinc carbonate, (*c*) zinc oxide, (*d*) zinc hydroxide.
23. Define the terms *basicity*, *acid salt*, *basic salt*, *normal salt*, illustrating your answer by means of examples.
24. How may the composition of the air be determined (*a*) volumetrically, (*b*) gravimetrically ?
25. Is air a mixture or a compound ? Give full reasons for your answer.

26. Upon what evidence is the formula H_2O assigned to a molecule of steam ?

27. Define *water of crystallization*, *efflorescence*, *deliquescence*, *hydrate*.

28. What is meant by *hardness* in water ?

29. What is hardness caused by ?

30. How may hard water be softened ?

31. How may the hardness of water be estimated ?

32. How would you test a given liquid to decide if it was water or not ?

33. How is ozone prepared ? What are its properties ?

34. Define *allotropy* and give two examples of the phenomenon.

35. Upon what evidence is the formula O_3 assigned to ozone ?

36. How is hydrogen peroxide obtained ?

37. What are the properties of hydrogen peroxide ?

38. What is the action of hydrogen peroxide on (*a*) lead sulphide and (*b*) potassium iodide solution ?

39. How may a solution of hydrogen peroxide be distinguished from a solution of ozone ?

40. Upon what evidence is the formula H_2O_2 given to hydrogen peroxide ?

CHAPTER XV

CHLORINE, BROMINE AND IODINE

The various members of a human family resemble one another more or less closely; they have, in fact, as we say, a "family resemblance." Yet we can easily distinguish them from one another, except in the case of a pair of identical twins—and even here the task is not as a rule absolutely impossible. A study of the chemical elements reveals the fact that some of them are very similar in their properties to others, and so chemists have arranged them in "families," each family consisting of a group of more or less similar elements. There is one difference between a human family and a chemical family which will strike you at once, namely, that in the former the similarity between the members is due to the fact that they have descended from the same parents, whereas we do not imagine the members of a chemical family to owe their resemblance to a cause of this sort. Modern research has shown, however, that there is reason to believe that all the chemical elements are composed of particles of positive and negative electricity, which we may therefore call, if we like, their Adam and Eve.

One of the most interesting and important chemical families is that which consists of fluorine, chlorine, bromine and iodine. These elements are all highly chemically active, and since they will all combine directly with metals, forming *salts*, they are called the *Halogens*—a word which is derived from the Greek, and means "salt-producers." Other families are the *alkali-metals* (lithium, sodium, potassium, rubidium and caesium), the *inert gases* (helium, neon, argon, krypton, xenon, radon) and the *nitrogen family* (nitrogen, phosphorus, arsenic, antimony and bismuth). All the members of the same family have similar properties: the similarity may be very great, as in the alkali-metals, or rather vague, but it is always sufficient to be noticeable. The similarity is not confined to the elements themselves, but extends to their compounds. Thus we shall find that the compound which hydrogen forms with chlorine (hydrochloric acid, HCl) is very similar indeed to the compound of hydrogen with bromine (hydrobromic acid, HBr), and this again to the compound of hydrogen with iodine (hydriodic acid, HI). At the end of the chapter you will find a table which shows the properties in which the halogen elements resemble one another, and you should make one to show those in which they differ. Fluorine is the scapegrace of the family, and has a row at every encounter with other elements (and most compounds)! Chlorine on the other hand is a hard-working, respectable element, anxious to get on in the world, but possessed of a somewhat fiery temper. Bromine is rather lazy, and has other objectionable habits which bring tears to our eyes, but the pet of the family is the modest and unassuming iodine. Even she, however, is not entirely without blemish, for when heated in a discussion she is apt to become purple in the face. Anyhow, no one will deny that they are a family worth knowing, so let us haste to make their acquaintance. Of fluorine we need not speak in this place; suffice it to say that although the chemical police had been on his track for a century, he always managed to elude them, until "a smart capture was effected in Paris" by Professor Henri Moissan in 1886.

Chlorine

Chlorine was the gas with which the Germans made a surprise attack upon the Allies in the spring of 1915. It is an extremely irritating and poisonous gas, and the bravery of the men who faced it without gas-masks or other protection passes description. Its poisonous nature can, however, be turned to a more humane purpose, and chlorine has found extensive use as a means of sterilizing germ-infected water and so rendering it fit for drinking.

Preparation of Chlorine.—Chlorine is prepared in the laboratory by heating manganese dioxide with concentrated hydrochloric acid. The apparatus employed is shown in Fig. 52. The manganese dioxide and hydrochloric acid are placed in a round-bottomed flask fitted with a cork carrying a delivery-tube. The delivery-tube leads to the bottom of a dry gas-jar, the mouth of which is loosely closed with a piece of cardboard pierced with a hole through which the tube passes.

On gently heating the flask, chlorine is at once evolved, and passes over into the gas-jar. It is much heavier than air (its vapour density is 35·5, whereas that of air is 14·4), so that it can be conveniently collected by this method of *displacement*. As the gas goes downwards, some people say that it is collected by *downward* displacement. Others say that as the air goes upward we ought to call this method *upward* displacement. You can choose which you like, only when you have made your choice stick to it, and in an examination *always put in a figure*, as your examiner may have made the opposite choice.

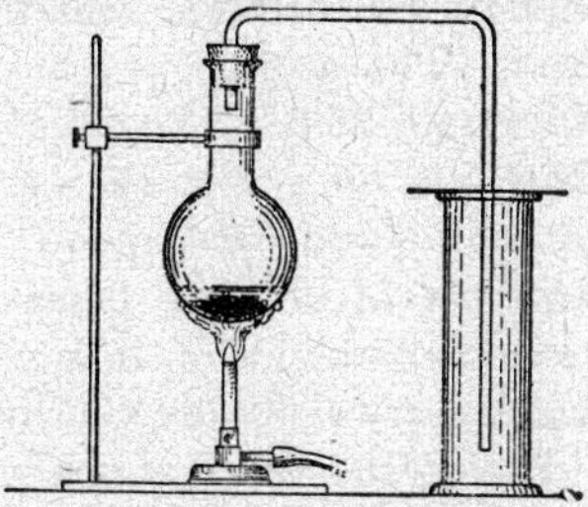

FIG. 52.—Preparation of Chlorine.

What happens in this reaction ? Well, manganese dioxide is blessed with a superabundance of oxygen. The ordinary valency of manganese is 2, so that the normal oxide is MnO. Manganese dioxide, however, has the formula MnO_2, *i.e.* the manganese has 1 atom of oxygen more than it is really entitled to. This is taken away from it by 2 molecules of hydrochloric acid, the hydrogen in the acid combining with the oxygen to form water. The chlorine is thus liberated and comes off—

$$MnO_2 + 2HCl = MnO + H_2O + Cl_2.$$

The manganese oxide which is left is a basic oxide, and reacts with more hydrochloric acid to give manganese chloride and water (acid + base = salt + water)—

$$MnO + 2HCl = MnCl_2 + H_2O.$$

Combining these two equations into one, we can write—

$$MnO_2 + 4HCl = MnCl_2 + 2H_2O + Cl_2.$$

From this equation we can see that, in this method of preparation, we get only half the chlorine that is contained in the hydrochloric acid we use, the other half remaining behind as manganese chloride. It is, therefore, rather a wasteful method. Let us see how much chlorine we should get if we started with 10 grams of manganese dioxide and enough hydrochloric acid to ensure that all the dioxide was used. The atomic weight of manganese is 55 and that of chlorine is 35·5. The molecular weight of manganese dioxide, MnO_2, is $55 + 2 \times 16$, *i.e.* 87. Using 1 molecule of manganese dioxide we get 1 molecule of chlorine (since the molecule of chlorine consists of 2 atoms); hence 1 gram-molecular-weight of manganese dioxide will yield 1 gram-molecular-weight of chlorine, that is $2 \times 35{\cdot}5$ or 71 grams.

Hence 10 grams of manganese dioxide would yield—

$$\frac{10}{87} \times 71 \text{ grams of chlorine} = 8{\cdot}2 \text{ grams.}$$

However, as chlorine is a gas, we shall probably want to know its volume rather than its weight. We can easily calculate this. We know that the gram-molecular weight of any gas at N.T.P. occupies 22·4 litres.

∴ 71 grams of chlorine occupy 22·4 litres at N.T.P.

∴ 8·2 grams of chlorine at N.T.P. occupy $\frac{8{\cdot}2}{71} \times 22{\cdot}4$ litres at N.T.P.

$$= 2{\cdot}59 \text{ litres.}$$

The volume at any other temperature and pressure can be found by applying the gas laws in the usual way.

If you think about the reaction between manganese dioxide and hydrochloric acid, you will see that the essential thing about it is the *removal of hydrogen* from the acid. Now, we have seen before (p. 180) that removal of hydrogen is called oxidation. What has happened, in fact, is that the excessive oxygen of the manganese dioxide has *oxidized* the hydrochloric acid, converting its hydrogen into water, and thus setting the chlorine free. This would lead us to expect that other oxidizing agents might have the same effect, and our expectation would be justified in practice. Practically any oxidizing agent, when heated with hydrochloric acid, will liberate its chlorine. Think of all the oxidizing agents you can, and try test-tube experiments in the laboratory to see which of them cause the liberation of chlorine when heated with hydrochloric acid.

We generally use manganese dioxide in the laboratory because it is cheap and efficient, and also because, since its molecular weight is low, a small quantity of it will yield a large volume of chlorine. The only objection to it is that it will not work in the cold. If your experiment is simply the preparation of chlorine, this does not matter much, but sometimes you want a stream of chlorine to use in another experiment. In this case, having to heat a flask may be a nuisance, so an alternative method is often employed in these circumstances. It consists in adding hydrochloric acid to potassium permanganate, $KMnO_4$, when chlorine is at once evolved without the application of heat. Potassium permanganate is one of the most powerful oxidizing agents known. It has 5 atoms of oxygen available for oxidizing purposes, as we shall see if we write the formula for 2 molecules of it $K_2O.2MnO.5O$. As potassium is univalent, the 2 atoms of it in the molecules of the permanganate hold 1 atom of oxygen between them; similarly the 2 manganese atoms hold an oxygen atom each. That accounts for 3 oxygen atoms; the other five are—we may imagine—held by false pretences, and are only too eager to get away. The result is that when hydrochloric acid is added to the potassium permanganate, the following reaction takes place:

$$2KMnO_4 + 16HCl = 2KCl + 2MnCl_2 + 8H_2O + 5Cl_2.$$

To understand this equation better we can split it up as follows:

$$2KMnO_4 = K_2O.2MnO.5O.$$

$$\begin{array}{ll} \text{(i)} & \left\{\begin{array}{l} K_2O + 2HCl = 2KCl + H_2O. \\ 2MnO + 4HCl = 2MnCl_2 + 2H_2O. \\ 5O + 10HCl = 5H_2O + 5Cl_2. \end{array}\right. \end{array}$$

(i), (ii), (iii) as above.

Adding (i), (ii) and (iii) together we get—

$$2KMnO_4 + 16HCl = 2KCl + 2MnCl_2 + 8H_2O + 5Cl_2,$$

the equation given above.

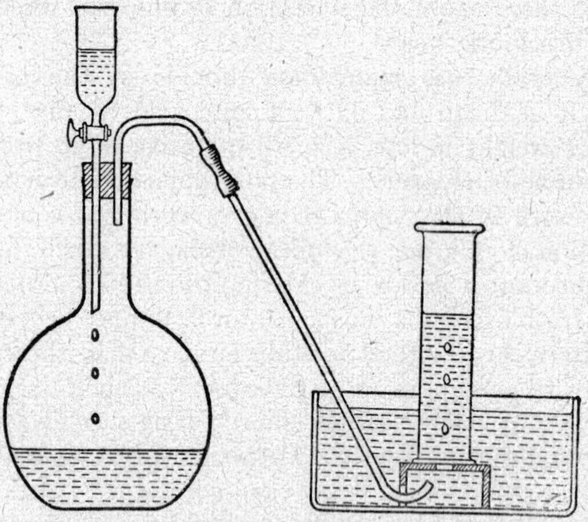

FIG. 53.—Preparation of Chlorine from Potassium Permanganate.

Calculate what volume of chlorine at 15° C. and 740 mm. pressure could be obtained if 15·8 grams of potassium permanganate were decomposed with hydrochloric acid. [K = 39.]

The apparatus which is used for preparing chlorine in this way is shown in Fig. 53. The hydrochloric acid is placed in a tap-funnel, whence it is allowed to drop slowly on to the potassium permanganate in the flask. The liquid in the trough is strong brine, over which chlorine may be collected.

A third method of getting chlorine in the laboratory is to

act upon bleaching-powder (see p. 217) with a dilute acid—

$$\text{"}CaOCl_2\text{"} + H_2SO_4 = CaSO_4 + H_2O + Cl_2.$$

Bleaching-powder   Calcium sulphate.

Properties of Chlorine.—Symbol, Cl. *Atomic Weight*, 35·5. *Valency*, 1. *Atomicity* (*number of atoms in molecule*), 2—hence formula is Cl_2.

Chlorine is a greenish yellow gas with a characteristic, pungent and very irritating smell. It can be liquefied if cooled and compressed, a fact which was discovered by FARADAY. Liquid chlorine is a golden yellow liquid which boils at − 33·6°, and on further cooling solidifies to a yellow crystalline solid whose melting-point is − 102°. Liquid chlorine is put on the market in steel cylinders. A 10-lb. cylinder is a convenient size for school use.

Chlorine is a very reactive element. It will combine directly with most metals, forming *salts* called chlorides. With sodium, for example, it combines to form sodium chloride or common salt, NaCl—

$$2Na + Cl_2 = 2NaCl.$$

This reaction may be brought about by heating sodium in a stream of chlorine. If a trace of moisture is present, the sodium takes fire and burns brilliantly. Salt, in the form of a white powder, is left. Bromine and iodine resemble chlorine in this property of combining directly with metals to form salts, and for this reason, as mentioned above, these three elements (together with the closely similar fluorine) are known as the *halogens* or salt-producers.

Several other metals will burn if heated in chlorine, and if they are finely divided they may even take fire of their own accord when plunged into the gas at ordinary temperatures. Thus powdered antimony—the metal which is so popular nowadays for making trinket-boxes, trays, etc.—takes fire when sprinkled into a jar of chlorine, forming *antimony chloride*.

Chlorine will also combine readily with several non-metals, such as hydrogen and phosphorus. If equal volumes of chlorine and hydrogen are mixed together in bright sunlight

—conditions which cannot often be fulfilled in this country!—the mixture explodes. It may also be exploded by igniting it with a lighted taper. The product is a colourless gas, *hydrogen chloride* or *hydrochloric acid gas*, which is formed according to the equation—

$$H_2 + Cl_2 = 2HCl.$$

We see from this equation that the volume of hydrochloric acid gas produced is equal to the volume of the mixture of hydrogen and chlorine before explosion, since we start with 2 molecules (1 of hydrogen and 1 of chlorine) and get 2 molecules formed. Hence, by arguing backwards from Avogadro's Hypothesis, 1 volume of hydrogen will combine with 1 volume of chlorine to form 2 volumes of hydrochloric acid gas. Thus, to combine with 50 c.c. of hydrogen we should require exactly 50 c.c. of chlorine, and we should get exactly 100 c.c. of hydrochloric acid gas formed—supposing, of course, that all the volumes were measured at, or corrected to, the same temperature and pressure.

Hydrochloric acid is a very important compound, which we shall study in detail later on (pp. 225–233).

When phosphorus is plunged into chlorine it first melts and then takes fire, burning quite vigorously. The product consists of a mixture of phosphorus pentachloride, PCl_5, and phosphorus trichloride, PCl_3—

$$2P + 5Cl_2 = 2PCl_5.$$
$$2P + 3Cl_2 = 2PCl_3.$$

For more about these compounds, see p. 284.

Chlorine will dissolve in water. The solution, which has the colour and smell of the gas, is called *chlorine water*. When chlorine water is exposed to sunlight, it gradually decomposes and oxygen is evolved—

$$2Cl_2 + 2H_2O = 4HCl + O_2.$$

The remaining liquid turns out to be a solution of hydrochloric acid, as indicated by the above equation. Chemists believe that when chlorine water decomposes, the first thing that happens is that a mixture of hydrochloric acid with another acid, called *hypochlorous acid*, is formed—

$$Cl_2 + H_2O = HCl + HClO.$$

Hypochlorous acid is an unstable compound, and readily splits up into hydrochloric acid and oxygen—

$$2HClO = 2HCl + O_2.$$

The sodium salt of hypochlorous acid, *sodium hypochlorite*, $NaClO$, is a very good germ-killer. It is the essential substance in the well-known antiseptic and disinfectant called *Milton*. Hypochlorous acid itself has the power of *bleaching* many coloured substances—that is, it discharges their colour and turns them white. The action is probably due to the ease with which it loses its oxygen and is converted into hydrochloric acid. The oxygen reacts with the dye, and splits it up into colourless compounds.

This will help us to understand a peculiar fact about chlorine. When a piece of dry dyed cloth is put into a jar of chlorine, nothing happens. But if the cloth be moistened, it is rapidly bleached. It is clear, therefore, that water must play an essential part in the bleaching action of chlorine, and possibly what happens is that hypochlorous acid—formed as described above—is the real bleaching agent. This, of course, could not be formed unless water was present. The bleaching action of chlorine may, therefore, be to some extent an *oxidation* of the dye brought about by the hypochlorous acid formed by the action of the chlorine upon water. [It should be noted that occasionally, but very rarely, *dry* chlorine will bleach a *dry* fabric. In this case, the bleaching must be due to the reaction of the chlorine with the dye itself.]

Chlorine will not burn, nor will it support combustion in the ordinary way. A burning wax taper, however, will continue to burn in chlorine; its flame becomes dull red, and deposits much soot, while white acid fumes are given off. We can understand what happens if we know that the wax of the taper is composed of carbon and hydrogen. Owing to its great affinity for chlorine, the hydrogen of the wax continues to burn, forming hydrochloric acid gas. The carbon is thus left and is deposited as soot. The formula for **wax** is of the type C_xH_y, where x and y are very large. Suppose the wax in a particular taper was $C_{60}H_{122}$. The equation for the reaction which would occur if such a taper were burnt in chlorine is—

$$C_{60}H_{122} + 61Cl_2 = 60C + 122HCl.$$

Compounds which consist of carbon and hydrogen only are called *hydrocarbons.* They can all be made to burn in chlorine, and the same sort of reaction goes on in each case —the hydrogen is converted into hydrochloric acid gas and the carbon is left. Thus, if a piece of cotton-wool is soaked in boiling turpentine ($C_{10}H_{16}$) and plunged into a jar of chlorine, the hot turpentine takes fire spontaneously, and burns with a reddish smoky flame—

$$C_{10}H_{16} + 8Cl_2 = 10C + 16HCl.$$

Action of Chlorine upon Bromides and Iodides.—The bromides (p. 239) and iodides (p. 247) are the salts of hydrobromic acid (HBr) and hydriodic acid (HI) respectively. When chlorine is passed into a solution of a bromide, bromine is liberated and the corresponding chloride is formed, *e.g.*—

$$\underset{\text{Potassium bromide.}}{2KBr} + Cl_2 = 2KCl + Br_2.$$

Similarly, chlorine will act upon a solution of an iodide, liberating iodine—

$$\underset{\text{Sodium iodide.}}{2NaI} + Cl_2 = 2NaCl + I_2.$$

In this connection it may be noted here that bromine (p. 233) also will act upon a solution of an iodide, liberating iodine—

$$\underset{\text{Potassium iodide.}}{2KI} + Br_2 = \underset{\text{Potassium bromide.}}{2KBr} + I_2.$$

Bromine, therefore, is intermediate in chemical activity between chlorine and iodine.

Action of Chlorine upon Alkalis.—When chlorine is passed into cold dilute caustic soda solution, it dissolves in the solution and reacts with the caustic soda according to the equation—

$$Cl_2 + 2NaOH = NaCl + NaClO + H_2O.$$

In this way, a mixture of *sodium chloride* (NaCl) and sodium *hypochlorite* (NaClO) is formed.

The same sort of reaction occurs with cold dilute caustic potash solution—

$$Cl_2 + 2KOH = KCl + \underset{\text{Potassium hypochlorite.}}{KClO} + H_2O,$$

and with lime-water (a solution of calcium hydroxide, $Ca(OH)_2$)—

$$2Cl_2 + 2Ca(OH)_2 = \underset{\text{Calcium chloride.}}{CaCl_2} + \underset{\text{Calcium hypochlorite.}}{Ca(ClO)_2} + 2H_2O.$$

Upon hot and concentrated solutions of alkalis, however, chlorine has a different action, a mixture of the *chloride* and *chlorate* of the metal being formed—

$$3Cl_2 + 6NaOH = 5NaCl + \underset{\text{Sodium chlorate.}}{NaClO_3} + 3H_2O$$

$$3Cl_2 + 6KOH = 5KCl + \underset{\text{Potassium chlorate.}}{KClO_3} + 3H_2O.$$

Since calcium hydroxide is not very soluble in water, it is impossible to make a concentrated solution of it. However, a thin paste of calcium hydroxide in water will do just as well for this purpose. Such a paste is known as *milk of lime*, and chlorine will react with hot milk of lime as follows—

$$6Cl_2 + 6Ca(OH)_2 = 5CaCl_2 + \underset{\text{Calcium chlorate.}}{Ca(ClO_3)_2} + 6H_2O.$$

This reaction is used in the manufacture of chlorates. The *chlorates* are salts of an acid called *chloric acid*, $HClO_3$.

Bleaching-powder.—We have already seen that chlorine can be prepared by the action of a dilute acid upon a substance called bleaching-powder, for which the formula $CaOCl_2$ has been suggested. Bleaching-powder, otherwise known as "chloride of lime," is a white powder made by passing chlorine over *dry* slaked lime or calcium hydroxide—

$$Ca(OH)_2 + Cl_2 = \text{"}CaOCl_2\text{"} + H_2O.$$

It is decomposed by all dilute acids, with liberation of chlorine. Even the carbon dioxide of the air, in combination with moisture (*i.e.* as *carbonic acid*, H_2CO_3), is sufficiently powerful to decompose bleaching-powder, which therefore always smells of chlorine when exposed to damp air. The equations for the reactions between bleaching-powder and various dilute acids are given below:

$$CaOCl_2 + H_2SO_4 = CaSO_4 + H_2O + Cl_2.$$
$$CaOCl_2 + 2HNO_3 = Ca(NO_3)_2 + H_2O + Cl_2.$$
$$CaOCl_2 + 2HCl = CaCl_2 + H_2O + Cl_2.$$
$$CaOCl_2 + H_2CO_3\ [\textit{i.e.}\ CO_2 + H_2O] = CaCO_3 + H_2O + Cl_2.$$

Since chlorine is such a powerful germ-killer, bleaching-powder is largely used as a disinfectant, although its main use is, as its name implies, in *bleaching*. The fabric to be bleached is first soaked in a solution of bleaching-powder, and then in a solution of a dilute acid. Chlorine is thus set free in the fibres of the fabric, which is therefore bleached. It would not do to stop here, for chlorine rapidly destroys the materials of which cloths are made; hence the fabric is transferred to another bath which contains a solution of a substance known as an *antichlor*. The purpose of the antichlor is to take away the unused chlorine left in the cloth and thus to prevent the latter from rotting. The compound which the photographers call "hypo"—sodium thiosulphate—is often employed; it reacts with the chlorine as follows—

$$4Cl_2 + \underset{\text{Sodium thiosulphate.}}{Na_2S_2O_3} + 5H_2O = 8HCl + H_2SO_4 + \underset{\text{Sodium sulphate.}}{Na_2SO_4}.$$

The cloth is next washed in water and then dried. Much bleaching is carried out by means of free gaseous chlorine, manufactured by one of the processes described below. Silk and wool are too delicate to be bleached either by free chlorine or by bleaching-powder, since chlorine quickly rots them. Linen and cotton goods are, however, not so readily attacked, and therefore may be safely bleached in this way. For silk, wool and straw, *sulphur dioxide* is generally employed as the bleaching agent (see p. 304).

EXERCISE.—If you were engaged in the bleaching trade, how many tons of bleaching-powder (supposing it to be pure $CaOCl_2$) would you have to buy in order to keep your works going for twelve weeks, using 1 ton of chlorine weekly ?

SUMMARY OF PROPERTIES OF CHLORINE

I. Physical Properties.

1. Greenish-yellow colour.
2. Characteristic pungent smell.
3. Soluble in water, forming "chlorine-water."
4. Much heavier than air (V.D. = 35·5).
5. Easily liquefied.

II. Chemical Properties.

1. Will not burn.
2. Will support combustion of some substances, such as phosphorus, hydrogen, and hydrocarbons (wax, turpentine, etc.).
3. Will react with metals to form salts, the *chlorides*.
4. Will bleach when moist, owing to formation of the very chemically active hypochlorous acid.
5. Will dissolve in caustic alkali solutions ; the nature of products depends upon concentration and temperature (see p. 217).
6. A mixture of chlorine and hydrogen will explode in bright sunlight, or if ignited. The product is hydrogen chloride—

$$H_2 + Cl_2 = 2HCl.$$

Manufacture of Chlorine.—Chlorine is a very important substance commercially, since it is used for bleaching, for the manufacture of bleaching-powder, in the dye industry, in the manufacture of drugs and chemicals and for many other purposes. It is therefore prepared on a large scale, nowadays by an electrical method, which has replaced a process known as DEACON'S PROCESS, after its inventor.

1. DEACON'S PROCESS.—We have seen that the principle of the ordinary laboratory methods for preparing chlorine is the *oxidation of hydrochloric acid, i.e.* removal of its hydrogen. Now, in industry it is important to keep down the cost of production as far as possible, so that the usual laboratory oxidizing agents such as manganese dioxide and potassium permanganate are out of the question. Deacon, however, said to himself, "There is plenty of oxygen in the air, and no one will charge me for that. Why should I not oxidize my hydrochloric acid with atmospheric oxygen instead of with the expensive manganese dioxide?"

He therefore tried the effect of heating a mixture of hydrochloric acid gas and air, but although a little chlorine appeared to be formed the action was too slow to be of any use. Still, he was not discouraged, for he knew that there were various ways of making a chemical reaction go more quickly. One of them is to add a suitable *catalyst* to the reacting substances, as we have seen when we were studying oxygen. Deacon therefore made a large number of experiments to see if he could find a substance which would act as a catalyst upon the oxidation of hydrochloric acid gas by atmospheric oxygen. After many failures he was at last successful: the magic substance was *copper chloride,* $CuCl_2$. If a mixture of air and hydrochloric acid gas is passed over heated copper chloride, the acid is readily oxidized to chlorine—

$$4HCl + O_2 \rightleftharpoons 2H_2O + 2Cl_2.$$

Experiments have shown that the greater the surface of the catalyst exposed to the mixture of gases, the greater is its action and the faster the oxidation proceeds. Hence, in Deacon's process, a mixture of hydrochloric acid gas and air was heated in pipes to about 450°, after which it passed into another series of tubes containing bricks soaked in copper chloride solution and maintained at a temperature of 480-500°. The bricks were porous, and as the copper chloride solution had penetrated throughout the pores, the surface of catalyst exposed was very large. The reaction goes very quickly and smoothly under these conditions. The gas which issued from the tubes was passed up a tower filled with coke over which water trickled; in this way the unused hydrochloric acid, which dissolved in the water, was regained, and the chlorine, which is much less soluble, passed on. It was dried by passing through concentrated sulphuric acid.

The chlorine obtained in this way was very dilute, being mixed with about fifteen times its own volume of nitrogen and unused air; it was therefore not suitable for compression into steel cylinders, since customers at a distance were not willing to pay carriage on cylinders of a gas which was only 6 per cent. chlorine. Chlorine prepared by Deacon's process was therefore either used on the spot for bleaching, or else was converted into bleaching-powder.

2. ELECTRICAL PROCESS.—In the electrical process a concentrated solution of common salt is electrolysed, when chlorine is given off from the anode. Caustic soda is obtained as another product in the same process: this is formed by the action of the sodium (which is liberated at the cathode) upon the water, in the usual way—

$$2Na + 2H_2O = 2NaOH + H_2.$$

It will be seen that still another valuable substance is obtained, namely *hydrogen*, which is used in the manufacture of ammonia, margarine, etc. This process is therefore an admirable example of the fulfilment of a chemical manufacturer's dream—to have no waste products whatever! If a manufacturer gets a great deal of a certain by-product in the course of his process, he always tries to find some use for it. Occasionally the waste-product turns out in the end to be more valuable than the main one.

Several different types of apparatus are employed in the electrolytic process for the manufacture of chlorine. The NELSON cell is shown in Fig. 54.

It consists of a vessel made of compressed asbestos surrounded by a steel net which forms the cathode. The brine to be electrolysed is placed in the vessel, and soon makes the walls damp throughout, though no liquid is actually lost. The anode is made of a stout graphite rod, dipping into the brine, and the cell as a whole is enclosed in an outer case through which steam can be blown. On passing the current,

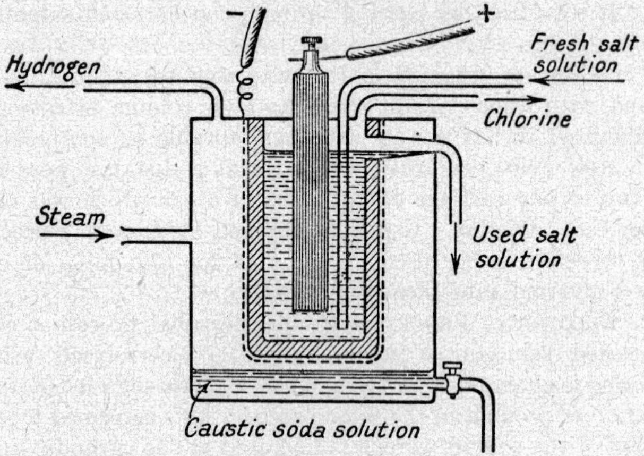

FIG. 54.—Nelson Cell.

chlorine is liberated at the anode, whence it is led away through a suitable pipe. The sodium which is set free at the cathode immediately reacts with the steam, forming caustic soda and hydrogen :

$$2Na + 2H_2O = 2NaOH + H_2.$$

The caustic soda solution is run off from time to time and evaporated, the fused caustic soda so obtained being allowed to set in suitable moulds as sticks or pellets. The hydrogen is a valuable by-product.

Occurrence of Chlorine.—Chlorine is so chemically active that it does not occur naturally in the free state. In the form of its compounds with sodium, potassium and magnesium, *viz.* sodium chloride, potassium chloride and magnesium chloride, it is widely distributed in large quantities. *Sodium* *chloride*, NaCl, is found as *rock-salt* in very large deposits in England (Cheshire), Galicia (near the town of Wielickza), and Germany (Stassfurt). It is also found dissolved in brine-springs (Droitwich, etc.) and in the sea. Potassium and magnesium chlorides are found in the solid state at Stassfurt, and in solution in sea-water. Silver chloride, AgCl, or *horn silver*, is also found native, though in comparatively small quantities. Chlorine is essential to the life of both plants and animals, which usually require it in the form of sodium chloride, common salt.

History of Chlorine.—Chlorine was discovered in 1774 by CARL WILHELM SCHEELE, who made it by the action of *muriatic acid* (the substance we now call hydrochloric acid, HCl) upon *pyrolusite* (the crude mineral form of manganese dioxide, MnO_2). At first it was regarded as a compound containing oxygen, but SIR HUMPHRY DAVY, in 1810, showed that it was an element, and gave it its present name "chlorine" (from the Greek *chloros*, greenish yellow).

Chlorine as an Oxidizing Agent.—Owing to its great affinity for hydrogen, chlorine will often remove the latter element from compounds containing it (*e.g.* wax). Now we have already seen that removal of hydrogen from a substance is equivalent in some respects to adding oxygen to it, so that the term *oxidation* includes cases of this sort. Hence chlorine is an *oxidizing agent*. However, its oxidizing actions are not confined to changes of the types just described, for in the presence of moisture the action of chlorine may sometimes result in the actual *addition of oxygen* to the substance concerned, the oxygen, of course, coming from the water. Thus when chlorine is passed into a solution of sulphur dioxide in water, sulphuric acid is produced; the chlorine is at the same time reduced to hydrochloric acid—

$$SO_2 + 2H_2O + Cl_2 = H_2SO_4 + 2HCl.$$

A solution of sulphur dioxide in water may be regarded as a solution of *sulphurous acid*, H_2SO_3 ($H_2O + SO_2 = H_2SO_3$). The above reaction is thus seen to be an oxidation of the sulphurous acid, H_2SO_3, to sulphuric acid, H_2SO_4, by addition of an atom of oxygen—

$$H_2SO_3 + O\,H_2 + Cl_2 = H_2SO_4 + 2HCl.$$

An example of the first kind of oxidizing action of chlorine is the change which occurs when hydrogen sulphide, H_2S, is passed into chlorine water. Hydrochloric acid is formed and sulphur is precipitated. In other words, the hydrogen sulphide has had its hydrogen removed and has therefore been oxidized. The chlorine is at the same time reduced to hydrochloric acid—

$$H_2S + Cl_2 = 2HCl + S.$$

This reaction may therefore be regarded either (*a*) as an oxidation of the hydrogen sulphide by the chlorine, or (*b*) as a reduction of the chlorine by the hydrogen sulphide.

In the section on oxidation, it was stated that the term oxidation has now come to include reactions in which the change is merely an increase in the proportion of electro-negative constituent of the molecule (or, of course, a decrease in the proportion of electro-positive constituent, which comes to the same thing). Chlorine is an electro-negative element, *i.e.* it appears at the *anode* in electrolysis. Hence, *if chlorine combines with a substance, that substance must be oxidized.*

Consider, for example, the case of ferrous chloride, $FeCl_2$. If chlorine is passed into a solution of ferrous chloride, combination occurs and *ferric chloride*, $FeCl_3$, is formed—

$$2FeCl_2 + Cl_2 = 2FeCl_3.$$

The ferrous chloride is therefore said to have been *oxidized.* Conversely, removal of chlorine from a substance is considered to be a *reduction.*

HOW TO DRY CHLORINE.—Chlorine has no action on sulphuric acid, and can therefore be dried by bubbling it through the concentrated acid in a Drechsel bottle (Fig. 56, p. 226). Chlorine cannot be collected over water, since it is soluble; neither should it be collected over mercury, which it attacks, forming *mercuric chloride*, $HgCl_2$. It can be collected over strong salt-solution, in which it is not very soluble, or—as mentioned above—by downward displacement.

COMPOUNDS OF CHLORINE.

Hydrochloric Acid, HCl.

Hydrochloric acid, or hydrogen chloride, which is a colourless gas, can be built up (*synthesized*) from its elements, by the explosion of a mixture of equal volumes of hydrogen and chlorine. In the laboratory, however, it is made by the action of concentrated sulphuric acid upon a metallic chloride. Any metallic chloride will do, but sodium chloride is always used in practice, since it is the cheapest. The sulphuric acid is poured through a thistle-funnel on to salt contained in a round-bottomed flask fitted with a cork and delivery-tube as shown in Fig. 55.

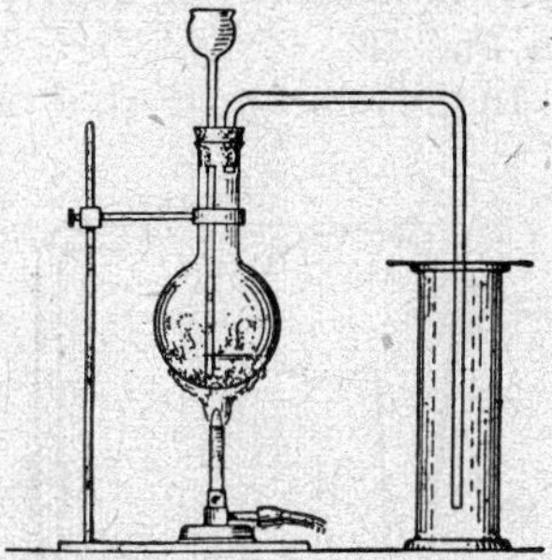

FIG. 55.—Preparation of Hydrochloric Acid Gas.

The reaction takes place in the cold, but is hastened, as usual, by the application of heat. The products are sodium *bi*-sulphate and hydrochloric acid gas—

$$NaCl + H_2SO_4 = NaHSO_4 + HCl.$$

[If a very high temperature is employed, the further reaction—

$$NaHSO_4 + NaCl = Na_2SO_4 + HCl$$

may be brought about. In the laboratory, however, only the first reaction occurs.]

The gas is collected by downward displacement, since it is heavier than air (V.D. = 18·25 ; V.D. of air = 14·4), and if required dry may be passed through concentrated sulphuric acid. Hydrogen chloride is extremely soluble in water, the solution formed being the ordinary "hydrochloric acid" of the laboratory. Since the gas is so soluble, we have to take special precautions when making a solution of it, to prevent the water from "sucking back" into the flask containing the sulphuric acid and salt. You can imagine what an explosion would take place if water came into contact with hot sulphuric acid!

When we are making a solution of a very soluble gas, therefore, such as hydrogen chloride, we adopt a device which keeps the water from running back. There are several sorts of apparatus in use; three of the commonest are shown in Fig. 56.

In the retort method, if the water sucks back it merely falls

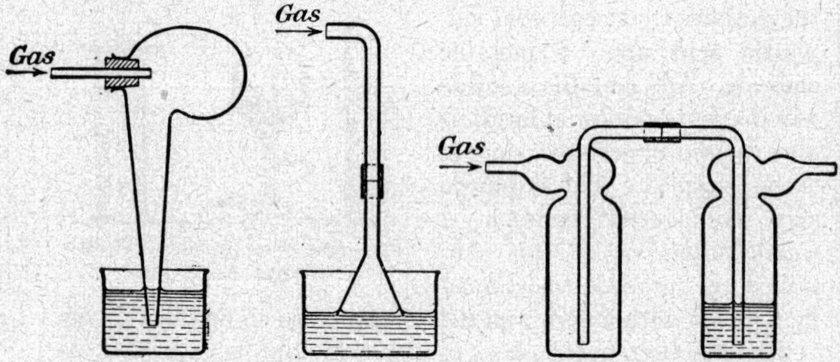

Retort Method. Funnel Method. Reversed Drechsel Bottle Method.

FIG. 56.—Methods of preventing "sucking back."

into the bulb of the retort and stays there: it can get no farther. In the second method, the delivery tube is connected with a funnel which *just touches* the water in the beaker. If the water begins to run up the funnel, the rim of the latter soon becomes clear of the surface of the water in the beaker, and hence the water which has risen drops back again. In the third method, if the water sucks back it simply passes into the empty Drechsel bottle, and can get no farther, since the bottle is connected up with the delivery-tube the wrong way round. This method is the best.

Properties of Hydrochloric Acid.—Hydrogen chloride ("hydrochloric acid gas") is a colourless gas with a pungent smell. It fumes strongly in moist air, owing to the formation of a cloud of tiny drops of hydrochloric acid solution. It is very soluble in water, 1 volume of which will dissolve no less than 450 volumes of the gas at 15° C. The solution, and the undried gas, possess strongly acid properties. Thus ordinary "hydrochloric acid" will turn blue litmus red, has an acid taste, will dissolve metals, and will liberate carbon dioxide from carbonates. For example, magnesium and zinc readily dissolve, forming the corresponding *chloride* and liberating hydrogen—

$$Mg + 2HCl = MgCl_2 + H_2.$$
$$Zn + 2HCl = ZnCl_2 + H_2.$$

Tin and aluminium are also dissolved by the hot solution—

$$Sn + 2HCl = SnCl_2 + H_2,$$
$$2Al + 6HCl = 2AlCl_3 + 3H_2,$$

but copper and lead are not appreciably attacked.

Typical examples of the action of hydrochloric acid solution upon a carbonate are as follows:

Sodium carbonate: $Na_2CO_3 + 2HCl = 2NaCl + H_2O + CO_2.$
Calcium carbonate: $CaCO_3 + 2HCl = CaCl_2 + H_2O + CO_2.$
Copper carbonate: $CuCO_3 + 2HCl = CuCl_2 + H_2O + CO_2.$

The salts of hydrochloric acid, *i.e.* the compounds derived from it by replacing its hydrogen by a metal, are called CHLORIDES. You will see that they are the same substances as are formed by the direct combination of the metals with chlorine.

Hydrochloric acid is the strongest acid known, being about equally strong with nitric acid and $1\frac{1}{2}$ times as strong as sulphuric. How is it, then, that sulphuric acid causes the liberation of hydrochloric acid when heated with a chloride? If hydrochloric acid is stronger than sulphuric, we should expect that the latter acid would be formed when hydrochloric acid acts upon a sulphate; it seems strange that this does not happen, but that sulphuric acid produces hydrochloric acid when it is heated with a chloride. Well, the fact is that in the second action we are not giving the hydrochloric acid a fair chance. If you were to undertake to fight a champion boxer, even your warmest supporter would not give much for your chances. But if the boxer, while retaining his strength, developed a distressing malady which had the effect of making him so unsteady upon his feet that the slightest touch sent him flying through the air, your chances would be considerably improved. You might even succeed in knocking him out of the ring, but no one would imagine you to be the stronger of the two: the astonishing result would simply be due to the fact that the fight was not under fair conditions. The contest between sulphuric and hydrochloric acids is somewhat similar. Sulphuric acid—a typically British production—has the typically British characteristic of being able to sit tight in a hot corner; or, to put it more prosaically, it is not volatile, but has a very high boiling-point. Hydrochloric acid, however, has the Gallic temperament—it is very *spirituel*, and, indeed, is a gas at ordinary temperature and pressure. Hence, when you heat sodium chloride with concentrated sulphuric acid, as soon as hydrochloric acid is formed it flies off and cannot retaliate by attacking the sodium sulphate. The sulphuric acid therefore is the victor.

To find out which really is the stronger of the two, we must let them fight under conditions which are fair to both. This we can do in several ways, one of which you will easily understand. We know that all acids have a great passion for caustic soda, which they seize with avidity whenever they get the chance. In this respect they are all alike. Well, suppose we dissolve equivalent weights of hydrochloric acid and sulphuric acid together in some water. They are now in a state where the volatility of the one and the non-volatility of the other make absolutely no difference. Now, suppose we add some caustic soda, *but not enough to satisfy both of them.* They will fight over the booty, and we can measure their relative strengths by finding out how much of the caustic soda each one manages to capture. We should find that the hydrochloric acid got three-fifths of it, and the sulphuric acid only two-fifths. Hence the hydrochloric acid is $\frac{3}{2}$ times as strong as the sulphuric acid.

Chlorides.—The metallic chlorides, or salts of hydrochloric acid, can be prepared in any of the following ways, most of which are of the usual types of methods used in the formation of salts of all kinds (see p. 442). One method, however, is peculiar, in that it consists in the direct union of the metal with chlorine (you will remember that this is why chlorine is called a halogen). It is obvious that we could not prepare, say, sulphates in this way, since the SO_4 group of atoms does not exist in the free state.

(i) Direct union of chlorine and metal, *e.g.*—

$$2Na + Cl_2 = 2NaCl.$$
$$2Fe + 3Cl_2 = 2FeCl_3 \text{ (ferric chloride).}$$

(ii) Action of hydrochloric acid upon the oxide or hydroxide of the metal, *e.g.*—

$$CuO + 2HCl = CuCl_2 + H_2O$$
$$Zn(OH)_2 + 2HCl = ZnCl_2 + 2H_2O$$
$$KOH + HCl = KCl + H_2O.$$

(iii) Action of hydrochloric acid upon the carbonate of the metal, *e.g.*—

$$MgCO_3 + 2HCl = MgCl_2 + H_2O + CO_2.$$

(iv) Action of hydrochloric acid upon the metal itself, *e.g.*—

$$Mg + 2HCl = MgCl_2 + H_2.$$

(v) In the case of an insoluble chloride, by double decomposition with a soluble chloride. Thus when sodium chloride solution is added to silver nitrate solution, a white curdy precipitate of silver chloride is obtained—

$$AgNO_3 + NaCl = AgCl \downarrow + NaNO_3.$$

Most metallic chlorides are soluble in water, the chief exceptions being silver chloride, $AgCl$, mercurous chloride, Hg_2Cl_2 (mercur*ic* chloride, $HgCl_2$, "corrosive sublimate," is soluble), and lead chloride, $PbCl_2$, which is only slightly soluble in cold water but more soluble in hot.

On heating with sulphuric acid, the chlorides yield hydrogen chloride; with a mixture of manganese dioxide and sulphuric acid, chlorides yield chlorine on application of heat—a reaction which is sometimes used for the preparation of chlorine. What happens is that the acid acting upon the chloride yields hydrochloric acid, which is then oxidized by the manganese dioxide. The equation for the action in the case of sodium chloride is—

$$2NaCl + MnO_2 + 3H_2SO_4 = 2NaHSO_4 + MnSO_4 + 2H_2O + Cl_2.$$

It should be noted that when a metal forms two chlorides (*e.g.* iron), direct action of chlorine upon the metal yields the *higher* chloride, *i.e.* the one containing the higher proportion of chlorine. Hydrochloric acid, when it acts upon such a metal, always yields the *lower* chloride. Thus with iron—

$$Fe + 2HCl = \underset{\text{Ferrous chloride.}}{FeCl_2} + H_2$$

$$2Fe + 3Cl_2 = \underset{\text{Ferric chloride.}}{2FeCl_3}$$

[An exception to be noted is copper. When chlorine acts upon heated copper, *cuprous chloride*, Cu_2Cl_2, and *not* cupric chloride, $CuCl_2$, is formed. This is because at the temperature of the reaction cupric chloride is unstable, and splits up into cuprous chloride and chlorine—

$$2CuCl_2 = Cu_2Cl_2 + Cl_2.]$$

Practically all metallic chlorides are reduced to metal if heated strongly in a current of hydrogen. The hydrogen is converted into hydrochloric acid.

Constitution of Hydrogen Chloride.—(i) When a mixture of 1 volume of hydrogen with 1 volume of chlorine is exploded, the hydrogen chloride formed is found, on cooling, to occupy the same volume as the original mixture, *i.e.* 2 volumes.

Hence, by Avogadro's Hypothesis, 2 molecules of hydrogen chloride contain 1 molecule of hydrogen and 1 molecule of chlorine.

∴ 1 molecule of hydrogen chloride contains $\frac{1}{2}$ molecule of hydrogen and $\frac{1}{2}$ molecule of chlorine.

But the molecule of hydrogen contains 2 atoms, and so does the molecule of chlorine.

Hence 1 molecule of hydrogen chloride consists of 1 atom of hydrogen and 1 atom of chlorine.

Therefore the formula is HCl.

(ii) This is confirmed by finding the vapour density (p. 93) of the gas. Measurement shows that the V.D. = 18·25. Therefore the molecular weight is 36·5, since M.W. = 2 V.D. (p. 94). But the atomic weight of chlorine is 35·5, hence the molecule of hydrogen chloride contains 1 atom of hydrogen and 1 of chlorine (1 + 35·5 = 36·5).

(iii) By placing a known volume of hydrogen chloride in a tube over mercury, and shaking it up with sodium amalgam (sodium dissolved in mercury). The acid is decomposed, yielding hydrogen (gas) and sodium chloride (solid). The volume of the hydrogen which is left is found to be exactly half that of the hydrogen chloride taken, ∴ by Avogadro's Hypothesis, 1 molecule of hydrogen chloride contains ½ a molecule of hydrogen.

∴ the hydrogen chloride molecule must be HCl_x. x is found from (ii), the vapour density.

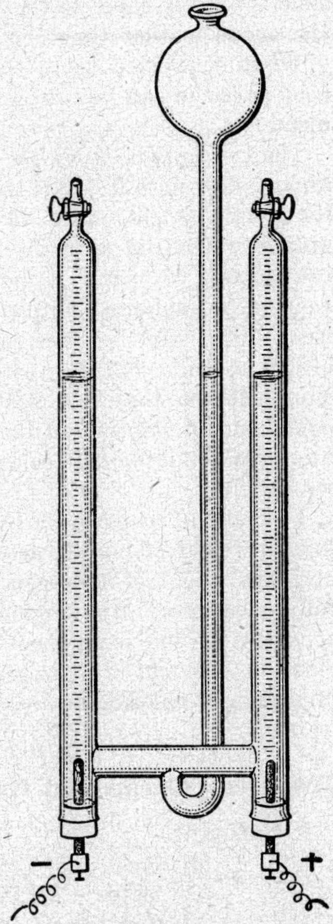

FIG. 57.

(iv) Electrolysis of concentrated hydrochloric acid, using a carbon anode (Fig. 57), yields hydrogen at the cathode and chlorine at the anode. After the liquid has become saturated with chlorine, it will be found that the volume of hydrogen which comes off from the cathode in a given time is exactly equal to the volume of chlorine evolved from the anode in that time.

What conclusion as to the structure of the hydrochloric acid molecule can you draw from the results of this experiment ?

The *composition by weight* of hydrochloric acid is of great importance, since it yields the *equivalent of chlorine* (and also its atomic weight, since its valency is 1), upon which the atomic weights of so many elements depend. That is, the equivalents of many elements—from which their atomic weights are obtained simply by multiplying by the valency (see p. 105)—have been determined by finding out what weight of them will combine with the equivalent of chlorine. You will see that if a mistake were made in finding the equivalent of chlorine, all these other equivalents, and therefore the atomic weights calculated from them, would also be wrong.

To find the composition by weight of hydrochloric acid, a known weight of pure hydrogen was burnt in pure chlorine, and the weight of hydrogen chloride so produced was carefully measured. By weighing also the chlorine used, the accuracy of the experiment was checked: the weight of chlorine + weight of hydrogen should be equal to the weight of hydrogen chloride.

Tests for Chlorine and Hydrochloric Acid.

1. CHLORINE.

(*a*) Smell. (*b*) Colour. (*c*) Bleaches moist litmus paper. (*d*) Will turn potassium iodide solution brown, owing to the liberation of iodine—

$$2KI + Cl_2 = 2KCl + I_2.$$

(If there is any doubt about the iodine, add starch solution, which iodine turns a deep blue colour.)

2. Hydrochloric Acid.

(i) *Gas.* (*a*) Smell. (*b*) Fumes in moist air. (*c*) Forms dense white fumes with ammonia, *ammonium chloride* being formed—

$$NH_3 + HCl = NH_4Cl.$$

(*d*) Turns blue litmus red.

(ii) *Solution.* (*a*) Smell. (*b*) Turns blue litmus red. (*c*) Gives a curdy white precipitate of silver chloride with silver nitrate solution—

$$AgNO_3 + HCl = AgCl \downarrow + HNO_3.$$

Bromine

Symbol: Br; *Valency:* 1; *Number of Atoms in Molecule:* 2 (therefore formula Br_2); *Atomic Weight:* 80; *Boiling-point:* 59°; Specific Gravity: 3·2.

Bromine is one of the two elements which are liquid at ordinary temperatures—the other is mercury. It was discovered by the Frenchman Balard in 1826. It was given its present name on account of its horrible smell (Greek, *bromos*, a stench).

Like chlorine, it does not occur free in nature since it is too chemically active. It is found in combination with metals as *bromides, e.g.* NaBr, sodium bromide; KBr, potassium bromide; and $MgBr_2$, magnesium bromide. These are contained in sea-water and in certain mineral springs in Ohio (U.S.A.) and elsewhere, and occur also in the solid state in the vast deposits at Stassfurt in North Germany.

Preparation.—Bromine may be prepared in the laboratory by heating a mixture of potassium bromide, manganese dioxide and sulphuric acid in a retort. (Cf. the method for the preparation of chlorine described on p. 229.) The bromine distils over and is collected in a cooled receiver (Fig. 58).

$$2KBr + MnO_2 + 3H_2SO_4 = 2KHSO_4 + MnSO_4 + 2H_2O + Br_2.$$

Potassium bisulphate. Manganese sulphate.

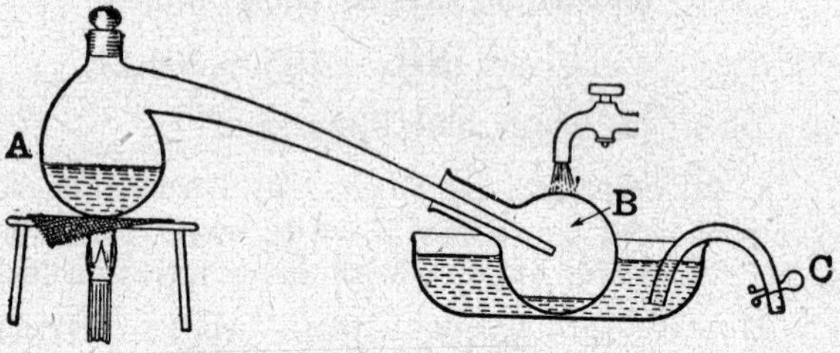

FIG. 58.—Preparation of Bromine.

[QUESTION: How much bromine could you get from 100 grams of potassium bromide, and how much manganese dioxide would you require ?]

Other bromides may be used, but the potassium salt is the one usually kept in the laboratory.

On the commercial scale, bromine is obtained from the bromides in the Stassfurt deposits and in the Ohio springs. A stream of chlorine is passed through hot concentrated solutions of the bromides, when bromine is liberated, according to the equations—

$$2KBr + Cl_2 = 2KCl + Br_2$$
$$2NaBr + Cl_2 = 2NaCl + Br_2$$
$$MgBr_2 + Cl_2 = MgCl_2 + Br_2.$$

The bromine vapour which comes off is passed through a spiral tube surrounded by water, and most of it is thus condensed and may be collected in a receiver. Any uncondensed bromine vapour is trapped by passing it up through a small tower containing wet iron filings, where iron bromide is formed ; this is used for making potassium bromide (p. 240).

The chief impurities in the bromine obtained in this way are chlorine and water. The water may be removed by shaking the bromine with concentrated sulphuric acid. The dry bromine is then distilled over potassium bromide (*i.e.* a little potassium bromide is added to the bromine in the distillation-apparatus), and is thus freed from chlorine, which replaces the bromine in the bromide and is left behind as potassium chloride—

$$2KBr + Cl_2 = 2KCl + Br_2.$$

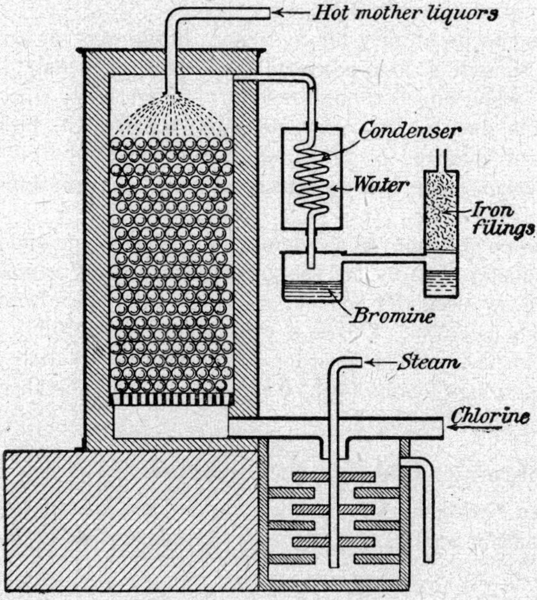

FIG. 59.—Manufacture of Bromine.

Properties.—Bromine is a reddish-brown, heavy, volatile liquid, which boils at 59°, freezes at − 7·3°, and has a specific gravity of 3·2. It readily passes into vapour at ordinary temperatures. If you look at a bottle of bromine which is only half full, you will notice that the upper portion is filled with heavy dark-red fumes. These fumes are bromine vapour: they have a very irritating action upon the eyes, nose, and throat. Liquid bromine should be used with care, since it produces yellow burns when dropped upon the skin.

Bromine dissolves slightly in water, forming a solution called *bromine-water*. In its chemical properties bromine closely resembles chlorine. Thus it combines directly with *hydrogen* (forming *hydrogen bromide*), with *metals* (forming salts, the *bromides*; hence it is a "*halogen*"), and with *phosphorus*, forming *phosphorus tri-bromide*, PBr_3, and *phosphorus penta-bromide*, PBr_5.

Owing to its affinity for hydrogen, bromine is an *oxidizing agent*, though a less powerful one than chlorine. It will bleach, when moist, though not very energetically (bleaching action is due to hypobromous acid, HBrO. Cf. bleaching action of chlorine, p. 215), and turns starch-solution *yellow* (distinction from iodine, which turns starch-solution blue. See p. 245).

Bromine is employed to some extent in medicine and in the dye industry, but by far the greater part of the annual production is used for conversion into ethylene dibromide, $C_2H_4Br_2$ (p. 337). This is a constituent of "ethyl" petrol, to which it is added in order to prevent the fouling of the sparking-plugs by the lead of the anti-knock substance, lead tetra-ethyl, $Pb(C_2H_5)_4$.

Hydrobromic Acid and the Bromides.

When hydrogen and bromine vapour are heated together, combination occurs, and *hydrogen bromide* or *hydrobromic acid*

FIG. 60.—Synthetic Preparation of Hydrogen Bromide.

gas, HBr, is formed. A convenient way of thus *synthesizing* the gas is to pass a mixture of hydrogen and bromine vapour through a tube containing a platinum spiral electrically heated (Fig. 60). The platinum, besides heating the gases, also acts as a catalyst.

The equation for the reaction is $H_2 + Br_2 = 2HBr$.

Note carefully that hydrobromic acid *cannot* be obtained pure by heating concentrated sulphuric acid with a bromide (contrast preparation of hydrochloric acid, p. 225), since it can act as a mild reducing agent, and as soon as it is formed it reduces some of the hot sulphuric acid to sulphur dioxide, being itself oxidized to bromine—

$$\text{(i)}\ KBr + H_2SO_4 = KHSO_4 + HBr,$$
$$\text{(ii)}\ H_2SO_4 + 2HBr = 2H_2O + SO_2 + Br_2,$$

$$\text{or}\ 2KBr + 3H_2SO_4 = 2KHSO_4 + 2H_2O + SO_2 + Br_2.$$

It is true that some of the hydrogen bromide escapes decomposition, but the mixture of gases evolved—hydrogen bromide, sulphur dioxide and bromine—cannot be conveniently purified.

Preparation in the Laboratory.—Hydrogen bromide is therefore generally prepared in another way, namely, *by the action of water on phosphorus tribromide*, PBr_3—

$$PBr_3 + 3H_2O = \underset{\text{Phosphorous acid.}}{H_3PO_3} + 3HBr.$$

[Similar reactions with the trichloride and tri-iodide of phosphorus give hydrochloric acid and hydriodic acid respectively :

$$PCl_3 + 3H_2O = H_3PO_3 + 3HCl.$$
$$PI_3 + 3H_2O = H_3PO_3 + 3HI.$$

Hydriodic acid, HI, is indeed prepared in this way (p. 246), but the method is not used for hydrochloric acid since simpler ones are available.]

The details of the preparation are as follows : Red phosphorus, water and sand are stirred up together into a fairly thick paste, which is put into a flask fitted with a cork carrying a tap-funnel and delivery-tube (Fig. 61).

The delivery-tube is connected to a U-tube containing bits of broken glass smeared with a paste of red phosphorus and water. Bromine is placed in the funnel and allowed to run in slowly. As each drop touches the phosphorus a bright flash occurs, and hydrogen bromide is given off.

Explanation of action:

The bromine combines with the phosphorus to form phosphorus tribromide—

$$2P + 3Br_2 = 2PBr_3.$$

This is then decomposed by the water present, yielding *phosphorous acid* and *hydrobromic acid*—

$$PBr_3 + 3H_2O = H_3PO_3 + 3HBr.$$

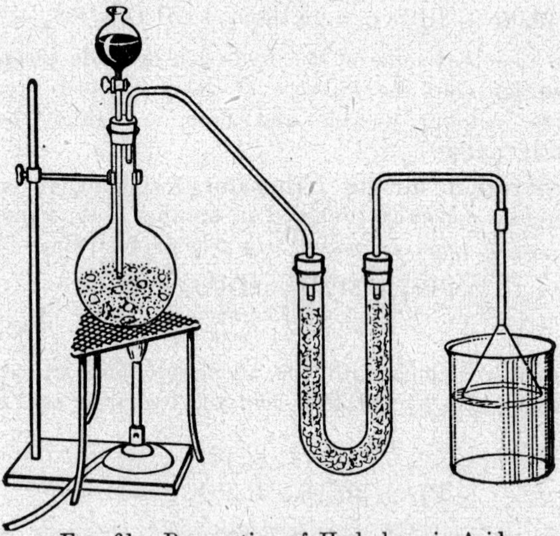

Fig. 61.—Preparation of Hydrobromic Acid.

Owing to the fact that bromine so easily vaporizes, the gas which comes off from the delivery-tube carries with it some bromine vapour. This is removed in the U-tube, where it is converted into hydrobromic acid by the water and phosphorus. The U-tube is, in fact, a secondary apparatus for producing hydrobromic acid.

The hydrogen bromide is then collected by downward displacement or over mercury. If a solution of it is required it may be obtained by using one of the usual forms of apparatus, as shown in the figure.

A solution of hydrobromic acid may also be prepared—

(i) By passing hydrogen sulphide through bromine-water and filtering off the sulphur which is precipitated—

$$H_2S + Br_2 = 2HBr + S \downarrow ,$$

or (ii) by passing sulphur dioxide through bromine-water, or bromine covered by a layer of bromine-water—

$$SO_2 + Br_2 + 2H_2O = H_2SO_4 + 2HBr.$$

From the mixture of dilute sulphuric and hydrobromic acids obtained in this way, dilute hydrobromic acid may be made by distillation. The first portion of the distillate contains most of the hydrobromic acid, while the sulphuric acid is left behind.

Properties.—Hydrogen bromide is a heavy colourless acid gas which fumes in moist air and dissolves readily in water, giving a strongly acid solution. In its general properties it closely resembles hydrogen chloride. It can be condensed to a colourless liquid, which boils at – 69° and freezes to a colourless crystalline solid at – 86°.

In solution in water hydrobromic acid slowly decomposes on exposure to air and light, the solution turning yellow owing to the liberation of bromine by oxidation—

$$O_2 + 4HBr = 2H_2O + 2Br_2.$$

Like hydrochloric acid, hydrobromic acid in solution will turn blue litmus red, will corrode and dissolve metals with evolution of hydrogen, and will liberate carbon dioxide from carbonates, *e.g.*—

$$Mg + 2HBr = MgBr_2 + H_2$$
$$Na_2CO_3 + 2HBr = 2NaBr + H_2O + CO_2.$$

Bromides.—The salts of hydrobromic acid are called *bromides.* They can be obtained from hydrobromic acid in any of the usual ways, and also from the metals themselves by the direct action of bromine—hence bromine is a *halogen* or salt-producer. The most important bromide is *potassium bromide,* KBr, which is widely used in the laboratory, in medicine, and in photography. It is made from the iron bromide obtained in the manufacture of bromine (p. 234) by dissolving it in water and adding potassium carbonate solution. Ferrous hydroxide is precipitated, carbon dioxide is evolved, and a solution of potassium bromide is left from which the salt may be obtained by evaporation and crystallization—

$$3FeBr_2 + 3K_2CO_3 + 3H_2O = \underset{\text{Ferrous hydroxide.}}{3Fe(OH)_2} + 6KBr + 3CO_2.$$

As the iron bromide from the bromine-works does not yield sufficient potassium bromide to satisfy the demand, more is made by adding bromine to iron filings, and is then converted into potassium bromide by the method described.

Potassium bromide may also be made by dissolving bromine in hot concentrated caustic potash solution, evaporating to dryness, and heating the residual mass of bromide and bromate alone or with charcoal.

(i) $3Br_2 + 6KOH = 5KBr + KBrO_3 + 3H_2O.$
(Cf. $3Cl_2 + 6KOH = 5KCl + KClO_3 + 3H_2O.$)

$KBrO_3$ is *potassium bromate.*

(ii) $2KBrO_3 = 2KBr + 3O_2.$
(Cf. $2KClO_3 = 2KCl + 3O_2.$)

If charcoal is used, then—

(iii) $2KBrO_3 + 6C = 2KBr + \underset{\text{Carbon monoxide.}}{6CO}.$

Potassium bromide is a white crystalline solid readily soluble in water. It is used in medicine as a sleeping-draught. When mixed with manganese dioxide and sulphuric acid, it yields bromine on heating. (See preparation of bromine, p. 233.) When solutions of silver nitrate and potassium bromide are mixed, a pale yellow precipitate of silver bromide, AgBr, is obtained—

$$AgNO_3 + KBr = AgBr \downarrow + KNO_3.$$

Silver bromide, like silver chloride, is used in photography. (See p. 249.) When bromine is dissolved in cold dilute solutions of caustic potash or soda, a mixture of the bromide and *hypobromite* of the metal is obtained—

$$Br_2 + 2KOH = KBr + KBrO + H_2O$$

Potassium hypobromite.

(Compare $Cl_2 + 2KOH = KCl + KClO + H_2O$.)

Potassium hypochlorite.

Potassium hypobromite is the salt of *hypobromous acid*, HBrO, corresponding to *hypochlorous acid*, HClO. It is very similar to potassium hypochlorite, but is much more unstable. A solution of it will bleach coloured fabrics.

Potassium bromate, $KBrO_3$, the formation of which has been mentioned above, is a white crystalline solid resembling potassium chlorate. When heated it splits up into potassium bromide and oxygen, just as the chlorate splits up into potassium chloride and oxygen.

Iodine

Symbol: I; *Valency:* 1; *Number of Atoms in Molecule (Atomicity):* 2 (therefore formula I_2); *Atomic Weight:* 127; *Melting-point:* 116°; *Specific Gravity:* 4·93.

Iodine was discovered in 1812 by a French saltpetre manufacturer named Courtois. It was first fully investigated by Gay-Lussac, who gave it the name of *iodine* on account of the violet colour of its vapour (Greek *ioeides*, like a violet). Like the other halogens, iodine is not found free in nature. It is, however, widely distributed (although in small quantities) in the form of its compounds the *iodides* (*e.g.* NaI, sodium iodide) and *iodates* (*e.g.* $NaIO_3$, sodium iodate). The chief iodides are those of sodium (NaI), potassium (KI), and magnesium (MgI_2), which occur in sea-water. It is an interesting fact that seaweeds have the power of absorbing iodine from sea-water. Thus, while the percentage of iodine in the sea is 0·001, the percentage in the dry matter of certain seaweeds is nearly 0·5. Sponges seem to possess this power to an astonishing degree: according to Hundeshagen, the dry weight of tropical sponges may contain as much as 14 per cent. of iodine!

Iodine is very important in the human body. Lack of it may give rise to serious disease, and it is finding increasing use in medicine for this reason.

Sodium iodate, $NaIO_3$, is found as an impurity (about 0·3 per cent.) in the mineral sodium nitrate, called *Chile saltpetre* or *caliche*, which occurs in large deposits in South America and is probably the fossilized remains of prehistoric seaweeds.

Extraction of Iodine.—Iodine is obtained both from seaweed and from *caliche*.

(i) *Extraction from Seaweed.*—The seaweed is dried during the summer months and is then burnt, forming an ash known as *kelp* in this country and as *varech* in Brittany and Normandy.

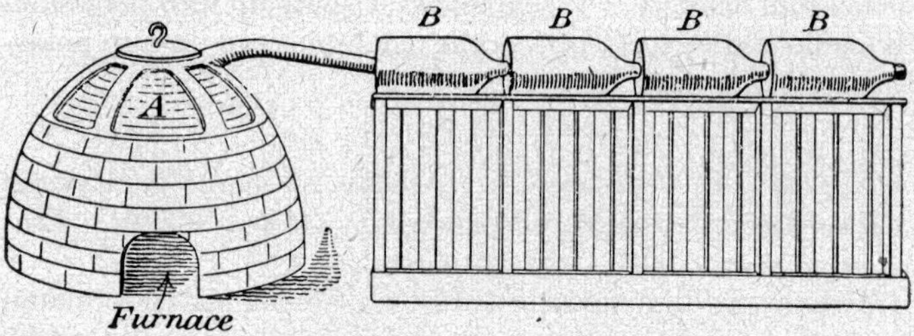

FIG. 62.—Manufacture of Iodine from Kelp.
A. Iron pot. *BB*. Udells.

The kelp consists of charcoal mixed with the iodides and other salts (sulphates, carbonates, chlorides, etc.) of sodium, potassium, and magnesium. It is stirred up with hot water in iron pots, and the insoluble matter allowed to settle. The clear solution is then run off and concentrated by evaporation. The sulphates and other salts, being less soluble, separate out, while the iodides remain in solution.

The concentrated solution of the iodides is mixed with manganese dioxide and concentrated sulphuric acid and heated in cast-iron pots. The iodine distils over and is collected in specially shaped condensers called *aludels* or *udells* (a word which comes to us from the Arab chemists; it should really be *al-athāl, al* meaning *the*). The equation for the reaction, as far as the *sodium* iodide is concerned (those for the potassium and magnesium iodides would be similar) is—

$$2NaI + MnO_2 + 3H_2SO_4 = 2NaHSO_4 + MnSO_4 + 2H_2O + I_2.$$

The iodine obtained in this way is washed, dried, and then purified by *sublimation, i.e.* by heating it and condensing the vapour, which is formed from, and passes back into, the solid state without going through the intermediate liquid state.

(ii) *Extraction from Chile Saltpetre or Caliche.*—The crude sodium nitrate is dissolved in water and the solution then concentrated by evaporation. Pure sodium nitrate crystallizes out while the sodium iodate is left in the solution or *mother-liquor.* The mother-liquor is run into wooden or lead-lined vats and mixed with a solution of *sodium bisulphite*, $NaHSO_3$, and *sodium sulphite*, Na_2SO_3, when the iodine comes down as a black precipitate—

$$2NaIO_3 + 2NaHSO_3 + 3Na_2SO_3 = 5Na_2SO_4 + H_2O + I_2 \downarrow.$$

The precipitated iodine is filtered off on filters made of coarse canvas, and is then pressed into cakes to get rid of the water. It is afterwards purified by sublimation.

Laboratory Preparation.—In the laboratory iodine is generally prepared by heating a mixture of potassium iodide and manganese dioxide with sulphuric acid, in a retort. Iodine sublimes over into the neck of the retort, whence it may be driven, by further heating, into a conical flask used as receiver.

$$2KI + MnO_2 + 3H_2SO_4 = 2KHSO_4 + MnSO_4 + 2H_2O + I_2.$$

Properties.—Iodine is a shiny black crystalline solid which sublimes if quickly heated, but if heated slowly melts at 116° to a black liquid. The liquid boils at 184°, forming a deep purple vapour. The vapour density of gaseous iodine at temperatures from just above 184° up to 600° is 127. Hence the molecular weight is 254. Therefore, since the atomic weight of iodine is 127, the molecules at this temperature must consist of 2 atoms, that is, they are *diatomic*—I_2. At 600°, the vapour density begins to get smaller, and continues to decrease on further heating, until at 1,600° it is only 63·5. Hence at 1,600° the molecular weight is 127, and the molecules must now be *monatomic*. At temperatures between 600° and 1,600°, the vapour density lies between 63·5 and 127, and the molecular weight thus lies between 127 and 254. These phenomena are explained by supposing that at 600° the diatomic molecules of iodine begin to *dissociate*, or to split up into simpler molecules—which in this case happen to consist of 1 atom only—

$$I_2 = I + I.$$

Above 1,600°, *all* the diatomic molecules have split up ; below 600°, *none* of them has split up ; between 600° and 1,600°, *some* of them have split up while others have not—the nearer the temperature is to 1,600° the greater the proportion of those which have done so. On cooling, the reverse changes take place, *i.e.* the monatomic molecules begin to join up together again to form the diatomic ones.

When the molecules of a substance split up into simpler ones on heating, and the simpler ones join together to form the original kind on cooling, the substance is said to **dissociate** *and the phenomenon is called* **dissociation.** Iodine vapour, then, *dissociates* on heating. Note that, for the change to be called "dissociation," it is essential that the simpler molecules should recombine on cooling. If they do not, then the change is *not* dissociation. Dissociation is therefore a type of *reversible reaction*, a fact which is indicated in the equation by the "reversed arrows" sign ; thus—

$$I_2 \rightleftharpoons I + I.$$

Other substances which dissociate on heating are—

Nitrogen peroxide (p. 278), $N_2O_4 \rightleftharpoons NO_2 + NO_2$.
Ammonium chloride (p. 267), $NH_4Cl \rightleftharpoons NH_3 + HCl$.
Hydriodic acid (p. 246), $2HI \rightleftharpoons H_2 + I_2 \rightleftharpoons H_2 + I + I$.
Phosphorus pentachloride (p. 284), $PCl_5 \rightleftharpoons PCl_3 + Cl_2$.

In each of these cases, the substances on the right-hand

side combine to form that on the left-hand side when the temperature is lowered. Contrast this with such an action as—

$$2KClO_3 = 2KCl + 3O_2.$$

This is an *irreversible* decomposition, and the potassium chloride and oxygen will not combine to form potassium chlorate again on cooling.

Iodine is only slightly soluble in water, but is much more soluble in liquids like benzene, chloroform, alcohol, and carbon disulphide. It will also dissolve readily in potassium iodide solution, forming a deep brownish-black liquid. In chemical behaviour, iodine is similar to the other halogens, but it is not so reactive. Still, a mixture of yellow phosphorus and iodine will take fire spontaneously, forming iodides of phosphorus. Iodine will also combine directly with many metals, forming the *iodides*, or salts of hydriodic acid, HI.

The most characteristic property of iodine is its reaction with starch. When iodine is added to starch "solution" a deep blue colour is produced. This reaction is so sensitive that 0·00001 gram of iodine in a litre of water may be detected by it. On heating, the blue colour disappears, but it comes back again on cooling. When the writer was a boy he mopped up some iodine solution with a handkerchief, which was thus naturally turned deep blue, owing to the starch in it. The washerwoman who washed the handkerchief got into a fearful state of mind, for it soon became white in hot water, but when she rinsed it out in cold water its gorgeous colour returned. Her remarks would not look well in print, particularly in a staid and sober text-book on chemistry.

The blue starch-iodine colour is permanently destroyed by addition of ammonia. The composition of the blue substance is unknown.

Hydriodic Acid, HI.

Like the other halogens, iodine will combine with hydrogen to form a colourless acid gas which in this case is *hydrogen iodide*, HI, or *hydriodic acid*. When a mixture of hydrogen and iodine vapour is heated, combination occurs, and hydriodic acid is formed. However, hydrogen iodide is a rather unstable substance, and easily splits up into hydrogen and iodine when it is heated. Hence the combination of hydrogen and iodine vapour can never be made complete by the action of heat: an equilibrium is set up, which can be indicated by the equation—

$$H_2 + I_2 \rightleftharpoons 2HI.$$

The proportion of hydrogen iodide in the equilibrium mixture varies with the temperature; thus at 448° it is 5 per cent.

Synthesis, then, is not a suitable method for preparing hydrogen iodide, which is more conveniently made by the action of water upon phosphorus iodide—

$$PI_3 + 3H_2O = H_3PO_3 + 3HI.$$

(Cf. action of water on phosphorus *trichloride* and *tribromide*. All these actions may be expressed by the equation—

$$P\begin{array}{l} \diagup X \quad\ \ H\,OH \\ - X + H\,OH \\ \diagdown X \quad\ \ H\,OH \end{array} = P\begin{array}{l} \diagup OH \quad\ \ HX \\ - OH + HX, \\ \diagdown OH \quad\ \ HX \end{array}$$

Phosphorous acid.

where $X = Cl$, Br or I.)

In practice, an apparatus similar to that employed for the preparation of hydrobromic acid (p. 238) is used. Water is placed in the tap-funnel, and a mixture of red phosphorus and iodine in the flask. On adding the water, drop by drop, hydriodic acid gas comes off. As iodine is not very volatile at ordinary temperatures, there is no necessity to have the U-tube on the delivery-tube.

The hydrogen iodide which comes off is collected by downward displacement. (*N.B.*—It *cannot* be collected over mercury, since it attacks it.)

An aqueous solution of hydriodic acid may be made by dissolving the gas in water, taking the usual precautions, since the gas is very soluble. It may also be made by passing hydrogen sulphide through iodine stirred up in water—

$$I_2 + H_2S = 2HI + S \downarrow.$$

(Cf. $Cl_2 + H_2S = 2HCl + S \downarrow$, and $Br_2 + H_2S = 2HBr + S \downarrow$.)

Hydriodic acid *cannot* be made by the action of concentrated sulphuric acid upon potassium iodide, since it is a reducing agent, and reduces the acid to sulphur, hydrogen sulphide and sulphur dioxide, being itself oxidized to iodine. Compare the action of concentrated sulphuric acid upon a bromide, p. 237.

Properties.—Hydriodic acid or hydrogen iodide is a colourless, heavy, acid gas, fuming in moist air, and readily soluble in water with which it gives a strongly acid solution. It can be condensed to a colourless liquid which boils at $-35{\cdot}5°$ and freezes at $-51°$ to a colourless crystalline solid.

In general chemical properties it closely resembles hydrochloric and hydrobromic acids. Unlike them, however, it is an *endothermic* substance, that is, when it is formed from its elements heat is *absorbed*, whereas when hydrogen and chlorine, or hydrogen and bromine, combine, heat is *evolved*, and hydrochloric and hydrobromic acids are therefore said to be *exothermic*. Moreover, hydriodic acid is a *powerful reducing agent*, since it readily gives up its hydrogen; hydrochloric acid, on the other hand, is not a reducing agent, and although hydrobromic acid may sometimes show reducing powers (see p. 237), yet it is not a reducing agent as a rule.

A solution of hydriodic acid in water is colourless when freshly prepared, but rapidly goes brown on exposure to air and light, owing to oxidation of the acid with liberation of iodine—

$$4HI + O_2 = 2H_2O + 2I_2.$$

The *iodides* are very similar to the chlorides and bromides. The most important is *potassium iodide*, KI. It is formed, together with *potassium iodate*, KIO_3, when iodine is dissolved in a hot concentrated solution of caustic potash—

$$3I_2 + 6KOH = 5KI + KIO_3 + 3H_2O.$$

(Cf. action of chlorine and bromine upon hot concentrated potash solution. See pp. 216 and 240.)

Potassium iodide and iodate are both white crystalline solids. The iodate when heated splits up, yielding potassium iodide and oxygen—

$$2KIO_3 = 2KI + 3O_2.$$

When solutions of silver nitrate and potassium iodide are mixed, a yellow curdy precipitate of silver iodide is thrown down—

$$KI + AgNO_3 = AgI \downarrow + KNO_3.$$

Summary and Comparison of the Properties of the Halogens

1. They are all non-metals.
2. They will all combine directly with metals, forming salts. Hence they are called *halogens* or salt-producers.
3. They all have diatomic molecules.
4. They are all univalent.
5. In the gaseous state they all have pungent smells.
6. They will all combine directly with hydrogen, forming colourless, heavy, fuming, acid gases of the formula HX where X = Cl, Br, I.
7. They are all *electro-negative*, *i.e.* they appear at the *anode* in electrolysis.
8. The similarity extends to (*a*) their methods of preparation, and (*b*) their compounds. For details, refer to appropriate sections above.
9. They will all react with hot concentrated caustic alkali solutions according to the equation—

$$3X_2 + 6KOH = 5KX + KXO_3 + 3H_2O [X = Cl, Br, \text{ or } I].$$

10. The salts of the type KXO_3 will all decompose on heating, yielding oxygen and the salt KX.

[The student should expand this list of comparisons by the introduction of suitable details.]

Use of Silver Chloride and Bromide in Photography

Silver chloride, AgCl, and silver bromide, AgBr, are peculiar compounds in that they are sensitive to light, which partially decomposes them. The effect produced upon them by a long exposure to light is obvious, since they go dark in colour, but even an exposure of a fraction of a second produces a distinct effect. Although this change is not visible to the naked eye, it can be rendered so by the process of *development*. If an image is thrown, by means of a lens, upon a film of silver bromide, the latter is partially *reduced to metallic silver* in those parts of the film upon which light falls. How much reduction occurs depends upon the intensity of the light and upon the length of exposure. If the film is now covered with a solution of a suitable reducing agent—the "developer"—such as "pyrogallic acid" or *pyrogallol*, further reduction occurs, but most quickly in those parts where the reduction has been already started by the light. The image is thus "developed," but it is a *negative* image, since those parts which were most fully illuminated, during the exposure, will have most silver deposited on them, and will therefore be blackest on development. When the image has been sufficiently developed, the unchanged silver bromide is dissolved out in a solution of sodium thiosulphate ("*hypo*"), and the image is thus fixed, since, of course, the metallic silver is not affected by light. *Positive* images can then be obtained by "printing off" the negative on paper covered with a film of silver chloride, and fixing as before.

In making a photographic plate the silver bromide is precipitated, in the form of grains, in a solution of gelatine, which serves the double purpose of holding the silver bromide and of making it more sensitive to light. The longer the gelatine is kept in the liquid state the larger become the granules of silver bromide, and the greater the sensitiveness of the plate to light. This process is called *ripening*. After it is complete, the gelatine containing the silver bromide is spread evenly over the plate and allowed to set.

The plate prepared in this way is most sensitive to the violet and blue rays of ordinary white light, but it may be made more sensitive to rays of other colours by staining the gelatine with various dyes.

Printing-out papers are covered with a film of gelatine containing a mixture of silver chloride with another silver salt called silver citrate [a salt of *citric acid*, the characteristic acid of lemon-juice]. The silver citrate increases the sensitiveness to light of the silver chloride. After the print has attained to a rather deeper shade than that required for the finished photograph, it is *toned* by means of a solution of "gold chloride," the action of which is to replace part of the silver in the print by gold, which gives a better colour. *Gaslight* papers are similar in nature to printing-out papers (except that silver bromide is used instead of silver chloride), but they are exposed for only a short time and the image is then developed as for a plate. It may be toned by means of a solution of sodium sulphide (Na_2S), which converts the silver into silver sulphide (Ag_2S).

Questions and Exercises

1. Write the names and symbols of those members of the halogen family which you have studied in this chapter.

2. What does the name "halogen" mean? Why was it given to these elements?

3. How would you prepare a jar full of dry chlorine?

4. What are the chief properties of chlorine?

5. Write equations for the following actions:

   (i) Hydrochloric acid upon potassium permanganate.
   (ii) ,, ,, ,, manganese dioxide.
   (iii) Hydrogen sulphide upon chlorine.
   (iv) Sulphur dioxide upon bromine water.
   (v) ,, ,, ,, chlorine water.

6. Under what conditions does chlorine bleach? How is the bleaching action explained?

7. What is bleaching-powder? How is it made? Write equations to show the action of dilute acids upon it.

8. Why does bleaching-powder always smell of chlorine?

9. Why does turpentine burn in chlorine?

10. Describe the chemical and physical properties of hydrogen chloride.

11. Upon what evidence is the formula HCl assigned to hydrochloric acid ?

12. How would you prepare (*a*) chlorine and (*b*) hydrochloric acid, starting from common salt ?

13. What volume of chlorine, measured at 16° C. 765 mm., is contained in 10 grams of hydrochloric acid gas ?

14. Complete the following equations—

$$\text{(i) } MnO_2 + 4HCl =$$
$$\text{(ii) } 2KCl + MnO_2 + 3H_2SO_4 =$$
$$\text{(iii) } 3Br_2 + 6KOH =$$

15. Mention four physical and four chemical properties of chlorine.

16. Write equations for the action of hydrochloric acid upon (*a*) zinc, (*b*) magnesium, (*c*) iron, (*d*) slaked lime, (*e*) aluminium, (*f*) caustic soda.

17. What are salts of hydrochloric acid called ? How may they be prepared ? (Give as many different methods as you can.)

18. How is bromine obtained commercially ?

19. How is bromine obtained in the laboratory ? Draw the apparatus.

20. Why cannot hydrobromic acid be prepared in the same kind of way as hydrochloric acid ?

21. Describe the laboratory method for the preparation of hydrobromic acid.

22. What is the action of chlorine upon a solution of (*a*) potassium bromide, (*b*) potassium iodide, (*c*) calcium hydroxide ?

23. In the preparation of hydrogen bromide, what weight of phosphorus would be needed to yield 11·2 litres of the gas at N.T.P. ?

24. From what sources is iodine obtained ?

25. How is iodine obtained commercially ?

26. How is iodine obtained in the laboratory ?

27. What do you mean by *sublimation* ?

28. What is *dissociation* ? Illustrate your answer by giving an example.

29. Describe a method for obtaining a solution of hydriodic acid.

30. Compare the action of sulphuric acid upon a chloride with its action upon (*a*) an iodide, (*b*) a bromide.

31. Explain the uses of silver chloride and bromide in photography.

32. What weight of silver chloride could be obtained by adding excess of silver nitrate to 50 c.c. of common salt solution containing 33 grams of sodium chloride per litre ?

33. How would you test for the presence of free iodine ?

34. From 12 tons of sodium chloride what weight of sodium bisulphate and what volume of hydrochloric acid gas (measured at 18° C. 750 mm.) could be obtained ? (1,000 kilograms = 0·9842 tons.)

35. How many grams of hydrochloric acid gas could be obtained from 25 grams of potassium chloride, KCl ?

36. Explain, by giving a comparison of their properties and those of their compounds, why the elements, chlorine, bromine and iodine, are classified together.

37. Describe Deacon's process for the preparation of chlorine.

38. Describe an electrical method for the preparation of chlorine.

39. Write a short account of chlorine as an oxidizing agent.

40. Write the formulæ for (*a*) hypochlorous acid, (*b*) phosphorous acid, (*c*) aluminium bromide, (*d*) potassium iodate, (*e*) phosphorus trichloride.

41. How could you distinguish between nitrogen peroxide and bromine vapour ?

42. Make a table to show the principal ways in which chlorine, bromine and iodine differ from one another.

CHAPTER XVI

NITROGEN AND PHOSPHORUS

Nitrogen

Symbol: N; *Valency:* 3 or 5; *Atomicity:* 2; *Atomic Weight:* 14.

The gas we call nitrogen the French call *azote*, because nothing can live in it. The word *nitrogen* means "nitre-producer," and this name was given to the gas because it is a constituent of nitre (saltpetre or potassium nitrate, KNO_3). Nitrogen was discovered in 1772 by Daniel Rutherford, Professor of Botany at Edinburgh University.

Occurrence.—In the uncombined state, nitrogen forms about 79 per cent. by volume and 77 per cent. by weight of the air. It is found combined in large quantities as sodium nitrate or *Chile saltpetre* ("caliche"), $NaNO_3$, and is widely distributed in smaller quantity in the soil as salts of ammonium (*e.g.* ammonium sulphate, $(NH_4)_2SO_4$), and as nitrates of sodium ($NaNO_3$), potassium (KNO_3), and calcium ($Ca(NO_3)_2$). Nitrogen is always found in the living matter of animals and plants.

Preparation.—(i) Nitrogen can be obtained from the air by extracting from the latter the water-vapour, carbon dioxide and oxygen it contains. For this purpose, the air is passed (*a*) through caustic soda solution, to remove carbon dioxide; (*b*) through tubes containing calcium chloride or pumice soaked in sulphuric acid, to remove the water; and (*c*) through a tube containing red-hot copper, which removes the oxygen (Fig. 63). The residual nitrogen may then be collected over mercury. If it is not required dry, the calcium

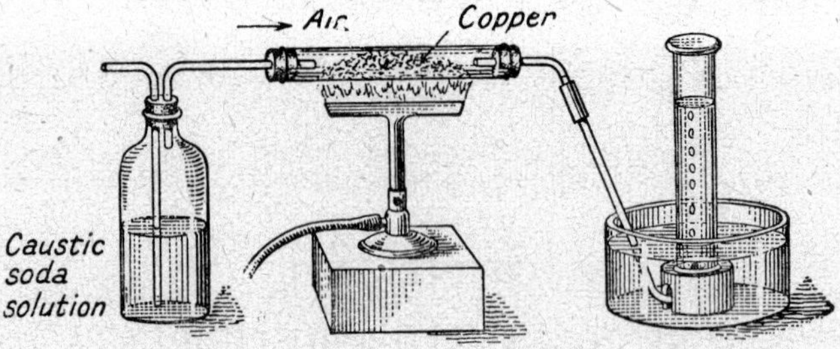

FIG. 63.—Apparatus to obtain Nitrogen from the Air.

chloride tubes may be omitted, and the nitrogen can then be collected over water (Fig. 63).

(ii) Another convenient way of getting nitrogen from the air is to shake the latter up with a solution of caustic soda and pyrogallol (the photographer's "pyro"). This absorbs both

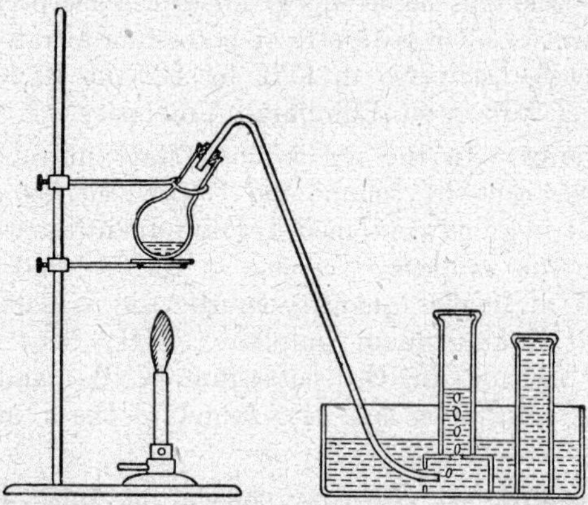

FIG. 64.—Preparation of Nitrogen from Ammonium Nitrite.

the carbon dioxide and the oxygen, turning dark brown during the reaction.

(iii) In the laboratory nitrogen is usually prepared by heating a solution of ammonium nitrite (NOT ammonium nitrate)—

$$NH_4NO_2 = N_2 + 2H_2O.$$

A suitable apparatus is shown in Fig. 64.

As, however, ammonium nitrite is an unstable compound it is never put on the market in the solid state, and even in solution is but rarely met with. It is better to use a mixture of equimolecular proportions of ammonium chloride and sodium nitrite, which in solution react to give ammonium nitrite and sodium chloride—

$$NH_4Cl + NaNO_2 \rightleftharpoons NaCl + NH_4NO_2.$$

The ammonium nitrite then splits up, when heated, according to the equation given above.

(iv) Sometimes nitrogen is prepared by passing chlorine into a concentrated solution of ammonia—

$$8NH_3 + 3Cl_2 = 6NH_4Cl + N_2.$$

The chlorine removes hydrogen from some of the ammonia, forming hydrochloric acid and nitrogen; the hydrochloric acid then combines with excess of ammonia to form ammonium chloride. Care must be taken not to pass the chlorine for too long a time, or the highly explosive nitrogen trichloride, NCl_3, will be formed. This is an extremely dangerous substance. It was discovered by DULONG (of "Dulong and Petit's Law") and rewarded him by exploding and blowing off one of his fingers and blinding him in one eye.

Properties.—Nitrogen is a colourless, odourless gas. It will not burn nor support combustion. It is very slightly soluble in water, less so than oxygen. It boils at − 194° and the liquid nitrogen freezes to a white solid at − 214°. Under ordinary conditions nitrogen behaves as a rather inert element, but of recent years much work has been done on the combination of nitrogen with other elements and the necessary conditions have been discovered. The compounds of nitrogen are very numerous, interesting, and important. Explosives, dyes, drugs, and artificial manures are mostly nitrogenous compounds, and nitrogen compounds are necessary to the life of plants and animals.

Nitrogen will combine directly with many metals, on heating, forming *nitrides*, *e.g.*—

$$3Mg + N_2 = Mg_3N_2, \text{ magnesium nitride.}$$

When magnesium nitride is acted upon by water, ammonia is liberated—

$$Mg_3N_2 + 6H_2O = \underset{\text{Magnesium hydroxide.}}{3Mg(OH)_2} + \underset{\text{Ammonia.}}{2NH_3}.$$

This may be detected by addition of Nessler's solution (p. 262), which with ammonia gives a brown precipitate or yellowish brown coloration.

When nitrogen and hydrogen, or nitrogen and oxygen, are sparked together for some time, *a little* combination occurs, and small quantities of ammonia in the first case and oxides of nitrogen in the second are formed. We shall see later that these reactions are of considerable importance to the price of food (p. 271).

COMPOUNDS OF NITROGEN.

Ammonia, NH_3.

In the form of its compound with hydrochloric acid, *ammonium chloride*, NH_4Cl, ammonia has been known for over 2,000 years. This salt occurs naturally in Armenia and other parts of Asia, and appears to have been called originally *sal armeniac* (" Armenian salt "). The early chemists, however, mixed it up with the natural sodium carbonate or *natron* found in the Libyan desert near a famous temple of the god JUPITER AMMON, and the name was changed in course of time into *sal ammoniac* through this mistake. Owing to the fact that ammonium chloride sublimes when heated, flying up to the cooler parts of the apparatus, the alchemists called it " the White Eagle."

PRIESTLEY was the first to collect ammonia gas (1774). He made it by heating a mixture of lime and sal ammoniac, and collected the gas over mercury. He called it *alkaline air*.

Ammonia occurs in the soil in small quantities, and in larger quantities, as ammonium sulphate $(NH_4)_2SO_4$, in the *soffioni* or *fumaroles* of Tuscany. It is obtained by the destructive distillation of many organic materials, such as horns, hoofs, bones, and coal. The old name for an aqueous solution of ammonia, *spirit of hartshorn*, indicates the method of preparation.

Preparation.—Ammonia is prepared in the laboratory by Priestley's method. A mixture of ammonium chloride and slaked lime, with a little water, is placed in a round-bottomed flask and heated. Ammonia comes off at once and calcium chloride is left—

$$Ca(OH)_2 + 2NH_4Cl = CaCl_2 + 2NH_3 + 2H_2O.$$

As ammonia is very soluble in water, but has a low vapour density $\left(\frac{17}{2} = 8{\cdot}5\right)$, it is collected by upward displacement. It may also be collected over mercury. It cannot be dried by means of sulphuric acid, phosphorus pentoxide, or calcium chloride, as it combines with these substances; it is therefore dried by passing through a glass "tower" containing lumps of quicklime. You should make a special note of this, as it is a hoary old examination trap.

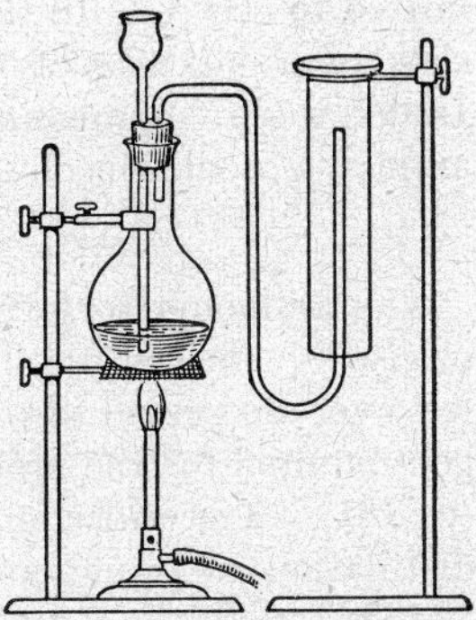

FIG. 65.—Preparation of Ammonia.

Commercial Preparation.—Ammonia is obtained commercially as a by-product in the manufacture of coal-gas (p. 317). Coal contains about 1·5 per cent. of nitrogen, and much of this is obtained in the form of ammonia when coal is heated in the absence of air. On passing the gases through water the ammonia dissolves, giving the so-called *ammoniacal liquor*. About 5 lb. of ammonia are obtained from every ton of coal. The ammoniacal liquor is heated with lime, when all the ammonia is driven off. It is collected in dilute sulphuric acid, and the solution of *ammonium sulphate* so obtained is evaporated to the point of crystallization—

$$2NH_3 + H_2SO_4 = (NH_4)_2SO_4.$$

The product is an impure ammonium sulphate ("sulphate of ammonia"); it is largely used as an artificial manure. Ammonia may be liberated from it, if desired, by heating with lime—

$$(NH_4)_2SO_4 + CaO = CaSO_4 + H_2O + 2NH_3.$$

If the gas is then passed into water, ammonia solution is obtained.

At the present day ammonia is mainly obtained *synthetically*, *i.e.* by direct combination of nitrogen and hydrogen. The process is known as HABER'S process. A mixture of pure nitrogen and hydrogen in the proper proportions is compressed to about 200 atmospheres and passed through tubes heated to 500° C. In the tube is placed a *catalyst*, which consists of a mixture of finely-divided iron and molybdenum. Under these circumstances a yield of about 30 per cent. of ammonia is obtained—

$$N_2 + 3H_2 \rightleftharpoons 2NH_3.$$

The ammonia so formed is cooled and dissolved in water or else liquefied, while the uncombined nitrogen and hydrogen left over are passed through the apparatus again. The hydrogen required for the process is obtained by the Bosch method (p. 161). The nitrogen is obtained partly by the fractional distillation of liquid air, but chiefly from "producer-gas." This is a mixture of carbon monoxide and nitrogen made by blowing air through red-hot coke. The nitrogen is freed from the carbon monoxide by the same method as is used to free the hydrogen from the latter in the Bosch method.

The Haber process is very successful, and as nitric acid may be obtained by the oxidation of ammonia, the supply of nitrates necessary for manures (see p. 271) is assured, even when the Chile saltpetre beds are exhausted—especially since nitric acid is nowadays obtained also from the air by another method (p. 271).

Joseph Priestley: The Leeds Portrait (c. 1763).

[*Reproduced by kind permission of the Royal Society.*]

Properties.—Ammonia is a colourless gas with a pungent smell. It is lighter than air, and therefore may be collected by upward displacement; it is extremely soluble in water, and therefore cannot be collected at the pneumatic trough except over mercury. Ammonia can easily be liquefied, as was first shown by FARADAY. Liquid ammonia is a colourless liquid boiling at − 33·5° and solidifying to a colourless crystalline solid at − 78°. It is used in commerce for *refrigerating* or ice-

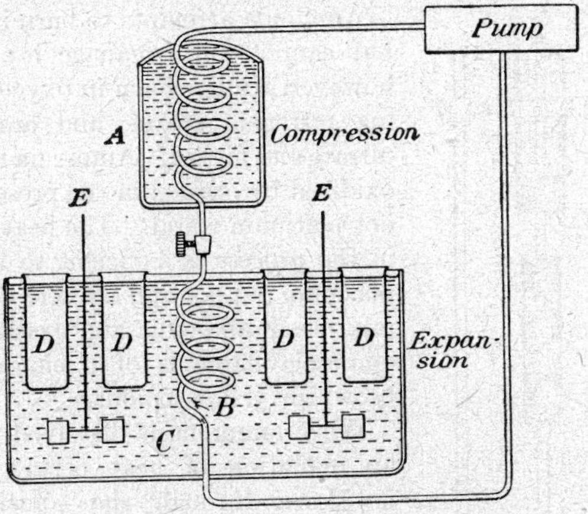

FIG. 66.—Ammonia Ice-making Machine.

A. The compressed ammonia is cooled in *A* (through which cold water circulates) and liquefies. *B*. In coil *B* the liquid ammonia is under reduced pressure and evaporates rapidly, the gas passing back to the pump whence it passes to *A* again, and so on. *C*. Vessel containing calcium chloride solution which does not freeze. *D, D*. Vessels containing water which is frozen. *E, E*. Stirrers.

making, since by rapidly evaporating it low temperatures are produced; the gaseous ammonia may then be liquefied again by passing it through a condenser surrounded by cold water and compressing it. (Fig. 66.) Household refrigerators work on the same principle, though the gas used is more often sulphur dioxide than ammonia.

Ammonia is not a base, since it combines directly with acids to form salts *without elimination of water*; it is, in fact, the *anhydride* of a base, the true base being *ammonium hydroxide*, NH_4OH, which is formed when ammonia is dissolved in water. The following equations illustrate the point—

$$NH_3 + HCl = NH_4Cl$$

basic anhydride + acid = salt *but no water.*

$$NH_4OH + HCl = NH_4Cl + H_2O$$

base + acid = salt + *water.*

Dry ammonia therefore has no action on litmus; moist ammonia turns red litmus blue.

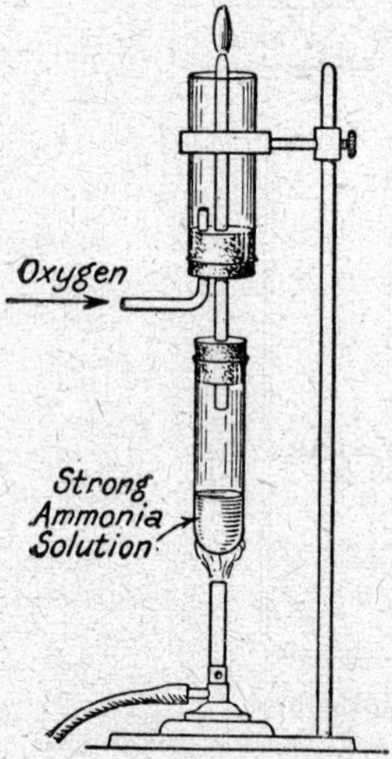

FIG. 67.—Ammonia burning in Oxygen.

Ammonia attempts to burn in the air but cannot quite manage it; it will, however, readily burn in oxygen, forming nitrogen, steam, and ammonium nitrate and nitrite. Ammonia is readily oxidized by oxygen in the presence of a hot platinum spiral. The heat evolved in the process is sufficient to keep the platinum red-hot and often to ignite the mixture of ammonia and oxygen. The ammonia flame is of a characteristic brownish yellow colour.

When ammonia is dissolved in water an evolution of heat occurs. If air is blown through the solution, the ammonia is rapidly driven off and heat is therefore absorbed. This reaction was at one time made use of in ice-making (CARRÉ'S process, now superseded by that previously described). The aqueous solution of ammonia contains ammonia and also ammonium hydroxide, NH_4OH. It forms a convenient source from which to obtain ammonia gas in the laboratory.

TESTS FOR AMMONIA.

(*a*) Smell. (*b*) Turns red litmus blue (when moist). (*c*) In solution gives a deep blue colour with copper sulphate solution. (*d*) Gives a brown ppt. or yellow coloration with NESSLER'S solution. To make Nessler's solution take some mercuric chloride solution and add potassium iodide solution until the first-formed ppt. of mercuric iodide is just re-dissolved. The solution now contains a peculiar compound called *potassium mercuri-iodide*, K_2HgI_4.

$$\text{(i)} \quad 2KI + HgCl_2 = 2KCl + HgI_2 \downarrow .$$
$$\text{(ii)} \quad HgI_2 + 2KI = K_2HgI_4.$$

Nessler's solution is a solution of potassium mercuri-iodide to which caustic soda has been added. It is used as a test for traces of ammonia and ammonium salts. The brown precipitate which it gives with these compounds is NHg_2I.

Under suitable conditions, Nessler's solution will detect 1 part of ammonia in 2,000,000 of water.

Composition of Ammonia.

(i) The vapour density of ammonia is 8·5, hence the M.W. is 17. As the atomic weight of nitrogen is 14, there clearly cannot be more than 1 atom of it in the molecule of ammonia.

Hence formula for ammonia is NH_3.

(ii) A measured volume of ammonia is placed in a eudiometer tube over mercury and sparked until no further change in volume occurs. The gas is now practically completely (98 per cent.) decomposed into nitrogen and hydrogen. The volume is noted, and a measured excess of oxygen introduced and a spark passed. Explosion occurs, all the hydrogen present being converted into steam, which condenses to liquid water, the volume of which is negligible compared with the volumes of the gases in the experiment. After cooling, the residual volume is noted. From the results, the formula for ammonia may be calculated. *Example*—

Volume of ammonia taken = 15 c.c.
Volume of mixture of nitrogen and hydrogen formed = 30 c.c.
Volume after addition of oxygen = 58 c.c.
Volume after explosion = 24·25 c.c.
∴ Contraction on explosion = 33·75 c.c.
Of this, $\frac{2}{3}$ will be hydrogen, since 2 volumes of hydrogen combine with 1 vol. of oxygen to form water,

i.e. 22·5 c.c.

But volume of nitrogen + hydrogen = 30 c.c.

∴ Volume of nitrogen = 30 − 22·5 = 7·5 c.c.

∴ 15 c.c. of ammonia yield 7·5 c.c. nitrogen and 22·5 c.c. hydrogen.

∴ 2 volumes " " 1 volume " " 3 vols. "

∴ by Avogadro, 2 molecules of ammonia yield 1 molecule nitrogen and 3 molecules hydrogen.

∴ 2 molecules of ammonia consist of 2 atoms of nitrogen and 6 of hydrogen.

∴ 1 molecule of ammonia contains 1 atom of nitrogen and 3 of hydrogen, and the formula is NH_3.

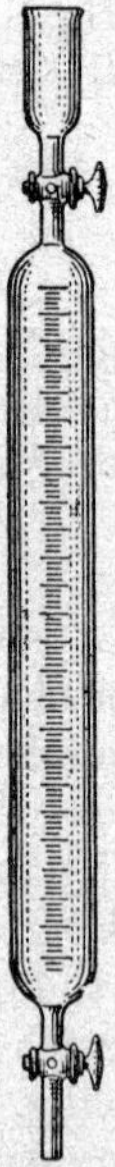

FIG. 68.—Hofmann's Apparatus.

(iii) HOFMANN'S METHOD.—A long tube (Fig. 68), fitted at each end with a tap and with a funnel attached at one end, is filled with chlorine. In the funnel is placed concentrated ammonia solution. When this enters the tube drop by drop, vigorous reaction occurs and the tube becomes filled with white fumes of ammonium chloride. After the reaction is complete the top tap is turned off, and the tube is placed in a pneumatic trough containing water. The bottom tap is then opened, when water rushes in, and, after levelling, the residual gas is found to occupy one-third of the volume of the original chlorine. This residual gas proves to be nitrogen. The hydrogen which was combined with this nitrogen in ammonia has been removed by the chlorine; now chlorine combines with its own volume of hydrogen, therefore the volume of hydrogen which was combined with the residual nitrogen is three times the volume of the latter. In other words, the ammonia consists of nitrogen and hydrogen in the proportions by volume of 1 to 3. Hence, by Avogadro's Hypothesis, the molecule of ammonia must be $(NH_3)x$; that is, the *empirical* formula of ammonia is NH_3. The *true* formula cannot be determined by Hofmann's method, which is therefore not so good as that given in (ii).

x may of course be found by a V.D. determination.

Ammonium.—The group of atoms NH_4 behaves in many respects like an atom of an alkali metal such as sodium or potassium. The following table shows certain of the resemblances.

Compound.	Ammonium.	Sodium.
Chloride	NH_4Cl	$NaCl$
Nitrate	NH_4NO_3	$NaNO_3$
Sulphate . . .	$(NH_4)_2SO_4$	Na_2SO_4
Hydroxide . . .	NH_4OH	$NaOH$
Carbonate . . .	$(NH_4)_2CO_3$	Na_2CO_3

The salts of the NH_4 group are very similar in appearance and properties to those of sodium, and for this reason the name *ammonium* was given to this group of atoms or *radical*, to indicate its apparent *metallic* nature (Latin names of *metals* end in *-ium* or *-um*). The ammonium group is univalent, since the nitrogen atom in it is quinquevalent, and only four of these valencies are used to attach hydrogen atoms—

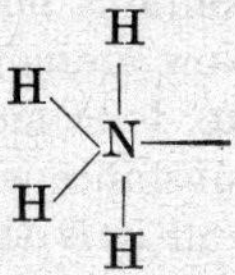

It is therefore capable of combining directly with a univalent acid radical (*e.g.* $-NO_3$ or $-Cl$) or of replacing an atom of sodium, potassium, or other univalent metal, in a compound. Although ammonia is well known, no one up to the present has succeeded in isolating ammon*ium*; it was at one time supposed that if it could be isolated it would present a metallic form. If a concentrated solution of ammonium chloride is poured over some sodium amalgam, the latter swells up and forms a peculiar mass called *ammonium amalgam*, which was considered to be an amalgam of mercury with ammonium, NH_4. On standing, the substance loses ammonia and hydrogen, and mercury is left. The question whether ammonium amalgam is really what it professes to be or not is still unsolved; there is evidence both ways. It would be very interesting if "ammonium" itself were isolated and proved to have metallic properties.

Ammonium Salts.

Ammonium hydroxide, NH_4OH, is formed when ammonia is dissolved in water—

$$NH_3 + H_2O \rightleftharpoons NH_4OH.$$

It is very unstable, and when gently heated splits up into ammonia and water, as shown by the reversed arrows in the equation. Even at ordinary temperatures a solution of it contains much free ammonia, as can easily be appreciated by smelling the liquid. Not until 1909 was ammonium hydroxide obtained pure; it is a white crystalline solid at low temperatures.

A solution of ammonium hydroxide often has two incorrect names applied to it. The first is "liquid ammonia," applied to it by apothecaries and druggists. This is obviously wrong, for liquid ammonia *is* liquid ammonia, *i.e.* the liquid obtained by cooling and compressing gaseous ammonia until it turns to a liquid. It contains no water. The second is "ammonium hydrate." Now ammonium hydrate would be the NH_4 group attached to 1 or more molecules of water, *i.e.* $NH_4.xH_2O$. No such substance is known. If ammonium hydroxide is a hydrate at all it is the hydrate of *ammonia*, *viz.* $NH_3.H_2O$. You must be careful over these points of nomenclature, and must not follow the names applied to substances by manufacturers and other people. In this connection notice that it is quite incorrect (for reasons similar to that given above) to call caustic soda and potash sodium *hydrate* and potassium *hydrate*: they are *not* the hydrates, but the *hydroxides* of these metals.

When ammonium hydroxide solution is added to solutions of salts of the heavy metals, the hydroxide of the metal is usually precipitated—

$$Al_2(SO_4)_3 + 6NH_4OH = 2Al(OH)_3 \downarrow + 3(NH_4)_2SO_4.$$
$$ZnCl_2 + 2NH_4OH = Zn(OH)_2 \downarrow + 2NH_4Cl.$$
$$FeCl_3 + 3NH_4OH = Fe(OH)_3 \downarrow + 3NH_4Cl.$$
$$CuSO_4 + 2NH_4OH = Cu(OH)_2 \downarrow + (NH_4)_2SO_4.$$

The pale-blue copper hydroxide readily dissolves in excess of ammonium hydroxide, forming a deep-blue solution. This reaction is used as a test for copper.

Ammonium chloride, NH_4Cl, is commonly known as *sal-ammoniac.* It is formed when ammonia and hydrogen chloride are allowed to come into contact; clouds of ammonium chloride are produced which quickly settle on the walls of the vessel—

$$NH_3 + HCl = NH_4Cl.$$

Commercially it is made by boiling ammonium sulphate with sodium chloride in aqueous solution—

$$(NH_4)_2SO_4 + 2NaCl \rightleftharpoons Na_2SO_4 + 2NH_4Cl.$$

On concentrating the solution the sodium sulphate crystallizes out first and may be removed; the solution of ammonium chloride may then be evaporated.

When ammonium chloride is heated, it passes from the solid state direct into that of gas or vapour, without going through the intermediate liquid stage. In other words, its boiling-point is *below* its melting-point, whereas in most cases the boiling-point of a substance is of course *above* the melting-point. When ammonium chloride vapour is cooled, it passes back directly to the solid again. This phenomenon, *solid* $\rightleftharpoons$ *gas,* is called *sublimation.* Ammonium chloride, then, sublimes when heated—not, as a boy once said, "I heated ammonium chloride *and it was sublime*!"

Ammonium chloride vapour is interesting because its vapour density is only half what we should expect it to be. The formula is NH_4Cl, $\therefore$ M.W. $= (14 + 4 + 35{\cdot}5) = 53{\cdot}5$; hence V.D. ought to be $\frac{53{\cdot}5}{2} = 26{\cdot}75$. As a matter of experimental fact, the V.D. is found to be 13·37. This strange phenomenon is explained by supposing that the ammonium chloride vapour has split up into ammonia and hydrochloric acid gas—

$$NH_4Cl \rightleftharpoons NH_3 + HCl,$$

in which case, of course, the V.D. of the vapour would be

half-way between those of ammonia (8·5) and hydrochloric acid (18·25), *i.e.* $\frac{8{\cdot}5 + 18{\cdot}25}{2} = 13{\cdot}37$, the figure actually found.

Substances, like ammonium chloride, the molecules of which on heating split up into simpler molecules, which recombine on cooling, are said to **dissociate,** and the phenomenon is called **dissociation.**

Dissociation is a *reversible* action and thus differs from *decomposition,* which is not reversible.

Ammonium chloride is used in soldering, as a "flux," because the hydrochloric acid which is set free on heating cleans the surface of the metal and thus enables the solder to "bite." It is also used in the manufacture of dyes and in calico-printing, and, of course, in the laboratory it is used as a source of ammonia.

Ammonium sulphate, $(NH_4)_2SO_4$, is obtained from ammonia prepared by the Haber process (p. 258) and from ammoniacal liquor (p. 257). It is a white crystalline solid very largely used as an artificial manure. It is decomposed on heating, one of the products being ammonia.

Ammonium nitrate, NH_4NO_3, is a white deliquescent crystalline solid, very soluble in water, the process of solution being accompanied by absorption of heat; it was therefore formerly used in refrigeration on a small scale, *e.g.* preparation of ice-cream. It is prepared by passing ammonia into fairly concentrated nitric acid. If heated, it splits up into nitrous oxide, N_2O, and water—

$$NH_4NO_3 = N_2O + 2H_2O.$$

This decomposition occasionally becomes very violent and an explosion may result. A mixture of ammonium nitrate and aluminium powder is called "ammonal," and was one of the explosives used in the Mills' bombs during the war of 1914–18. Ammonium nitrate explosives are usually fairly safe to handle.

Ammonium carbonate is made commercially by heating ammonium sulphate with powdered limestone; the sublimate obtained is a complex substance, containing but little of the normal carbonate, $(NH_4)_2CO_3$. It is a white crystalline solid, which smells of ammonia, and is used for filling "smelling-bottles."

All ammonium salts yield ammonia when heated with caustic soda, caustic potash, or lime.

Nitric Acid, HNO_3.

Nitric acid has been known from very remote times, but not until the work of LAVOISIER and CAVENDISH in the eighteenth century was its composition discovered. The old name for nitric acid is *aqua fortis* ("strong water"), and was given to it on account of its strong corrosive action upon metals and other substances. A mixture of nitric acid with concentrated hydrochloric acid is sometimes known as *aqua regia* ("royal water"), because it will dissolve the "noble" metal gold.

Preparation.—Nitric acid is prepared in the laboratory, and also commercially, by heating potassium or sodium nitrate with concentrated sulphuric acid (Fig. 69)—

$$\text{(i)}\ KNO_3 + H_2SO_4 = KHSO_4 + HNO_3,$$

and, on further heating,

$$\text{(ii)}\ KHSO_4 + KNO_3 = K_2SO_4 + HNO_3.$$

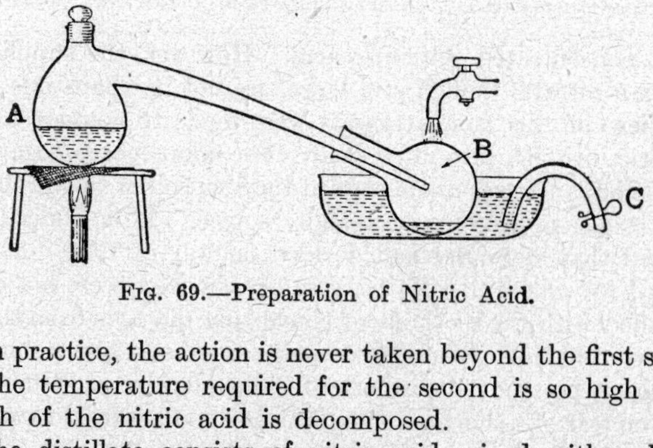

FIG. 69.—Preparation of Nitric Acid.

In practice, the action is never taken beyond the first stage as the temperature required for the second is so high that much of the nitric acid is decomposed.

The distillate consists of nitric acid mixed with a little

water, which may be removed by addition of concentrated sulphuric acid followed by redistillation. The acid so obtained is of a yellow colour; this is due to the presence in it of the yellow gas nitrogen peroxide. If a current of dry air or dry carbon dioxide is blown through the acid the nitrogen peroxide is swept away and the resulting acid is colourless.

Manufacture.—Much nitric acid is made, as already described, by heating sodium nitrate (caliche or Chile saltpetre)

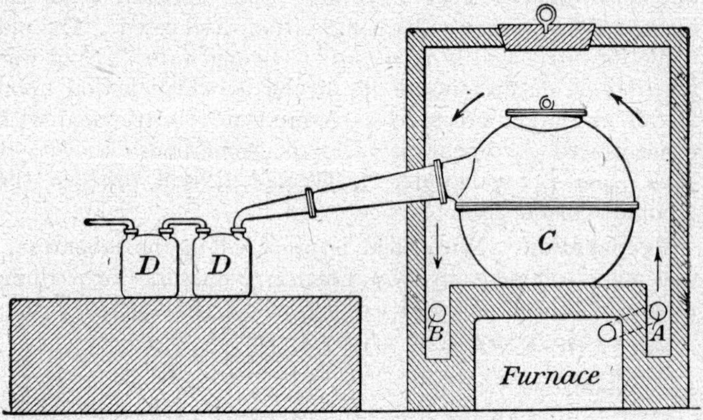

FIG. 70.—Manufacture of Nitric Acid.

A. Entrance for furnace gases. *B.* Exit for furnace gases. *C.* Iron retort. *D.* Receivers.

with concentrated sulphuric acid. However, the supplies of Chilean nitrate, though still large, are not inexhaustible, and in view of this fact, attempts were made to convert atmospheric nitrogen into nitric acid. For many years no appreciable advance was made toward the solution of this problem, but it has now been successfully solved. It is, indeed, reported that Germany had decided on war in 1913, but was forced to wait until 1914 because her chemists were not quite satisfied with the methods of converting nitrogen from the air into nitric acid. When these methods were at last perfected, Germany became independent of Chile saltpetre, and therefore had no fear of a shortage of explosives, or of artificial manures.

The exhaustion of the Chile beds, which cannot be indefinitely delayed, was a matter of grave concern to the world at large, for this reason: Ordinary unmanured soil gives a yield of about 18 bushels per acre when planted with wheat. If the soil is manured with sodium nitrate, the yield is increased to about 36–38 bushels per acre. Taking the world's supply of food as a whole, it is found that *there would not be enough to go round except for the increased crop obtained by manuring with nitrates.*

There was, therefore, an immediate necessity to obtain supplies of nitric acid and nitrates from other sources. The only source which is at all suitable is the atmosphere, where two of the constituents of nitric acid, namely, oxygen and nitrogen, occur in unlimited quantities.

After the serious nature of the problem was pointed out by SIR WILLIAM CROOKES in 1898, chemists set to work to discover methods of converting atmospheric nitrogen into nitric acid and nitrates, a process which is known as the *fixation of nitrogen.* Success was finally achieved, as mentioned above, and our wheat supply is no longer likely to suffer through shortage of nitrogenous manures.

FIXATION OF NITROGEN.—(i) In BIRKELAND and EYDE'S process air is passed through an electric arc drawn out to a thin disc of flame, some 6–8 feet in diameter, by means of a powerful electro-magnet. The issuing gas contains oxides of nitrogen (about 2 per cent.) and is passed into water, where nitric acid is formed. This is usually mixed with excess of lime and so converted into a basic calcium nitrate (*air-saltpetre* or *Norwegian saltpetre*—because it is made chiefly in Norway), which is used as a manure in place of sodium nitrate.

(ii) Another process consists in the oxidation of synthetic ammonia (see p. 258). A mixture of carefully purified air and ammonia is passed over platinum (or some other suitable catalyst) at about 500–550° C., when the ammonia is oxidized to nitric oxide, NO:

$$4NH_3 + 5O_2 = 4NO + 6H_2O.$$

This is cooled to 150° C. and mixed with more air, when nitrogen peroxide is formed :

$$2NO + O_2 = 2NO_2.$$

On dissolving nitrogen peroxide in water in the presence of air, nitric acid is obtained :

$$4NO_2 + 2H_2O + O_2 = 4HNO_3.$$

This second process (which has almost completely displaced that of Birkeland and Eyde) is so successful that, in Europe, sodium nitrate prepared by neutralizing synthetic nitric acid with sodium carbonate is actually cheaper than Chile saltpetre (p. 384).

Properties.—Nitric acid is a colourless fuming liquid of sp. gr. 1·53 and m.p. − 41°. Ordinary " commercial " concentrated nitric acid contains about 68 per cent. by weight of pure acid. When nitric acid is boiled it partially dissociates into nitrogen peroxide, oxygen, and water—

$$4HNO_3 \rightleftharpoons 4NO_2 + O_2 + 2H_2O.$$

Nitric acid is the strongest acid known, being equally strong with hydrochloric acid. It is also a powerful oxidizing agent, and these two characteristics often clash. When nitric acid acts upon metals, we may imagine that hydrogen is first formed, in the usual way, but that the excess of nitric acid then oxidizes the hydrogen and is itself reduced to nitric oxide (NO), nitrous oxide (N_2O), nitrogen peroxide (NO_2), etc.

Any or all of these gases may therefore be obtained when nitric acid acts upon a metal. With magnesium, *dilute* nitric acid acts so rapidly that some of the hydrogen escapes oxidation, and may be detected in the gases evolved ; this, however, is very exceptional.

Examples of the Action of Nitric Acid.

(i) *Lead.* $Pb + 4HNO_3 = Pb(NO_3)_2 + 2H_2O + 2NO_2.$

(ii) *Copper.* $3Cu + 8HNO_3 = 3Cu(NO_3)_2 + 4H_2O + 2NO.$

(iii) *Tin.* $5Sn + 20HNO_3 = H_{10}Sn_5O_{15} + 5H_2O + 20NO_2$

($H_{10}Sn_5O_{15}$ is a white insoluble substance called *metastannic acid*; on heating it yields *stannic oxide* and water—

$$H_{10}Sn_5O_{15} = 5SnO_2 + 5H_2O).$$

(iv) *Sulphur* → sulphuric acid, H_2SO_4.

(v) *Phosphorus* → phosphoric acid, H_3PO_4.

(vi) *Iodine* → iodic acid, HIO_3.

(vii) *Arsenic* → arsenic acid, $HAsO_3$.

(viii) *Ferrous sulphate* reduces nitric acid to nitric oxide, which combines with excess of ferrous sulphate to form a dark brown compound $(FeSO_4)_2.NO$. This is the principle of the "*brown-ring*" test for nitrates. The suspected nitrate is dissolved in a little water and a few drops of ferrous sulphate solution added. Sulphuric acid is then carefully poured in and sinks to the bottom as a lower layer. Where the two layers meet, a brown ring is formed if a nitrate is present. Nitric acid is first liberated by the sulphuric acid and then reduced by the ferrous sulphate as above—

$$6FeSO_4 + 3H_2SO_4 + 2HNO_3 = \underset{\text{Ferric sulphate.}}{3Fe_2(SO_4)_3} + 2NO + 4H_2O$$

$$4FeSO_4 + 2NO = 2(FeSO_4)_2NO.$$

(ix) With *bases*, nitric acid yields *nitrates*, all of which are soluble.

Action of heat on the nitrates—

A. *Potassium* and *sodium* nitrates first melt, then evolve oxygen; the *nitrite* of the metal is left—

$$2KNO_3 = 2KNO_2 + O_2.$$

B. *Ammonium* nitrate yields nitrous oxide—

$$NH_4NO_3 = N_2O + 2H_2O.$$

C. Nitrates of *heavy metals*, except silver and mercury, yield the oxide of the metal, nitrogen peroxide, and oxygen—$2Pb(NO_3)_2 = 2PbO + 4NO_2 + O_2$.

(Copper nitrate crystals yield nitric acid vapour and steam as well.)

D. *Silver* and *mercury* nitrates yield the metal, nitrogen peroxide, and oxygen—

$$Hg(NO_3)_2 = Hg + 2NO_2 + O_2.$$

Solid nitrates are powerful oxidizing agents, and are therefore used in the preparation of explosives. Gunpowder, for instance, consists of potassium nitrate (75 per cent.), with sulphur (10 per cent.), and charcoal (15 per cent.).

Oxides of Nitrogen.

Nitrogen forms at least five *oxides* or compounds of nitrogen and oxygen, *viz.*—

Nitrous oxide, N_2O.
Nitric oxide, NO.
Nitrogen trioxide or nitrous anhydride, N_2O_3.
Nitrogen dioxide, peroxide or tetroxide, NO_2 or N_2O_4.
Nitrogen pentoxide or nitric anhydride, N_2O_5.

It will be noticed that these compounds well illustrate the Law of Multiple Proportions (p. 84), since the ratio of the weights of oxygen which combine with a constant weight of nitrogen in the five oxides is 1 : 2 : 3 : 4 : 5.

Nitrous oxide, N_2O.

Nitrous oxide was discovered by Priestley in 1772, but was more carefully investigated by Sir Humphry Davy in 1799. Davy showed that it could be made by heating ammonium nitrate—

$$NH_4NO_3 = N_2O + 2H_2O.$$

This method is still the one which is most suitable for preparing nitrous oxide in the laboratory. The apparatus employed is shown in Fig. 71.

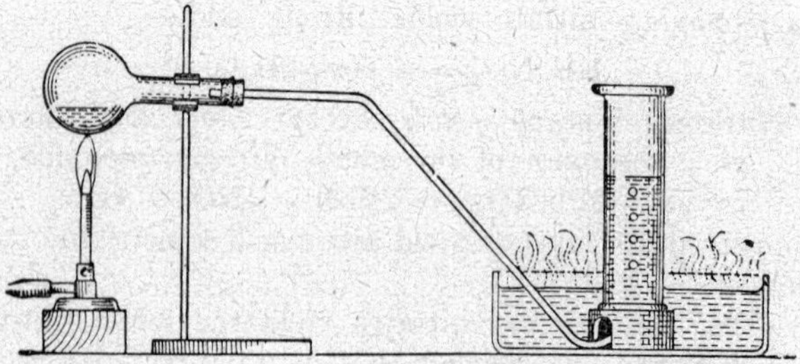

Fig. 71.—Preparation of Nitrous Oxide.

Dry ammonium nitrate is placed in a round-bottomed flask fitted with a cork carrying a delivery-tube leading to a pneumatic trough. On heating the flask the ammonium nitrate melts and then begins to decompose. The nitrous oxide which is evolved is collected over HOT water, as it is soluble in cold. The heating should be stopped while there is still some ammonium nitrate left, otherwise a serious explosion may occur. The terrible disaster which occurred a few years ago at a German chemical factory (Oppau) was due to the explosion of ammonium nitrate.

The nitrous oxide obtained in this way always contains traces of nitric oxide. This may be removed by bubbling the gas through a solution of ferrous sulphate, $FeSO_4$, in which the nitric oxide is soluble while the nitrous oxide is insoluble.

Properties.—Nitrous oxide is a colourless gas with a sweet and not unpleasant smell. It is soluble in cold water, and is therefore usually collected over hot water, although, since it has a density of 22 (air = 14·4), it may conveniently be collected by downward displacement *when cold.* If the gas is required dry, it is passed through strong sulphuric acid and collected over mercury.

Nitrous oxide is used as an anæsthetic in dentistry and minor surgical operations. It is sometimes called "laughing-gas," since the inhalation of a mixture of nitrous oxide and air produces hysterical laughter. It is very readily decomposed, on heating, into a mixture of nitrogen and oxygen, containing 33·3 per cent. by volume of the latter, so that substances burn very readily in it—nearly as well as in pure oxygen. Heat is given out during the decomposition of the nitrous oxide, and this assists in raising the temperature and therefore aids the combustion. A glowing splint is re-lit by nitrous oxide, but the latter gas may easily be distinguished from oxygen by the following tests :

(i) Nitrous oxide has a characteristic sweet smell.

(ii) Nitrous oxide is much more soluble in cold water than is oxygen.

(iii) Nitrous oxide when mixed with nitric oxide gives no

brown fumes of nitrogen peroxide, such as are given by oxygen with nitric oxide.

(iv) On burning a piece of phosphorus in nitrous oxide, *the residual gas on cooling has the same volume as that of the nitrous oxide started with*—

$$5N_2O + 2P = \underset{\text{Solid.}}{P_2O_5} + 5N_2.$$

The last experiment shows us that 1 volume of nitrous oxide contains 1 volume of nitrogen,

∴ by Avogadro's Hypothesis,

1 molecule of nitrous oxide contains 1 molecule of nitrogen,

∴ formula is N_2O_x.

x is found by a V.D. determination—

$$V.D. = 22 \therefore M.W. = 44.$$

Of these 44 parts, 28 are nitrogen (from formula N_2O_x, above), ∴ 16 are oxygen. But 16 is the A.W. of oxygen, ∴ $x = 1$ and the FORMULA is N_2O.

Nitric oxide, NO.—Nitric oxide, like nitrous oxide, is a gas. It is made by pouring moderately concentrated nitric acid upon copper turnings, and is collected over water—

$$3Cu + 8HNO_3 = 3Cu(NO_3)_2 + 4H_2O + 2NO.$$

A suitable apparatus is shown in Fig. 72. If the gas is

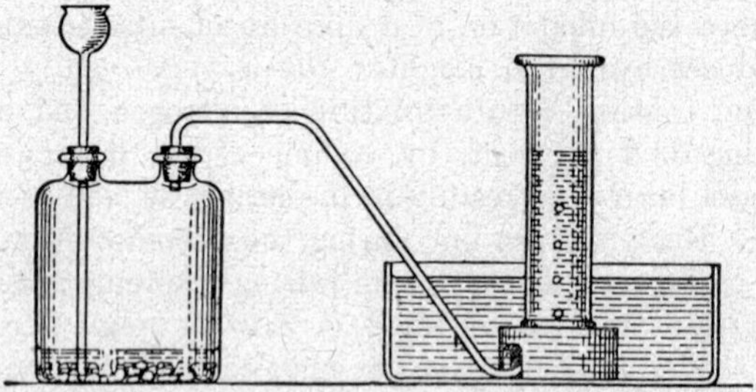

FIG. 72.—Preparation of Nitric Oxide.

required dry it is passed through calcium chloride and collected over mercury.

Properties.—Nitric oxide is a colourless gas, which immediately combines with free oxygen when the two are brought into contact; it is therefore impossible to say whether it has any taste or smell. The brown fumes which are formed when nitric oxide is exposed to air or oxygen consist of *nitrogen peroxide*, NO_2 (p. 278)—

$$2NO + O_2 = 2NO_2.$$

Nitric oxide will not burn, but will support combustion if the burning substance is hot enough to decompose the gas into nitrogen and oxygen. Nitric oxide is more stable than nitrous oxide, so that the temperature required to bring about this decomposition is correspondingly higher. Thus, feebly burning phosphorus is extinguished if plunged into nitric oxide, but if strongly burning it continues to burn in the gas.

Both nitrous and nitric oxides are neutral to litmus; since, however, nitric oxide so readily forms nitrogen peroxide when it can get at free oxygen, and since nitrogen peroxide dissolves in water to form an acid solution, nitric oxide often *appears* to redden litmus.

Composition of Nitric Oxide.—The composition of nitric oxide is determined by enclosing a measured volume in a eudiometer tube over mercury. The eudiometer contains a spiral of thick iron wire which may be raised to a red heat by means of an electric current. On heating, the wire reacts with the nitric oxide, forming solid oxide of iron (whose volume is practically equal to that of the iron from which it came, and may therefore be neglected) and nitrogen. After cooling, it will be found that the volume of the residual nitrogen is half that of the nitric oxide taken.

1 volume of nitric oxide contains $\frac{1}{2}$ volume of nitrogen,

$\therefore$ by Avogadro's Hypothesis,

1 molecule of nitric oxide contains $\frac{1}{2}$ molecule of nitrogen,

$\therefore$ formula is NO_x.

x is found as for nitrous oxide.

Nitric oxide is practically insoluble in water, and may therefore be collected at the pneumatic trough. A mixture of carbon disulphide vapour and nitric oxide burns with a bright blue flash, and was formerly used by photographers for taking flashlight photographs.

Nitrogen peroxide, NO_2 or N_2O_4.—This gas is the commonest oxide of nitrogen. It is alternatively known as nitrogen dioxide or nitrogen tetroxide, and is prepared by the action of heat upon lead nitrate—

$$2Pb(NO_3)_2 = 2PbO + 4NO_2 + O_2.$$

The mixture of gases is passed through a U-tube surrounded by a freezing mixture ; the oxygen passes on while the nitrogen peroxide (which is usually impure) condenses to a greenish-yellow liquid.

Properties.—Nitrogen peroxide is a brown gas with a char-

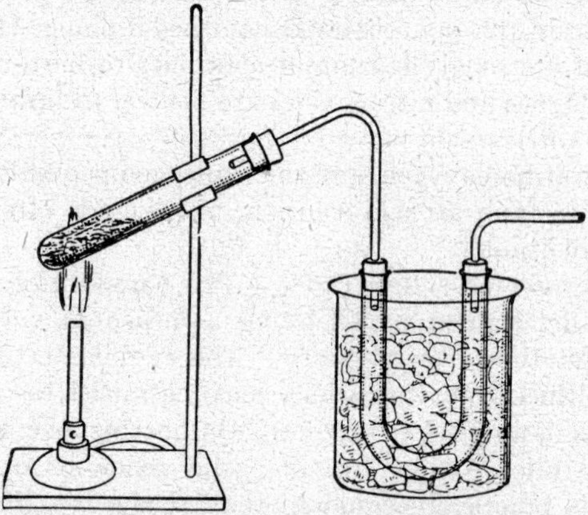

FIG. 73.—Preparation of Nitrogen Peroxide.

acteristic pungent smell. It will not burn nor will it support combustion (unless—as in the case of nitric oxide—the temperature of the burning body is high enough to split it up into oxygen and nitrogen). From vapour density determinations, it is found that at temperatures just above the boiling-point of the substance (22° C.), the molecular weight is 92. This corresponds to the formula N_2O_4 ($2 \times 14 + 4 \times 16$). At higher temperatures, however, the V.D. gradually diminishes until at 150° it reaches a minimum value of 23. This corresponds to a M.W. of 46 and a formula NO_2.

On heating, therefore, nitrogen peroxide *dissociates, i.e.*

its molecules split up into simpler ones, the reverse change taking place on cooling—

$$N_2O_4 \rightleftharpoons 2NO_2.$$

At temperatures below 150°, the gas consists partly of NO_2 molecules and partly of N_2O_4 molecules, the higher the temperature the greater being the proportion of the former.

Nitrogen peroxide is a very poisonous gas, and may quickly give rise to septic pneumonia. *It should therefore on no account be inhaled*: a special word of warning is necessary here, as nitrogen peroxide is so often made in school laboratories. Nitrogen peroxide is far more dangerous than most of those gases concerning which danger-signals are hoisted.

Nitrogen peroxide converts moist sulphur dioxide into sulphuric acid—

$$SO_2 + H_2O + NO_2 = H_2SO_4 + NO,$$

and is used for this purpose in the manufacture of sulphuric acid by the lead-chamber process (p. 307).

Phosphorus

Symbol: P; *Valency:* 3 or 5; *Atomicity of Vapour:* 4; *Atomic Weight:* 31.

Phosphorus is an element which shows many resemblances to nitrogen, and this similarity extends to the compounds of the two. The discovery of phosphorus was made in 1669 by the German chemist, Brandt, but it was not until Scheele, in 1771, showed that it could easily be obtained from bone-ash, that phosphorus was anything more than a chemical curiosity.

Occurrence.—Phosphorus is very chemically active, and so is found only in the form of compounds, the chief of which is *calcium phosphate*, $Ca_3(PO_4)_2$. Bone-ash, *i.e.* the ash left after burning bones, is composed mainly of calcium phosphate, and large quantities of *phosphorite* and *Redonda phosphate* (both impure calcium phosphate) occur naturally. Some of the principal deposits are in Morocco and Algeria.

Preparation.—Phosphorus is manufactured by strongly

heating a mixture of coke, silica (SiO_2, p. 349) and calcium phosphate in an electric furnace (Fig. 74)—

$$Ca_3(PO_4)_2 + 5C + 3SiO_2 = \underset{\text{Calcium silicate.}}{3CaSiO_3} + 2P + 5CO.$$

The phosphorus vapour which comes off is condensed under water in copper vessels, and the liquid phosphorus is then allowed to set in tubular moulds—hence the familiar "sticks."

Properties.—Phosphorus exists in several allotropic modifications, of which the chief are "yellow" (or "white") phosphorus, and "red" phosphorus.

Yellow Phosphorus.—This is a semi-transparent pale-yellow waxy crystalline solid, which can easily be cut with a knife. It gradually darkens on exposure to air, becoming finally very dark brown. It is practically insoluble in water, but dissolves readily in carbon disulphide. When gently warmed in air it takes fire spontaneously (30° C.), so that it is always kept under water, and should never be touched with the fingers.

The name "phosphorus" (*light-bearer*) was given to the element on account of its peculiar property of glowing in the dark. NICOLAS LÉMERY, in his *Cours de Chimie* (1694), mentions certain practical jokes which had been carried out by means of the phosphorescence and ready ignition of phosphorus. He says also that a piece of phosphorus accidentally found its way into the bed of a visitor to Boyle; a servant had to extinguish the conflagration by throwing buckets of water over both bed and visitor.

The glow is due to the slow combustion of the phosphorus, which gradually oxidizes, forming a mixture of its oxides, chiefly phosphor*ous* oxide, P_4O_6. When phosphorus is burnt in air or oxygen, the main product is phosphor*ic* oxide or phosphorus pentoxide, P_2O_5—

$$4P + 5O_2 = 2P_2O_5.$$

Yellow phosphorus is very chemically active. It will combine directly with chlorine, igniting spontaneously when plunged into the gas. The product is *phosphorus pentachloride*, PCl_5—

$$2P + 5Cl_2 = 2PCl_5.$$

It is extremely poisonous, and is occasionally used as a rat-poison. *Red phosphorus* is a red powder which appears to be amorphous. Close examination, however, has shown that it is really crystalline, although the crystals are very minute. It is made by heating the yellow form in a cast-iron pot to a temperature of 230–250°, in the absence of air. A trace of iodine may be used as a catalyst when the action is carried out on a small scale.

Red phosphorus is not so chemically active as the yellow variety. It is insoluble in water, and is not poisonous when swallowed. It will not dissolve in carbon disulphide, and takes fire in the air only when heated to a comparatively high temperature (260° C.). It does not glow in the air, and will not take fire spontaneously in chlorine (contrast the yellow form).

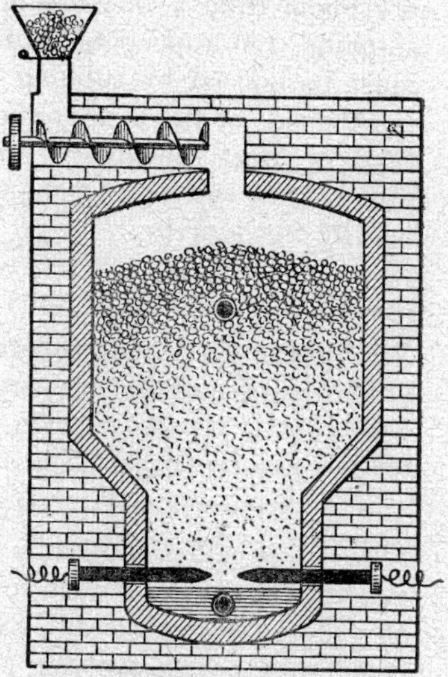

FIG. 74.—Manufacture of Phosphorus.

Transformation of Red Phosphorus into Yellow and of Yellow into Red.—(i) *Yellow to red.* Heat to 240° in nitrogen or other inert gas, with a crystal of iodine as catalyst.

(ii) *Red to yellow.* Heat in an inert gas until the vapour is produced (above 550°). On rapidly cooling the vapour, yellow phosphorus is formed.

To show that both the yellow and red forms are the same element, equal weights of the two may be burnt in oxygen. It will be found that equal weights of phosphorus pentoxide are obtained.

Other allotropic forms of phosphorus are known. One of them, " scarlet phosphorus," is used in making certain kinds of matches. " Strike anywhere " matches are sometimes tipped with a mixture of scarlet phosphorus, potassium chlorate, red-lead, gum, and a colouring matter. When they are rubbed, the heat produced by the friction is sufficient to cause the phosphorus to be ignited by the oxidizing agents present, and the combustion of the phosphorus sets fire to the wood. In most "strike anywhere" matches, however, scarlet phosphorus is replaced by a compound of phosphorus and sulphur, called *phosphorus sesquisulphide*, P_4S_3. "Safety" matches are made from a mixture of potassium chlorate, antimony sulphide, red-lead, potassium dichromate, and gum. They must be ignited by rubbing on a specially prepared surface (on the side of the box) containing red phosphorus, powdered sand or glass, antimony sulphide and gum. Most of the processes in the modern manufacture of matches are carried out by machinery.

Compounds of Phosphorus.

Phosphine or Phosphoretted Hydrogen, PH_3.

Phosphine was first prepared by heating yellow phosphorus with caustic potash solution. This method is still employed for laboratory preparation of the gas (Fig. 75)—

$$4P + 3KOH + 3H_2O = 3KH_2PO_2 + PH_3.$$

KH_2PO_2 is called potassium hypophosphite. To conduct the experiment caustic potash (or soda) solution and some pieces of yellow phosphorus are placed in a round-bottomed flask fitted with a cork carrying a delivery-tube and another tube which admits coal-gas. All air is first swept from the apparatus by a stream of coal-gas, and the flask is then heated. Phosphine comes off, and as each bubble rises from the water of the trough into the air, it ignites spontaneously and forms a vortex ring of white phosphorus pentoxide.

Phosphine may also be prepared by the action of water upon calcium phosphide, Ca_3P_2—

$$Ca_3P_2 + 6H_2O = 3Ca(OH)_2 + 2PH_3.$$

Properties.—Phosphine is a colourless gas with a very unpleasant smell, rather like that of decaying fish, and is extremely poisonous. It is only slightly soluble in water, in this respect differing from the corresponding compound of nitrogen, *viz.*, ammonia (p. 261). It is, however, a *basic anhydride*, like ammonia, and combines directly with acids to form salts, the *phosphonium* salts, *e.g.*

$PH_3 + HI = PH_4I$, phosphonium iodide, a white crystalline solid.

The base itself, *phosphonium hydroxide*, PH_4OH, is unknown, and a solution of phosphine in water has no action on litmus.

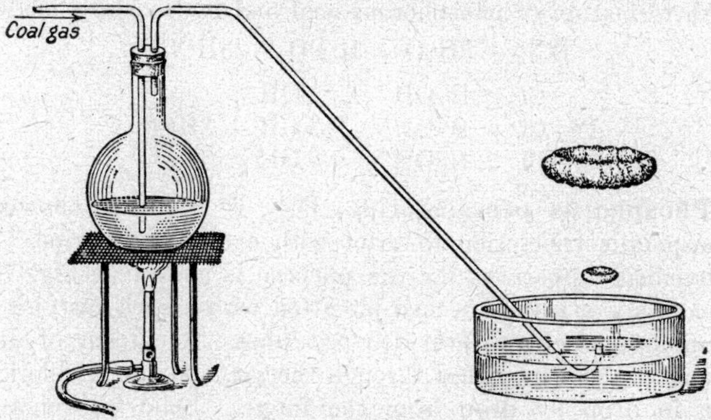

FIG. 75.—Preparation of Phosphine.

As generally prepared, phosphine is spontaneously inflammable in air. When pure, although it will burn readily when ignited, it does not take fire spontaneously. The products of combustion are water and phosphorus pentoxide—

$$2PH_3 + 4O_2 = P_2O_5 + 3H_2O.$$

Calcium phosphide, Ca_3P_2, is made by heating calcium phosphate with carbon in the electric furnace—

$$Ca_3(PO_4)_2 + 8C = Ca_3P_2 + 8CO.$$

Commercial calcium phosphide is a reddish brown solid which yields spontaneously inflammable phosphine on treatment with water. Mixed with calcium carbide it is therefore used in *Holmes' signals*, which consist of tins containing the mixture, attached to a buoy. When required for use, the tins are pierced at each end and thrown into the sea.

The acetylene evolved is ignited by the ignition of the phosphine it contains, and the sea is lit up.

Phosphorus trichloride, PCl_3, is prepared by passing chlorine through molten phosphorus in a retort from which all air has previously been removed by a stream of carbon dioxide. The phosphorus takes fire and burns in the chlorine, and the phosphorus trichloride distils over as a colourless oily liquid. It fumes in the air, and is decomposed by water with formation of phosphorous acid and hydrochloric acid—

$$PCl_3 + 3H_2O = H_3PO_3 + 3HCl,$$

$$P\begin{cases} Cl \\ Cl \\ Cl \end{cases} + \begin{matrix} H\ OH \\ H\ OH \\ H\ OH \end{matrix} = P\begin{cases} OH \\ OH \\ OH \end{cases} + 3HCl.$$

Phosphorus pentachloride, PCl_5, is made by allowing phosphorus trichloride to react with excess of chlorine. A convenient apparatus for the purpose is shown in Fig. 76. It consists of a wide-necked jar fitted with a cork carrying a dropping-funnel and two delivery-tubes. A current of dry chlorine is slowly passed through the jar, and the trichloride run in drop by drop from the funnel. Solid phosphorus pentachloride collects in the jar. It is a yellowish crystalline substance with a peculiar smell. It sublimes on heating, and the vapour is dissociated into phosphorus trichloride and chlorine—

$$PCl_5 \rightleftharpoons PCl_3 + Cl_2.$$

It fumes in the air, and is vigorously attacked by water; the first change results in the formation of a colourless oily liquid, *phosphorus oxychloride*, $POCl_3$, and this is then acted upon by more water, yielding *orthophosphoric acid*, H_3PO_4—

$$PCl_5 + H_2O = POCl_3 + 2HCl.$$
$$POCl_3 + 3H_2O = H_3PO_4 + 3HCl.$$

Phosphorous oxide or **phosphorus trioxide,** P_2O_3 or P_4O_6, is formed, together with the pentoxide, when phosphorus is burnt in a limited supply of air. The phosphorus is burnt in a long hard-glass tube, and the products of combustion are passed through a plug of glass wool. This stops the pentoxide, which is solid, but the more volatile trioxide, being still in the gaseous state, passes through and is condensed in a cooled U-tube. It is a white crystalline solid, which melts at 23°, and rapidly absorbs oxygen from the air forming the pentoxide—

$$P_2O_3 + O_2 = P_2O_5.$$

It dissolves in water, forming *phosphorous acid*, H_3PO_3, of which it is therefore the *anhydride*—

$$P_2O_3 + 3H_2O = 2H_3PO_3.$$

Phosphorus trioxide is a poisonous substance with a smell resembling that of garlic.

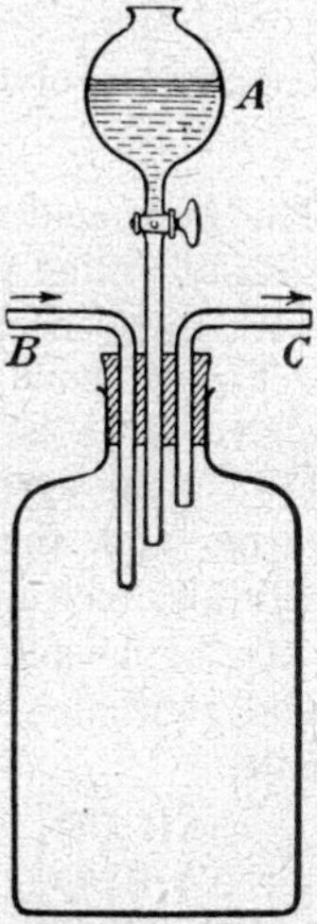

FIG. 76.—Preparation of Phosphorus Pentachloride.

A. Phosphorus trichloride. *B*. Chlorine in. *C*. Excess chlorine out.

Phosphoric oxide or **Phosphorus pentoxide,** P_2O_5, is made by burning phosphorus in *excess* of air or oxygen.

It is a white crystalline solid with a great affinity for water; it is, indeed, the most effective *drying-agent* known. It is very quickly turned to a semi-liquid mass, *metaphosphoric acid*, HPO_3, on exposure to air, and dissolves in water with a hissing noise forming metaphosphoric acid in the cold but orthophosphoric acid if the water is hot—

(i) $P_2O_5 + H_2O = 2HPO_3$.
(ii) $P_2O_5 + 3H_2O = 2H_3PO_4$.

In addition to its drying powers it possesses the property of taking the elements of water out of many substances which contain them. Thus it yields nitrogen pentoxide with nitric acid and sulphur trioxide with sulphuric acid.

(i) $2HNO_3 - H_2O = N_2O_5$.
(ii) $H_2SO_4 - H_2O = SO_3$.

Phosphorus pentoxide is the anhydride of phosphoric acid, of which there are three varieties, as described below.

Orthophosphoric acid, H_3PO_4, is the most important acid of phosphorus. It may be obtained by decomposing calcium phosphate with sulphuric acid—

$$Ca_3(PO_4)_2 + 3H_2SO_4 = 3CaSO_4 + 2H_3PO_4,$$

and evaporating the solution after filtration from the calcium sulphate. It is also formed when phosphorus pentoxide is added to *boiling* water—

$$P_2O_5 + 3H_2O = 2H_3PO_4,$$

and when a solution of metaphosphoric acid, HPO_3, is boiled—

$$HPO_3 + H_2O = H_3PO_4.$$

The pure acid may be most conveniently prepared by cautiously boiling yellow or red phosphorus (preferably the latter) with nitric acid.

The aqueous solution of the acid obtained in any of the above ways is concentrated until the temperature rises to 140°. The syrupy liquid is then allowed to cool in a desiccator, and the acid separates out as colourless rhombic crystals, melting at 41·7°.

Orthophosphoric acid is soluble in water, giving a feebly acid solution. It is a *tribasic* acid and forms three sodium salts—

NaH_2PO_4, sodium dihydrogen orthophosphate.
Na_2HPO_4, disodium hydrogen orthophosphate.
Na_3PO_4, trisodium orthophosphate, or normal sodium orthophosphate.

Normal sodium phosphate gives a strongly *alkaline* solution.

The disodium salt, Na_2HPO_4, is ordinary laboratory "sodium phosphate." It has a *slightly* alkaline reaction in solution.

The monosodium salt, NaH_2PO_4, has a very slightly acid reaction in solution.

A solution of ordinary "sodium phosphate" has a marked stimulating effect when drunk, and was given to German soldiers during the war of 1914–18 to invigorate and refresh them. It is also a constituent of the "iced phosphate" drinks perpetrated by American Soda Fountains.

The constitution of orthophosphoric acid is represented by the formula—

$$O = P \begin{cases} OH \\ OH. \\ OH \end{cases}$$

Titration with caustic soda using litmus or phenolphthalein as indicator gives the disodium salt; with methyl orange the colour change occurs at the stage corresponding to NaH_2PO_4.

Calcium superphosphate, $CaH_4(PO_4)_2$, is an important fertilizer made by acting upon mineral calcium phosphate with sulphuric acid—

$$Ca_3(PO_4)_2 + 2H_2SO_4 = 2CaSO_4 + CaH_4(PO_4)_2.$$

Pyrophosphoric acid, $H_4P_2O_7$, is formed when orthophosphoric acid is cautiously heated at a temperature of about 215–220°. Two molecules of the orthophosphoric acid lose one molecule of water—

$$2H_3PO_4 = H_4P_2O_7 + H_2O.$$

It is a white crystalline solid, and yields salts called the *pyrophosphates.*

Meta-phosphoric acid, HPO_3, may be made by heating the ortho or the pyro acid to redness—

$$H_3PO_4 = H_2O + HPO_3,$$
$$H_4P_2O_7 = 2HPO_3 + H_2O,$$

or by adding phosphorus pentoxide slowly to cold water—

$$P_2O_5 + H_2O = 2HPO_3.$$

It is a glassy transparent solid, and is put on the market as "glacial phosphoric acid." It is a monobasic acid and the chief salt is *sodium metaphosphate*, $NaPO_3$. This is formed when sodium ammonium hydrogen orthophosphate, or *microcosmic salt* (so-called because it is found in the excretory products of the "microcosm," *i.e.* man), is strongly heated—

$$NaNH_4HPO_4 = NaPO_3 + H_2O + NH_3.$$

Fused sodium metaphosphate dissolves many metallic oxides to form coloured orthophosphates; microcosmic salt is therefore sometimes used instead of borax for the "bead" test in analysis.

Tests for Phosphates.—All the phosphoric acids and their salts when heated with ammonium molybdate solution, $(NH_4)_2MoO_4$, and excess of concentrated nitric acid, give a yellow precipitate of variable composition called *ammonium phosphomolybdate*.

With *silver nitrate* solution, orthophosphates give a yellow precipitate,
pyrophosphates give a white precipitate,
metaphosphates also give a white precipitate.

With a solution of *white of egg*, metaphosphates cause coagulation,
ortho- and pyro- phosphates have no action.

Questions

1. Who discovered nitrogen ?
2. What does "nitrogen" mean ? What does "azote" mean ?
3. How does nitrogen occur in nature ?
4. How could you obtain nitrogen from air ?
5. Describe the preparation and properties of pure dry nitrogen.
6. Write the formulæ for (*a*) magnesium nitride, (*b*) ammonium nitrite, (*c*) Chile saltpetre, (*d*) nitre, (*e*) ammonia.
7. What is the origin of the name *ammonia* ?
8. Describe the preparation and properties of ammonia.
9. How would you dry ammonia ?
10. Describe a synthetic process for obtaining ammonia commercially.
11. Describe a modern ice-making machine.
12. Mention the chief tests for ammonia and ammonium salts.
13. Upon what evidence is the formula NH_3 assigned to ammonia ?
14. Explain the difference between *ammonia* and *ammonium*.
15. How have people tried to obtain ammonium ?
16. Why is it wrong to call a solution of ammonia "ammonium hydrate" or "liquid ammonia" ?
17. Write equations for the action of ammonium hydroxide upon solutions of (*a*) copper sulphate, (*b*) ferrous chloride, (*c*) zinc sulphate, (*d*) aluminium chloride.
18. Mention a test for copper.
19. Explain the term *sublimation*. Why did the alchemists call sal ammoniac the "White Eagle" ?

20. What do you understand by the term "dissociation"? Describe examples of this phenomenon.

21. What is the action of heat upon (*a*) ammonium nitrate, (*b*) ammonium nitrite, (*c*) ammonium chloride?

22. What are (*a*) *aqua fortis*, (*b*) *aqua regia*?

23. How is nitric acid prepared in the laboratory? What are its chief properties?

24. What do you mean by the *fixation of nitrogen*?

25. Describe methods of obtaining nitric acid (*a*) directly from the air, (*b*) from ammonia.

26. What is the action of nitric acid upon (*a*) tin, (*b*) copper, (*c*) sulphur, (*d*) phosphorus, (*e*) marble?

27. Describe the brown-ring test for nitrates.

28. Give a short account of the action of heat upon nitrates.

29. Describe the preparation and properties of nitric oxide.

30. ,, ,, ,, ,, ,, nitrous oxide.

31. ,, ,, ,, ,, ,, nitrogen peroxide.

32. Upon what evidence are the formulæ N_2O and NO assigned to nitrous and nitric oxide respectively?

33. How would you distinguish between oxygen and nitrous oxide? Why are you likely to confuse these two gases?

34. How does phosphorus occur in nature?

35. How is phosphorus manufactured?

36. Compare and contrast the properties of yellow phosphorus with those of red phosphorus.

37. How may yellow phosphorus be converted into red phosphorus and *vice versâ*?

38. Describe the preparation of phosphine.

39. Compare and contrast the properties of phosphine with those of ammonia.

40. Chemists classify nitrogen and phosphorus together. Show, by a consideration of the properties of these elements and of their compounds, that this classification is justified on chemical grounds.

41. Describe the preparation and properties of the chlorides of phosphorus.

42. How are (*a*) phosphorus trioxide and (*b*) phosphorus pentoxide prepared? What are their chief properties?

43. Write the formula and give the names of the three phosphoric acids.

44. Mention some tests for the phosphoric acids and their salts.

CHAPTER XVII

SULPHUR

Symbol: S; *Atomic Weight:* 32; *Valency:* 2, 4 or 6; *Specific Gravity:* about 2; *Boiling-point:* 444°.

History of Sulphur.—The word sulphur shows us that this element and one of its most characteristic properties have been known for some thousands of years, for "sulphur" is the Latin form of the Sanskrit word *sulvari* or "*enemy of copper.*" Sanskrit is the language of the ancient Hindoos, so that these people were acquainted with sulphur 3,000 years or more ago, and knew also that it "destroys" copper when the two are heated together. The black substance so formed we now call *cuprous sulphide* (Cu_2S). (See p. 295.) To the Greeks and Romans sulphur was well known, since it occurs naturally in Sicily and other volcanic regions of the Mediterranean. JABIR, the greatest of the Arab chemists (he is said to have lived at the time of the Caliph Harun al-Rashid, eighth century A.D.), put forward the theory that all metals were composed of sulphur and mercury—a theory which was afterwards modified into the phlogiston theory of Becher and Stahl, about which you have read earlier in this book.

The properties of sulphur were thoroughly investigated in the Middle Ages, and many sulphur compounds were described. That sulphur is an *element* was first shown by LAVOISIER in 1777.

How Sulphur occurs in Nature.—Sulphur in the free state (that is, in the form of the element itself) is found in vast quantities in Sicily and Italy and, at a depth of about 700 feet, in Texas and Louisiana (U.S.A.). Compounds of sulphur with metals—the *sulphides*—are also widely distributed in large quantities, *e.g.* *iron pyrites*, FeS_2; *galena*, PbS; *cinnabar*, HgS (mercuric sulphide), and *copper pyrites*, $CuFeS_2$. Much sulphur also occurs in the form of metallic *sulphates*, *e.g.* calcium sulphate, *gypsum*, $CaSO_4.2H_2O$.

Extraction.—In Sicily the natural sulphur is mixed with soil and stones and other impurities. Lumps of the crude sulphur ore are built up into heaps, which are covered over with the residue from a previous operation. The heaps are built on the side of a hill, and are set alight. Part of the

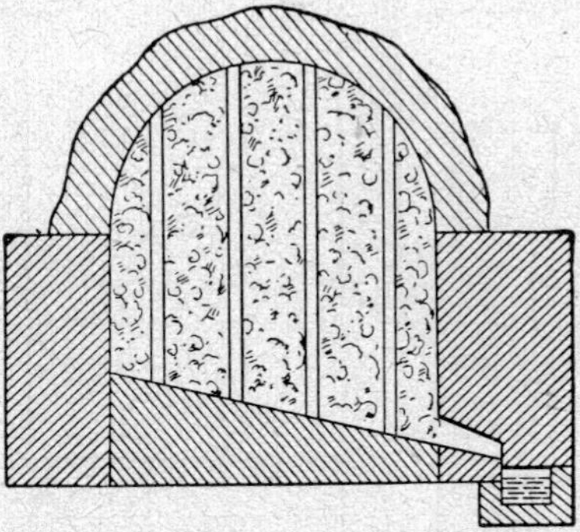

FIG. 77.—Extracting Sulphur in Sicily.

sulphur burns and melts the rest, which sinks to the bottom of the heap and flows out into wet wooden boxes placed to receive it.

It is still not pure enough for general use, so it is boiled in iron pots and the vapour condensed in a brickwork chamber (Fig. 78).

At first, the walls of the chamber (C) are cold, and the sulphur vapour then condenses to a fine powder (" flowers of sulphur "), but they gradually become heated by the vapour until they are above the melting-point of solid sulphur, and then the vapour condenses not to the solid but to the *liquid* state. The flowers of sulphur first formed are scraped out through the trap-door at the top of the chamber. The liquid sulphur which later collects on the floor is run out and poured into cylindrical moulds, where it solidifies and forms the so-called "roll-sulphur."

In Louisiana and Texas, superheated steam is blown down through a pipe into the sulphur bed. The sulphur is thus melted, and is then forced up through another pipe by means of compressed air. It is very pure (99·5 per cent.), and does

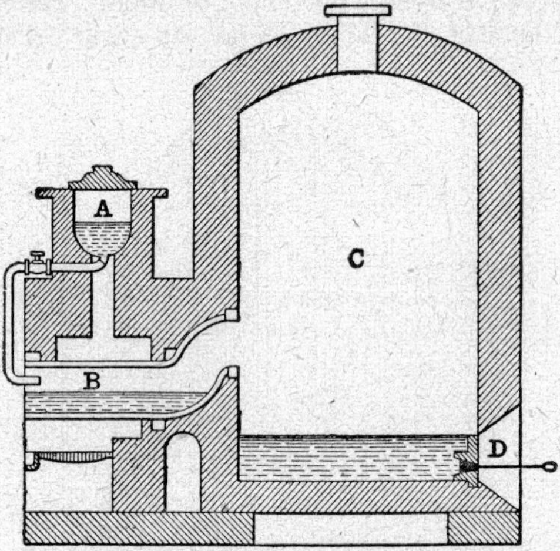

FIG. 78.—Refinement of Sulphur.

not require refinement. A single "well" often produces as much as 500 tons a day.

Properties.—Sulphur exists in several different forms, called *allotropes* or *allotropic forms* of sulphur. You have already studied allotropy when you learnt about ozone and oxygen, so you will remember what it is: *When an element can exist in more than one form, those forms being physically and often chemically distinct, it is said to exhibit allotropy, and the different forms are called allotropes, or allotropic forms, of the element.*

The chief forms of sulphur are (i) ordinary sulphur, which is generally called *rhombic* sulphur from the shape of its crystals and (ii) *monoclinic* or *prismatic* sulphur, the crystals of which have a very different shape—they are long, thin, and needle-like (Fig. 79*a*).

RHOMBIC SULPHUR is the ordinary, naturally-occurring form. It will dissolve in the inflammable liquid known as *carbon disulphide*, and when the solution is evaporated, the sulphur is left again still in the form of rhombic crystals (Fig. 79*b*).

MONOCLINIC OR PRISMATIC SULPHUR can be prepared by melting rhombic sulphur in a Battersea crucible, allowing the liquid to cool until a thin crust has just formed on the surface, piercing this with two holes and pouring out the remaining liquid through one of these while air enters through the other. If the crust is now removed, the crucible will be found to be lined with long, transparent, needle-like crystals of monoclinic sulphur. Monoclinic sulphur gradually changes back again into rhombic sulphur at ordinary temperatures, but above 95·3° the reverse is true, *i.e.* rhombic slowly changes into monoclinic. *At* 95·3°, neither form shows any tendency to pass into the other: this temperature is called the *transition-point.* Like rhombic sulphur, monoclinic sulphur readily dissolves in carbon disulphide, but when the solution is evaporated the crystals deposited are *rhombic.*

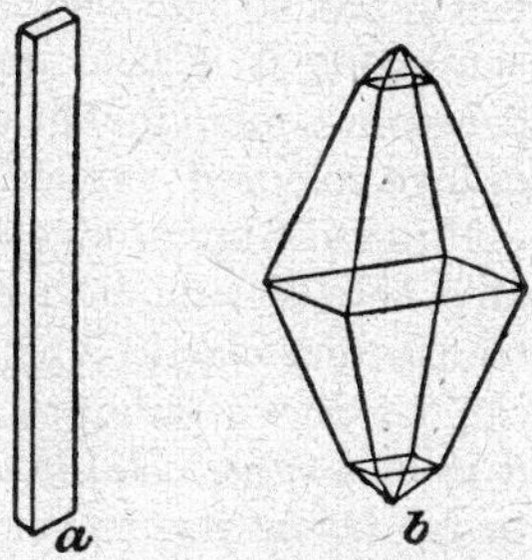

FIG. 79.—Monoclinic and Rhombic Sulphur.

To show that each form consists of sulphur and nothing else, equal weights of the two could be taken separately and burnt in a current of oxygen. The sulphur dioxide (p. 300) so formed could be absorbed in a weighed solution of caustic soda (in which it is soluble), and the increase in weight noted. This would be the weight of sulphur dioxide produced, and it would be found that the weight of sulphur dioxide from the known weight of rhombic sulphur exactly equalled the weight of sulphur dioxide from the same weight of the monoclinic sulphur. Hence monoclinic and rhombic sulphur must be identical in chemical composition, and if one is sulphur so must the other be.

In their chemical properties, the two forms of sulphur are practically identical, so that what follows may be taken to apply to them both.

When sulphur is heated it melts, forming a pale amber-coloured liquid which runs about easily (*i.e.* it is *mobile*). At 160°, the liquid suddenly turns dark brown in colour and becomes quite sticky or *viscous.* It goes on darkening and becoming more and more sticky until at 235° it is practically black, and so viscous that it will not flow out if the test-tube containing it is held upside-down. At higher temperatures it becomes more mobile again, and at 444° it boils, forming an orange-coloured vapour.

PLASTIC SULPHUR.—If the nearly-boiling liquid is poured in a thin stream into cold water, it forms a very viscous, transparent elastic substance known as plastic sulphur. This can be drawn out into long threads, and chemists consider it to be a *supercooled liquid,* that is, a liquid cooled so rapidly, to far below its freezing-point, that it has not had time to crystallize. Glass is another example of a super-cooled liquid.

On standing, plastic sulphur is gradually converted into ordinary rhombic sulphur, a change which takes place more quickly if the plastic sulphur is kneaded and pulled about with the fingers.

MILK OF SULPHUR.—If slaked lime is stirred up with water a turbid liquid called milk of lime is produced. Boiling milk of lime readily dissolves sulphur, forming a solution of a substance called *calcium polysulphide,* the formula for which is unknown : it may be represented as CaS_2. If hydrochloric acid is added to this solution of calcium polysulphide, sulphur is precipitated as a *white* powder which is known as *milk of sulphur* (or, in the druggists' shops, *lac sulphuris*).

AMORPHOUS SULPHUR.—An amorphous form of sulphur is also known.

FURTHER PROPERTIES OF SULPHUR.—In many ways, sulphur resembles oxygen, and chemists indeed put these two elements into the same "family." Both are non-metals, and they form compounds of the same types, as may be seen from the following table:

Typical Compounds of Oxygen.	Typical Compounds of Sulphur.
Water, H_2O.	Hydrogen sulphide, H_2S.
Carbon dioxide, CO_2.	Carbon disulphide, CS_2.
Copper oxide, CuO.	Copper sulphide, CuS.
Arsenic oxide, As_2O_3.	Arsenic sulphide, As_2S_3.
Sodium hydroxide, $NaOH$.	Sodium hydrosulphide, $NaSH$.
Silver oxide, Ag_2O.	Silver sulphide, Ag_2S.
Hydrogen peroxide, H_2O_2.	Hydrogen persulphide, H_2S_2.

Moreover, they both exist in allotropic forms, and they both have a valency of 2 (although sulphur may also have a valency of 4 or 6).

When sulphur is strongly heated it can be ignited in air or oxygen, and burns with a blue flame, forming *sulphur dioxide*, SO_2—

$$S + O_2 = SO_2.$$

If sulphur vapour is passed over red-hot carbon, the two combine, forming carbon disulphide, CS_2—

$$C + 2S = CS_2.$$

Sulphur will also combine directly with hydrogen, for if hydrogen is passed through boiling sulphur, hydrogen sulphide, H_2S, is formed in small quantities—

$$H_2 + S = H_2S.$$

Most metals will combine directly with sulphur on heating. Thus a mixture of iron filings and sulphur, if gently heated, soon becomes incandescent, owing to the vigour with which the iron and the sulphur combine to form *ferrous sulphide*, FeS—

$$Fe + S = FeS.$$

Similarly copper burns brightly in sulphur vapour, the product being *cuprous sulphide*, Cu_2S—

$$2Cu + S = Cu_2S.$$

Sulphur and mercury may be made to combine simply by rubbing the two together in a mortar—

$$Hg + S = HgS \text{ (\textit{mercuric sulphide})}.$$

The only common metal which will not combine directly with sulphur is gold.

Sulphur will not dissolve in dilute acids, but it dissolves in hot concentrated nitric acid, being converted into sulphuric acid.

Uses.—Sulphur is used in the manufacture of sulphuric acid, carbon disulphide and other compounds. It is also employed to keep vines from becoming mouldy: the sulphur is burnt in the vineyards and the sulphur dioxide, SO_2, which is formed, kills the moulds and other fungi. Much sulphur is used in the manufacture of matches and gunpowder, while *vulcanite* is made by treating ordinary india-rubber with sulphur under special conditions.

Compounds of Sulphur.

Hydrogen sulphide, H_2S.

This gas is alternatively known as *sulphuretted hydrogen.* It is a colourless gas. Although it can be made by passing hydrogen through boiling sulphur, as mentioned above, this

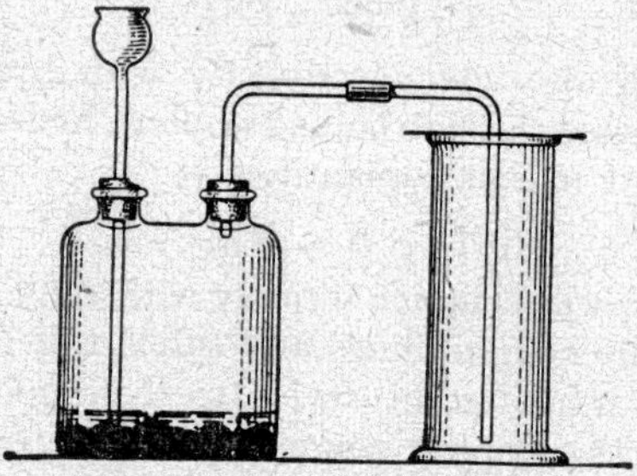

Fig. 80.—Preparation of Sulphuretted Hydrogen.

is not a convenient method of preparing the gas. It is usually prepared in the laboratory by the action of a dilute acid upon *ferrous sulphide*: hydrochloric acid is the acid generally used—

$$FeS + 2HCl = \underset{\text{Ferrous chloride.}}{FeCl_2} + H_2S.$$

[What volume of dry hydrogen sulphide, measured at N.T.P., could you obtain from 4·4 grams of ferrous sulphide, and what weight of ferrous chloride would be formed at the same time ?]

The apparatus for the purpose is shown in Fig. 80.

As the gas is heavier than air (V.D. = 17 ; V.D. of air = 14·4), it can be collected by downward displacement. It cannot be collected over water, in which it is soluble, or over mercury, which it attacks.

Since ferrous sulphide almost always contains iron, the hydrogen sulphide obtained in this way is contaminated with hydrogen ($Fe + 2HCl = FeCl_2 + H_2$). A purer gas can be made by using *antimony sulphide*, Sb_2S_3, instead of ferrous sulphide—

$$Sb_2S_3 + 6HCl = \underset{\text{Antimony chloride.}}{2SbCl_3} + 3H_2S.$$

The gas should be washed by passing it through a *little* water. This removes any hydrogen chloride carried over.

As the gas is very often required in the laboratory, forms of apparatus have been invented which are automatic in action. The well-known apparatus devised by KIPP (Fig. 81) is generally used. You will understand how it works when you see it in action.

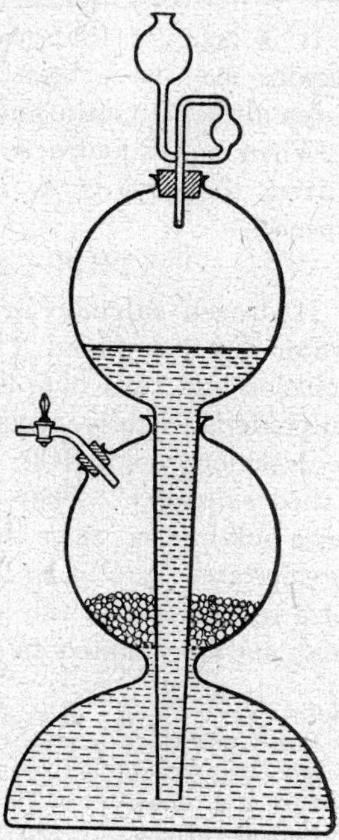

FIG. 81.—Kipp's Apparatus.

Properties.—Hydrogen sulphide is a colourless gas with a sweetish and unpleasant smell of rotten eggs. Bad eggs, in fact, owe their smell to the fact that they contain hydrogen sulphide, which is formed when white of egg decomposes.

It is a poisonous gas, and, if breathed, rapidly produces

headache. It will burn in air with a blue flame, forming steam and sulphur dioxide if there is plenty of air—

$$2H_2S + 3O_2 = 2H_2O + 2SO_2.$$

If, however, there is not enough air, sulphur is deposited—

$$2H_2S + O_2 = 2H_2O + 2S.$$

It is believed that the sulphur which occurs in volcanic regions may have been formed in this way, since volcanic gases always contain hydrogen sulphide.

When moist hydrogen sulphide and sulphur dioxide are mixed, the two gases react, and sulphur and water are formed—

$$2H_2S + SO_2 = 2H_2O + 3S.$$

Hydrogen sulphide is readily soluble in water (1 litre of water dissolves about 3 litres of the gas at 15° C.), and the solution will turn blue litmus red, *i.e.* it is *acid*. Hydrogen sulphide is therefore sometimes called *hydrosulphuric acid* (cf. hydrochloric acid, HCl). The salts of hydrogen sulphide are called *sulphides*. They can be made by heating the metal with sulphur, or, since they are mostly insoluble, they can be precipitated by passing hydrogen sulphide through a solution of a soluble salt of the metal. Examples of sulphides which may be precipitated in this way are—

Sulphide—		
Lead (black) . .	$Pb(NO_3)_2 + H_2S$	$= PbS \downarrow + 2HNO_3$.
Mercuric (black) . .	$HgCl_2 + H_2S$	$= HgS \downarrow + 2HCl$.
Bismuth (black) . .	$2Bi(NO_3)_3 + 3H_2S$	$= Bi_2S_3 \downarrow + 6HNO_3$.
Copper (black) . .	$CuSO_4 + H_2S$	$= CuS \downarrow + H_2SO_4$.
Cadmium (yellow) .	$CdCl_2 + H_2S$	$= CdS \downarrow + 2HCl$.
Arsenic (yellow) . .	$2AsCl_3 + 3H_2S$	$= As_2S_3 \downarrow + 6HCl$.
Antimony (orange) .	$2SbCl_3 + 3H_2S$	$= Sb_2S_3 \downarrow + 6HCl$.
Tin—		
Stannous (brown) .	$SnCl_2 + H_2S$	$= SnS \downarrow + 2HCl$.
Stannic (dirty yellow) .	$SnCl_4 + 2H_2S$	$= SnS_2 \downarrow + 4HCl$.

Of those sulphides which are insoluble in water, some will, however, dissolve in dilute hydrochloric acid, while others will not. The examples given above are those which are *not* soluble in a dilute acid. It is owing to its power of precipitating the sulphides of metals that hydrogen sulphide is used so largely in qualitative analysis.

Hydrogen sulphide will react directly with chlorine, bromine or iodine, especially in the presence of water. Thus if it is passed through a solution of chlorine or bromine, or through water in which iodine is stirred up, the following actions occur—

$$\text{(Chlorine.)} \quad Cl_2 + H_2S = 2HCl + S\downarrow.$$
$$\text{(Bromine.)} \quad Br_2 + H_2S = 2HBr + S\downarrow.$$
$$\text{(Iodine.)} \quad I_2 + H_2S = 2HI + S\downarrow.$$

In each case, a solution of the halogen acid is obtained, and sulphur is precipitated. These reactions may be regarded as *reductions* of the halogens (Cl, Br, or I) by the hydrogen sulphide, which is itself oxidized to sulphur.

If hydrogen sulphide is passed through sulphuric acid, it reduces the latter to sulphur dioxide, and is itself oxidized to sulphur—

$$H_2S + H_2SO_4 = 2H_2O + SO_2 + S.$$

Hence, *sulphuric acid cannot be used to dry the gas*; neither, of course, can *quicklime*, which is a base and would react with hydrogen sulphide—

$$CaO + H_2S = CaS + H_2O.$$

It is best, therefore, to dry hydrogen sulphide by passing it through **U**-tubes containing *calcium chloride.*

Formula of Hydrogen Sulphide.—A known volume of the gas is placed in a eudiometer tube over mercury [if it is quite dry its action on mercury is extremely slow], and sparks are passed through it for some time. It is thus decomposed into hydrogen (gas) and sulphur (solid, hence volume can be neglected). The volume of hydrogen formed is found to be the same as that of the original hydrogen sulphide.

Hence, by Avogadro's Hypothesis—

1 molecule of the gas contains 1 molecule of hydrogen.

But the molecule of hydrogen is H_2.

∴ formula for hydrogen sulphide is H_2S_x, where x is still to be found.

To find x—

Determine the Vapour Density. This is found to be **17.**

$\therefore$ Mol. Wt. is 34.

But of these 34 parts we know that 2 are hydrogen.

$\therefore$ 32 parts are sulphur.

But the atomic weight of sulphur is 32, $\therefore x = 1$, and the FORMULA is H_2S.

OXIDES OF SULPHUR.

Sulphur forms several oxides, of which the chief are *sulphur dioxide*, SO_2 (gas), and *sulphur trioxide*, SO_3 (solid).

Sulphur dioxide, SO_2.—If we may judge from their accounts of their experiments, one of the chief amusements of the alchemists was burning sulphur or sulphides, so that they must have made sulphur dioxide innumerable times. In those days, however, the chemistry of gases was not yet studied, and gases were thought to be nothing more than varieties—generally impure—of ordinary air. The first man to collect, and examine the properties of, sulphur dioxide was PRIESTLEY, who in the year of the discovery of oxygen (1774) made it by heating sulphuric acid with mercury—

$$Hg + 2H_2SO_4 = HgSO_4 + 2H_2O + SO_2.$$

Three years later (1777) it was investigated by LAVOISIER, who showed that it was a compound of sulphur and oxygen.

PREPARATION.—When sulphur is heated in air to a sufficiently high temperature it takes fire and burns with a ghostly blue flame; the product is sulphur dioxide—

$$S + O_2 = SO_2.$$

This, however, is not a convenient way of preparing the gas in the laboratory, although it is used on the commercial scale. In the laboratory we prefer to make it by heating concentrated sulphuric acid with copper. Other metals will do (*e.g.* mercury—see above—and zinc), but copper is chosen, since it is cheaper than mercury and because the action goes very quietly. The equation for the reaction is usually given as follows, though in all probability the changes are much more complex—

$$Cu + 2H_2SO_4 = CuSO_4 + 2H_2O + SO_2.$$

[Note that the residue in the flask is *black*, because some cuprous sulphide, Cu_2S, is formed in a side-reaction.]

The apparatus employed is shown in Fig. 82.

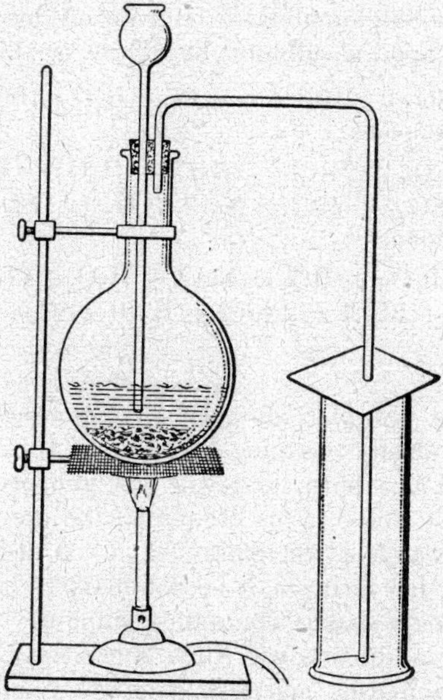

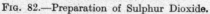

FIG. 82.—Preparation of Sulphur Dioxide.

White fumes (sulphur trioxide, etc.) contaminate the sulphur dioxide prepared in this way. They may be removed by bubbling the gas through cold concentrated sulphuric acid.

Since sulphur dioxide is soluble in water but heavier than air (V.D. = 32 ; V.D. of air = 14·4), it is collected by downward displacement. It can be collected over mercury, and if required dry should be bubbled through concentrated sulphuric acid.

Commercial Preparation.—Sulphur dioxide is prepared commercially by burning sulphur or iron pyrites in air—

$$\text{(i) } S + O_2 = SO_2,$$
$$\text{(ii) } 4FeS_2 + 11O_2 = 2Fe_2O_3 + 8SO_2,$$

or by heating coke with concentrated sulphuric acid—

$$C + 2H_2SO_4 = 2SO_2 + 2H_2O + CO_2.$$

Formation.—Sulphur dioxide is given off by the action of a dilute acid upon a sulphite, bisulphite or thiosulphate—

$$\underset{\text{Sodium sulphite.}}{Na_2SO_3} + 2HCl = 2NaCl + H_2O + SO_2.$$

$$(\text{Cf. } Na_2CO_3 + 2HCl = 2NaCl + H_2O + CO_2.)$$

$$\underset{\text{Sodium bisulphite.}}{NaHSO_3} + HCl = NaCl + H_2O + SO_2.$$

$$(\text{Cf. } NaHCO_3 + HCl = NaCl + H_2O + CO_2.)$$

$$\underset{\text{Sodium thiosulphate.}}{Na_2S_2O_3} + 2HCl = 2NaCl + H_2O + SO_2 + S\downarrow.$$

PROPERTIES.—Sulphur dioxide is a colourless gas with a very pungent smell (" burning sulphur "). It is much heavier than air, will not burn, and will not support combustion. Germs and the lower forms of animal life are readily killed by the gas, which is therefore used as a disinfectant. In many schools, for instance, it is customary to burn weekly in the dormitories a candle containing sulphur.

Moist sulphur dioxide will turn blue litmus red, and will bleach many colouring matters. It is easily soluble in water, and the solution has the same acidic and bleaching properties. When sulphur dioxide dissolves in water, combination occurs, and an unstable compound called *sulphurous acid*, H_2SO_3, is formed—

$$H_2O + SO_2 = H_2SO_3.$$

Chemists have attempted to get this substance out of the solution, but have always failed. If the solution is boiled, the sulphurous acid splits up again and sulphur dioxide is given off.

Sulphur dioxide can be liquefied without much difficulty;

you will see the liquid in a glass bottle fitted with a metal valve. If the valve is loosened, sulphur dioxide gas comes off, while if the bottle is inverted liquid sulphur dioxide can be run out.

Sulphurous acid, H_2SO_3.—Although this acid is not known in the pure state, as mentioned above, yet its salts, the *sulphites*, are fairly stable and can be obtained in the solid state. Sulphurous acid is a weak acid, but is stronger than carbonic, for when its solution is poured upon a carbonate effervescence takes place, carbon dioxide is evolved, and a solution of a sulphite is left—

$$e.g.\ Na_2CO_3 + H_2SO_3 = Na_2SO_3 + H_2O + CO_2 \uparrow .$$

The only sulphite you are likely to meet with is *sodium sulphite*, Na_2SO_3, which is a white crystalline solid. It can be made in the way just described, or by passing sulphur dioxide into caustic soda solution—

$$2NaOH + SO_2 = Na_2SO_3 + H_2O.$$

[Cf. $2NaOH + CO_2 = Na_2CO_3 + H_2O$, and note that sulphur dioxide, like carbon dioxide, is absorbed by caustic soda solution.]

The sulphites, like the carbonates, effervesce when a dilute acid is poured upon them, sulphur dioxide coming off—

$$Na_2SO_3 + H_2SO_4 = Na_2SO_4 + H_2O + SO_2.$$
$$K_2SO_3 + 2HNO_3 = 2KNO_3 + H_2O + SO_2.$$
$$CaSO_3 + 2HCl = CaCl_2 + H_2O + SO_2.$$

Sulphurous acid is a good *reducing agent*, since it is easily oxidized to sulphuric acid—

$$H_2SO_3 + \text{oxygen} = H_2SO_4.$$

Moist sulphur dioxide naturally behaves in the same way.

Examples.—

(i) Sulphur dioxide when passed into chlorine water reduces the chlorine to hydrochloric acid—

$$Cl_2 + SO_2 + 2H_2O = 2HCl + H_2SO_4$$
$$(\text{or } Cl_2 + H_2O + H_2SO_3 = 2HCl + H_2SO_4).$$

(ii) Sulphur dioxide reduces an acidified potassium dichromate solution, the colour of the liquid changing from the orange of the dichromate to the green of the chromium salt—

$$K_2Cr_2O_7 + 3H_2O + 3SO_2 + H_2SO_4 = K_2SO_4 + Cr_2(SO_4)_3 + 4H_2O.$$

For the action of sulphur dioxide upon hydrogen sulphide, see p. 298.

Bleaching Action of Sulphur Dioxide.—That the fumes of burning sulphur can be used for bleaching was known to the Romans, for PLINY, who was killed in the great eruption of Vesuvius which overwhelmed Pompeii in A.D. 79, mentions the fact in his *Natural History*. Nowadays, sulphur dioxide is used for bleaching delicate fabrics—silk, wool and straw—which would be rotted by chlorine. The colouring-matter is *reduced* to a colourless substance, while the moist sulphur dioxide is oxidized to sulphuric acid. The colourless substances formed in sulphur dioxide bleaching are usually easily oxidized back to the colouring-matter again, especially in the presence of sunlight. Hence, straw hats, which are light in colour at the beginning of the season, have usually gone quite yellow by the end.

FORMULA FOR SULPHUR DIOXIDE.—The apparatus employed is the same as that used in finding the formula of carbon dioxide (p. 328). Sulphur is placed on the boat and ignited by passing a current through the platinum wire. After the action is over it is found that the volume of sulphur dioxide formed is equal to that of the oxygen in which the sulphur was burnt.

Hence, 1 vol. of sulphur dioxide contains 1 vol. of oxygen.

$\therefore$ by Avogadro's Hypothesis—

1 molecule of sulphur dioxide contains 1 molecule of oxygen.

But the molecule of oxygen is O_2.

$\therefore$ formula for sulphur dioxide is S_xO_2.

To find x, take the V.D. This is found to be 32, $\therefore$ M.W. = 64. Of these 64 parts 32 are oxygen, $\therefore$ 32 are sulphur. But A.W. of sulphur = 32, $\therefore x = 1$, and—

FORMULA = SO_2.

Sulphur trioxide, SO_3, is a white crystalline solid made by passing a mixture of sulphur dioxide and oxygen over heated platinized asbestos, which acts as a catalyst—

$$2SO_2 + O_2 = 2SO_3.$$

It is a very hygroscopic substance, and dissolves in water with a hissing noise, forming *sulphuric acid*, H_2SO_4, of which it is therefore the *anhydride*.

Sulphuric acid, H_2SO_4, is not only very important in the laboratory; it is also the most important chemical of commerce. It is used directly or indirectly in practically every art and trade. Nearly 14,000,000 tons are produced annually.

Manufacture of Sulphuric Acid.

1. Lead-Chamber Process.—In this process a hot mixture of air and sulphur dioxide, containing also oxides of nitrogen, has a fine spray of water projected into it, when sulphuric acid is formed. Nitric oxide acts as an oxygen-carrier, combining with atmospheric oxygen, and handing it on to the sulphur dioxide, thus forming sulphur trioxide, which is immediately converted by the water present into sulphuric acid. The nitric oxide is regenerated—

(i) $NO + \frac{1}{2}O_2$ (from air) $= NO_2$.
(ii) $H_2O + SO_2 + NO_2 = H_2SO_4 + NO$.
(iii) $NO + \frac{1}{2}O_2 = NO_2$.

The above equations show that there is no loss of nitric oxide in the operation; from this point of view, therefore, nitric oxide may be said to act as a catalyst in the reaction.

The sulphur dioxide required for the process is obtained by roasting iron pyrites, FeS_2, in a current of air. The gas issuing from the pyrites burners contains about 7 per cent. of sulphur dioxide, 83 per cent. nitrogen, and 10 per cent. oxygen. A small supply of oxides of nitrogen is now fed into the gas, to make up for the inevitable slight losses of these substances which occur in working. The oxides of nitrogen are prepared by the catalytic oxidation of ammonia by means of heated platinum in the presence of oxygen;

they were formerly prepared by the action of concentrated sulphuric acid upon nitre.

The mixture of air, sulphur dioxide, nitrogen, and *small* amounts of oxides of nitrogen now passes up the GLOVER tower, which is made of brickwork lined with lead, inside which again is another lining of fireproof bricks. The tower is packed with acid-proof tiles, and down it trickles a mixture of (*a*) dilute "chamber" acid (65 per cent. H_2SO_4) and (*b*) concentrated sulphuric acid (containing dissolved oxides of nitrogen) from the GAY-LUSSAC tower at the other end of the plant. As the hot gases pass up the Glover tower (i) they

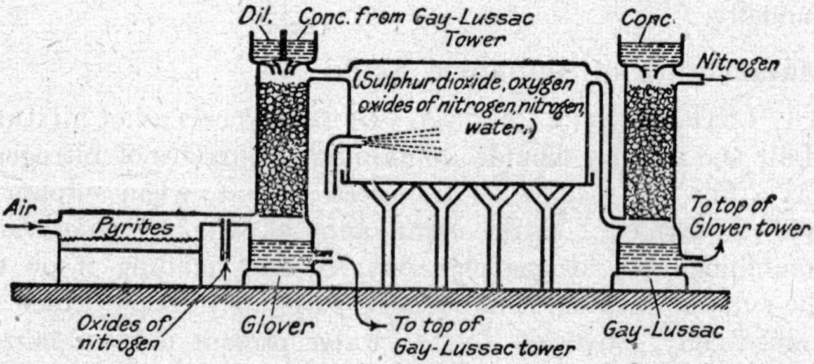

FIG. 83.—Diagram of Sulphuric Acid Plant.

are cooled to the proper temperature for reaction, (ii) they take up the necessary oxides of nitrogen by driving these out from the descending acid (remember that the oxides of nitrogen previously introduced are *only to make up for loss*; the main quantity of these oxides is taken up in the Glover tower), and (iii) they concentrate the acid which flows down the tower.

After the gases leave the Glover tower, they pass into a series of lead-chambers, where the main portion of the sulphuric acid is formed. (Some is formed in the Glover tower.) A fine spray of water is blown into the chambers from the roof and sides, and "chamber acid" collects on the floor, whence it can be drawn off. Chamber acid is never allowed to reach a concentration of more than 70 per cent. H_2SO_4, since stronger acid would dissolve the lead of the chambers.

The number and size of the chambers are so arranged that the conversion of sulphur dioxide into sulphuric acid is practically complete by the time the gases leave the last chamber. The residual gases consist chiefly of nitrogen and oxides of nitrogen. To recover the latter the Gay-Lussac tower is used. This is filled with acid-proof tiles, down over which a stream of cold concentrated sulphuric acid flows. This dissolves the oxides of nitrogen, probably forming a compound with them, while the nitrogen passes on into the chimney stack. The acid from the Gay-Lussac tower is then returned to the Glover tower, in which it loses its oxides of nitrogen as already described.

Summary of the Lead-Chamber Process.

Materials.— (i) Air.
(ii) Sulphur dioxide (by burning pyrites, FeS_2).
(iii) Spray of water.
(iv) Oxides of nitrogen (to act as catalyst). Used over and over again.

Passage of Gases.—

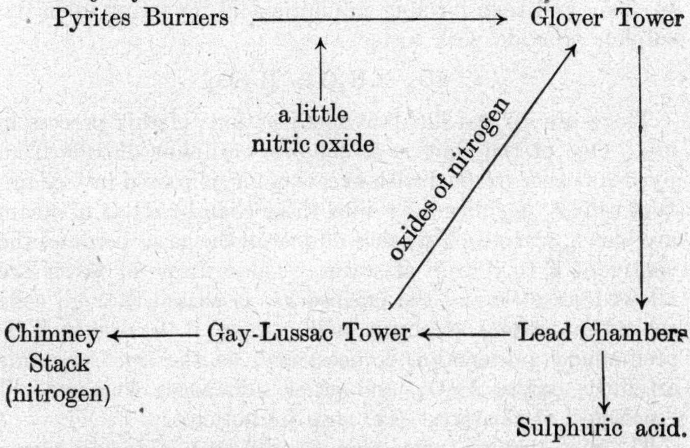

Use of Various Parts of Plant.—
(i) Pyrites Burners—formation of sulphur dioxide.

[(ii) Apparatus for catalytically oxidizing ammonia, to provide oxides of nitrogen to make up for working losses.]

(iii) Glover Tower—introduction of oxides of nitrogen, which have been dissolved in conc. sulphuric acid in the Gay-Lussac tower.

(iv) Lead Chambers—formation of sulphuric acid.

(v) Gay-Lussac Tower—absorption of residual oxides of nitrogen in conc. sulphuric acid, which is then pumped to the Glover Tower.

Concentration of the Chamber Acid.—The chamber acid (65–70 per cent.) is concentrated by passing it in a fine spray down a tower (the GAILLARD tower), made of acid-resisting lava, through which a current of hot gas from a coke furnace passes in the opposite direction. An acid of 92–97 per cent. strength collects at the base of the tower.

Another method of concentration is to blow a stream of hot air over the dilute acid contained in silica pans.

2. CONTACT PROCESS.—This consists in making sulphur trioxide according to the catalytic process already described (p. 305), and then forming sulphuric acid by acting upon the sulphur trioxide with water—

$$SO_3 + H_2O = H_2SO_4.$$

There are several different modifications of this process in use. One of the chief is as follows: Sulphur dioxide from pyrites burners, mixed with excess of air, is passed into chambers called "scrubbers"; into these chambers jets of steam are blown, when each particle of dust in the gases becomes the centre of a tiny drop of water. These drops of water are allowed to settle and the purified gas is passed through coke soaked in strong sulphuric acid, where it is dried. This preliminary purification is necessary, as the dust contains arsenious oxide, As_2O_3, and other substances which would "poison" the catalyst (*i.e.* stop its action).

The pure dry gas, consisting of sulphur dioxide and excess of air, is now passed through a series of tubes containing the catalyst, which consists of platinized asbestos, that is, asbestos which has been soaked in platinum chloride solution and then strongly heated, when the platinum chloride loses its chlorine and the platinum is left in a state of extremely fine division throughout the asbestos. In these tubes the reaction occurs. Heat is given out during the reaction, so that when it has been started by external heat it proceeds automatically, the rate of flow of the gases through the tubes being regulated in such a way that the heat evolved is just sufficient to keep the temperature at 400–450°.

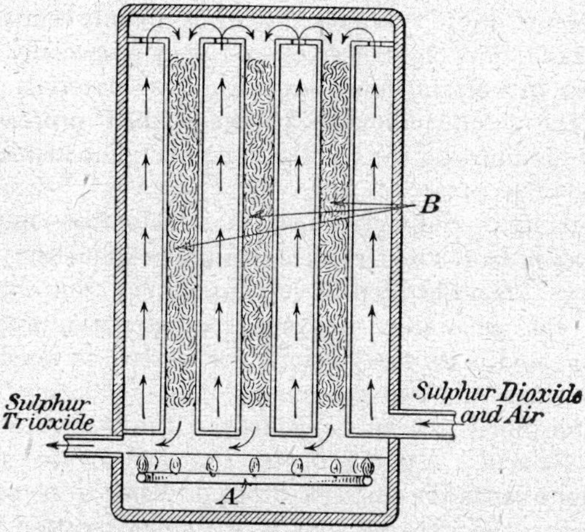

FIG. 84.—Diagram of the Contact Process.
A. Ring of gas burners. *B.* Catalyst.

The sulphur trioxide so produced is absorbed in 98 per cent. sulphuric acid in a large vat, water being run in at the same time at such a rate that the concentration of the acid in the vat remains constant at 98 per cent. When the vat is nearly full, the water may be turned off and the concentration of acid raised to 100 per cent. If sulphur trioxide is still passed in, it dissolves in the 100 per cent. acid, and forms *fuming sulphuric acid* or *oleum*, a solution of the trioxide in sulphuric acid.

At first, attempts were made to dissolve the sulphur trioxide in water directly, but this produced a mist of sulphuric acid which filled the works and proved extremely unpleasant to the workmen; moreover, much of the trioxide was converted into a glassy modification which dissolves in water much more slowly than the ordinary form.

Comparison of Lead-chamber and Contact Processes.—The lead-chamber process is the cheaper of the two, but gives a less pure acid. As for many purposes sulphuric acid need not be very pure, "chamber" acid still has a wide sale. At the present day, "contact" acid is mainly employed in the manufacture of explosives and dyes (especially indigo), and also in certain processes with food-materials such as beer. The sulphur dioxide for the contact process is frequently obtained by the combustion of sulphur instead of the roasting of pyrites.

PROPERTIES.—Sulphuric acid is a colourless oily liquid which can be frozen to a white crystalline solid melting at 10·5°. Ordinary "concentrated" sulphuric acid contains about 3 per cent. of water. A very characteristic property of sulphuric acid is its great avidity for water; so much heat is evolved when the two are mixed that in diluting the acid the latter must always be added to the water, and *never water to the acid.* Addition of water to concentrated sulphuric acid might cause the first few drops of water to be converted into steam, the expansion of which would scatter the acid explosively.

The great attraction which exists between sulphuric acid and water makes it an excellent drying agent for gases (*except* ammonia, with which it combines to form ammonium sulphate; hydrogen sulphide, which it oxidizes to sulphur; and nitric oxide, acetylene and ethylene, which it absorbs).

Sulphuric acid will often remove the *elements of water* from substances containing them; thus it chars moist sugar—

$$C_{12}H_{22}O_{11} = 12C + 11H_2O,$$

leaving a black mass of carbon. Paper, $(C_6H_{10}O_5)_n$, is similarly charred, while alcohol, C_2H_5OH, is converted into ethylene, C_2H_4—

$$C_2H_5OH = C_2H_4 + H_2O.$$

It is a dibasic acid, and forms two series of salts, *e.g.* with sodium it forms *sodium hydrogen sulphate*, $NaHSO_4$, and *normal sodium sulphate*, Na_2SO_4.

When passed through a red-hot silica tube sulphuric acid is split up into water, sulphur dioxide, and oxygen.

Questions

1. What does the word "sulphur" mean? Why is it an appropriate name for the element?
2. How does sulphur occur in nature?
3. How is sulphur extracted and refined?
4. Define *allotropy* and mention examples of the phenomenon.
5. How would you prepare (*a*) plastic sulphur, (*b*) monoclinic sulphur?
6. Describe the preparation and properties of hydrogen sulphide.
7. Upon what evidence is the formula H_2S given to hydrogen sulphide?
8. Write equations for the action of hydrogen sulphide upon solutions of the following salts: (*a*) lead nitrate, (*b*) mercuric nitrate, (*c*) bismuth chloride, (*d*) copper chloride, (*e*) cadmium nitrate, (*f*) arsenic chloride, (*g*) antimony chloride, (*h*) stannous chloride, (*k*) stannic chloride, (*l*) sodium carbonate.
9. What is the action of hydrogen sulphide upon (*a*) chlorine water, (*b*) bromine water, (*c*) sulphur dioxide?
10. How would you dry hydrogen sulphide?
11. Describe the preparation and properties of sulphur dioxide.
12. Contrast the bleaching action of chlorine with that of sulphur dioxide.
13. Upon what evidence is the formula SO_2 assigned to sulphur dioxide?
14. Describe the lead-chamber process for the manufacture of sulphuric acid.
15. Describe the contact process for the manufacture of sulphuric acid.

CHAPTER XVIII

CARBON AND SILICON

Carbon and silicon are two non-metallic elements which are put by chemists in the same family. There are several other elements in this family, of which the chief are tin and lead. All the members of the family have a valency of four, *i.e.* they are *quadrivalent*. Occasionally they may be *bivalent* as well. We shall see that carbon and silicon form compounds which are in many ways similar to one another, but carbon is a very remarkable element. It forms an enormous number of compounds—at least three-quarters of a million—which, while they are all more or less closely related, differ markedly in many ways from compounds of all other elements. For this reason, the study of carbon compounds has been made into a special branch of chemistry, called *organic* chemistry. The name " organic " refers to the fact that most of the substances which can be obtained from living or dead *organisms*—plants or animals—are carbon compounds, and it was at one time thought that these " organic compounds " could not be made in the laboratory, and did not obey the ordinary chemical laws. This we now know to have been a mistake, but the name is still retained. The chemistry of the compounds of other elements is called *inorganic* chemistry, and in a course of inorganic chemistry we usually study carbon itself and a few of its simpler compounds. In this book we shall consider not only these simple carbon compounds but also a few of the more complicated ones such as starch, sugar, alcohol and soap.

CARBON

Symbol : C ; *Valency :* 4 (very rarely 2) ; *Atomic Weight :* 12.

Occurrence.—Vast quantities of more or less impure carbon occur naturally as *coal,* which consists of fossilized remains of ancient plants. The *diamond* is a crystalline form of carbon, while *graphite* or " black lead " is also crystalline, but the crystals are not the same shape as those of the diamond. Carbon *compounds* are very widely distributed in large quantities. Thus there are the metallic *carbonates* (salts of *carbonic acid,* H_2CO_3), the chief being calcium carbonate, $CaCO_3$, which is found as limestone, chalk, marble, etc., and *dolomite* (of which the Dolomitic Alps are largely composed), a double carbonate of magnesium ($MgCO_3$) and calcium ($CaCO_3$). Other carbonates occur in smaller quantities.

In the air, carbon is always present as *carbon dioxide,* CO_2, which forms about 0·03–0·04 per cent. of the atmosphere by volume and is of vital importance to plant life (see p. 353). *Petrol* and *petroleum,* two essentials of modern civilization, are compounds consisting of carbon and hydrogen only ; such compounds are called *hydrocarbons.* The " natural gas " which comes off from gas-wells in various parts of the earth also consists of mixtures of hydrocarbons.

Carbon is the principal constituent of all living matter, and we shall see later that there is a continuous circulation of it from the atmosphere into the bodies of plants and animals and thence back again into the atmosphere—a circulation the necessary energy for which is derived from sunlight.

Properties.—Like oxygen and phosphorus and many other elements, carbon has the power of existing in *allotropic forms* (see pp. 202 and 292). Two of these are crystalline, *viz.* diamond and graphite, while the other is generally, though incorrectly, described as *amorphous,* or non-crystalline. All three forms are of great importance to mankind, but chemically the diamond and graphite are comparatively uninteresting.

To show that all three forms of carbon consist of the same element, and nothing else, we can make use of the facts (*a*) that when carbon is heated in air or oxygen it burns, forming carbon dioxide, and (*b*) that carbon dioxide is absorbed by caustic potash or soda solution (p. 383). If, therefore, we take known weights of (i) diamond, (ii) graphite, and (iii) pure "amorphous" carbon, burn them in a stream of oxygen, absorb the carbon dioxide so formed in a weighed solution of caustic soda, and so find the weight of the carbon dioxide produced, we shall be able to calculate the weight of carbon dioxide formed from 1 gram of each of the three allotropic

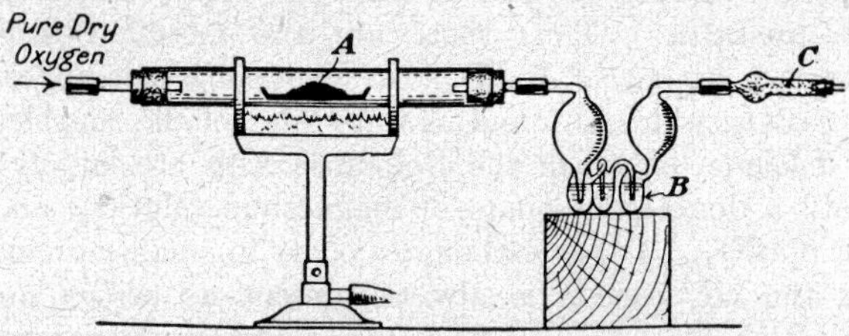

FIG. 85.—Apparatus to show that Diamond, Graphite and Amorphous Carbon are all allotropic forms of the same element.

forms. Experiments on these lines have shown that (i) from 1 gram of diamond we get 3·67 grams of carbon dioxide, (ii) from 1 gram of graphite we get 3·67 grams of carbon dioxide, and (iii) from 1 gram of amorphous carbon we get 3·67 grams of carbon dioxide, and *nothing else* in any one of the three cases. Hence all three substances are nothing but allotropic forms of the same element. The principle of the experiment is illustrated diagrammatically in Fig. 85. To get accurate results in practice the apparatus has to be modified considerably.

The weighed diamond or graphite or amorphous carbon is placed in a clean, dry, weighed porcelain boat A, and heated in a current of pure dry oxygen. The carbon dioxide is absorbed in the weighed bulbs B, which contain caustic soda solution. A calcium chloride tube C, weighed with the bulbs B, is provided to prevent loss of moisture from B. As the bulbs are originally weighed full of air, after the combustion is over the oxygen in the apparatus must be swept out with a current of dry air.

Diamond.

The diamond has been prized as a gem from time immemorial. It is found in many parts of the world, particularly South Africa, Brazil, and Australia. In South Africa diamonds occur in a blue clay, which is mined, exposed to the air for some months so that it may fall to a powder, and then stirred up in a stream of water. In this way the lighter particles are carried away, and the diamonds and heavier particles remain. The concentrated earth is then washed over a layer of grease, to which the diamonds stick, and from which they can afterwards be picked out by hand. The largest diamond ever discovered was the Cullinan (Transvaal, 1905). Before cutting it weighed 3,025¾ carats, or over a pound and a quarter (1 *carat* = 0·2054 gm.). Colourless diamonds are the most valuable; the "black diamonds" (*carbonado*) are used for making glass-cutters, etc., and for cutting and polishing the colourless stones.

The specific gravity of the diamond is 3·5, and it is the hardest substance known. It is very unreactive chemically. Acids have no effect upon it, but if it is heated to about 800° in the air it takes fire and burns brilliantly, forming carbon dioxide—

$$C + O_2 = CO_2.$$

It is thought that diamonds have been formed in the earth by the crystallization of carbon from its solution in iron, or perhaps in a silicate (p. 349), possibly under great pressure. Attempts to make diamonds artificially have not been very successful, though small ones may have been obtained by the great French chemist Moissan.

Graphite.

The name "graphite" was given to this substance on account of its use as a writing material (Greek *grapho*, I write). It was called *plumbago* or *blacklead* possibly because, like lead, it will mark paper, or because it was supposed to be a lead compound. It was not until 1800 that graphite was shown to be merely a crystalline form of carbon. Graphite occurs in large quantities in many different places: Bohemia, Ceylon, Siberia and California are the chief.

At Niagara it is prepared by heating coke with a little sand and pitch in an electric furnace for about 24–30 hours. In a finely powdered state it is used as a lubricant, and also to protect iron and steel (*e.g.* fenders, stoves and grates) from rust. Another important application of graphite is in the manufacture of pencils. The "lead" in pencils is made of powdered graphite mixed with clay.

Graphite forms shiny black crystals which feel greasy to the touch. It is a reasonably good conductor of heat and electricity, and is very unreactive chemically.

"Amorphous" Carbon.

Coal.—Coal has been formed by the decay of plant remains in the absence of air and under high pressure. There are several different varieties of coal, the composition of some of which is roughly given in the following table:

Variety.	Carbon. per cent.	Hydrogen. per cent.	Nitrogen and Oxygen. per cent.	Ash. per cent.
Lignite	60	5	30	5
Bituminous coal. . .	80	5	12	3
Cannel coal	83	5	10	2
Anthracite	93	3	2	2

Lignite or brown coal is a fossilized wood, something like peat but harder. *Bituminous coal* is the ordinary house coal. It is composed of the remains of flowerless plants which flourished in an amazing manner in the Carboniferous Age. These plants are now represented on the earth only by insignificant descendants such as the ferns and horse-tails. *Cannel coal* is so called because a piece of it if lit will burn like a *candle*. It is chiefly used for making coal-gas. *Anthracite* is a hard coal which may contain as much as 97 per cent. of carbon. It is used for heating boilers (hence the name *steam-coal*) and also in anthracite stoves.

Distillation of Coal.—When coal is heated in iron retorts in absence of air, four main products are formed:

(i) Coke (left in the retorts).

(ii) A watery liquid called the *ammoniacal liquor*. This contains ammonia, and is the source of much of tho ammonium su phate of commerce.

(iii) Coal-tar.

(iv) Coal-gas.

(i) COKE.—This consists chiefly of carbon (about 80 per cent.). It is used as a *fuel* and as a source of *gaseous fuels* (p. 348). It is also employed in obtaining metals from their ores (*e.g.* iron, p. 414).

(ii) AMMONIACAL LIQUOR.—For treatment of this liquid see p. 257.

(iii) COAL-TAR.—Tar is a black liquid containing many important substances, such as benzene ("benzol"), toluene ("toluol"), naphthalene (of which "moth-balls" are made), and phenol or carbolic acid. It is re-distilled, and as its chief constituents have different boiling-points they can be separated by collecting the distillate in various fractions. Benzene is important as a motor-fuel, and it and the other substances in coal-tar are converted by chemists into dyes (aniline dyes, etc.), explosives, drugs, and many other products of the greatest value. It is not too much to say that practically every industry and art in the country depends to some extent upon substances made from coal-tar.

(iv) COAL-GAS.—The crude gas which passes on from the receivers in which the ammoniacal liquor and tar are condensed is purified in chambers called "scrubbers" and "purifiers," and is then stored in large chambers called gasometers. It consists chiefly of hydrogen, methane or marsh-gas (p. 333), and carbon monoxide (p. 329). The proportions by volume are shown in the table:

Gas.	Volume percentage.
Hydrogen	43·0—55·0
Methane (CH_4)	25·0—35·0
Carbon monoxide (CO)	4·0—11·0
Other gases	4·5—21·5

Hydrogen, methane and carbon monoxide all burn with non-luminous flames. The luminosity of ordinary coal-gas flames is due to the presence in the gas of traces of acetylene (C_2H_2), benzene (C_6H_6), and ethylene (C_2H_4), all of which burn with luminous flames.

Coal-gas is supplied to consumers under a pressure of about 4 inches of water more than atmospheric pressure. This is very wasteful, and some companies are now supplying it at much higher pressures, thus giving a better service, and also doing away with the necessity of bulky and unsightly gasometers. When the gas is under high pressure the gas-mains themselves are quite large enough to store the whole quantity required.

Coal-gas used to be sold on the basis of so much per cubic foot. Since, however, practically all gas-burners are now of the incandescent mantle type, and since gas is very widely used as a fuel, it is clear that what the consumer is buying is really *heating power*. Hence gas is now sold at so much *per therm*, a therm being a measure of heating-power, *viz.* the amount of heat required to raise the temperature of 100,000 lb. of water through 1° Fahrenheit, or 100,000 British Thermal Units. If the heating value of a gas is stated to be 4·5 therms per 1,000 cubic feet, this means that 1,000 cubic feet of the gas when burnt produce enough heat to raise the temperature of 450,000 lb. of water 1° Fahrenheit. This method of charging is much fairer than the old way, for the heating value of gas may vary very considerably.

By treating coal with hydrogen under suitable conditions, it is possible to obtain petrol. This "hydrogenation of coal" has enormous commercial possibilities, and may render Europe independent of American and Asiatic oil.

Retort-carbon is a very hard form of carbon deposited as a lining on the retorts in gas-works. It is a good conductor of electricity, and is used for making the "carbons" for arc-lamps. *Soot* and *lampblack* are also forms of amorphous carbon. Lampblack contains oil and other substances as impurities. It is used in making *printers' ink* and for filling rubber for motor-car tyres.

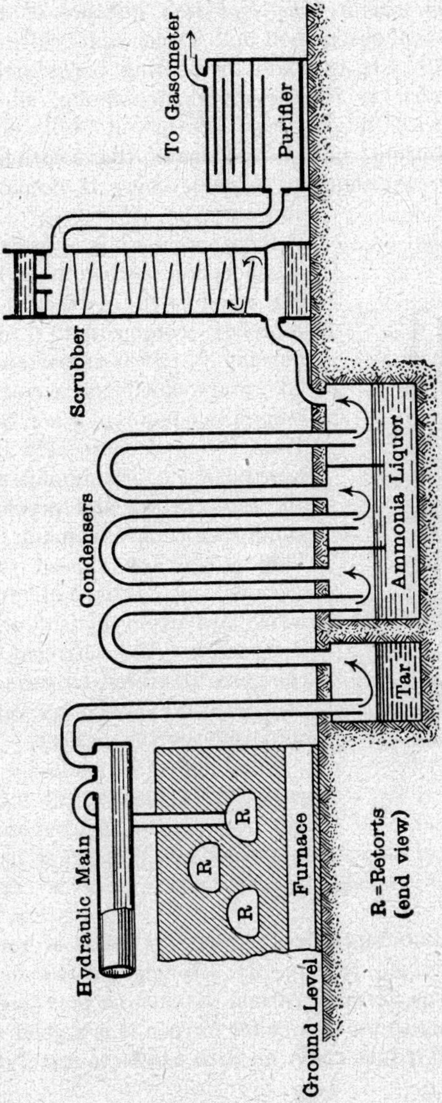

FIG. 86.—The Manufacture of Coal-gas.

Animal charcoal or *bone-black* is a mixture of about 10 per cent. amorphous carbon and 90 per cent. calcium phosphate (p. 279). It is made by heating bones strongly in absence of air. It is used in sugar-refining, since when boiled up with a coloured solution it will often absorb the colouring matter and leave the solution colourless. The brown solution of crude sugar is decolorized in this way.

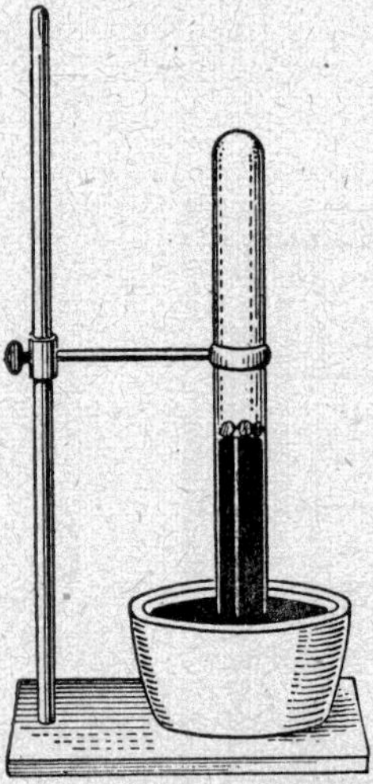

FIG. 87.—Absorption of Gases by Charcoal.

Wood charcoal is a porous form of amorphous carbon made by burning wood with insufficient air for complete combustion ("charcoal-burning"). It is important in the laboratory chiefly on account of its remarkable power of absorbing gases. Thus 1 c.c. of charcoal will absorb nearly 200 c.c. of ammonia at ordinary temperature and pressure, and almost as much sulphur dioxide. This property has been turned to account in "charcoal biscuits," which are eaten by sufferers from indigestion. The charcoal absorbs the gases produced by fermentation of food in the alimentary canal, and thus relieves the patient.

Pure carbon is made by heating pure sugar in air until it is completely charred, and then reheating the charred mass first in a current of chlorine and then in a current of hydrogen. The product is called sugar-carbon and is extremely pure.

CHEMICAL PROPERTIES OF CARBON.—Carbon is not a very chemically active element. If strongly heated in air or oxygen it burns, forming carbon dioxide, as previously mentioned. Owing to its affinity for oxygen it is a good *reducing agent*, and will reduce many metallic oxides to metal if heated with them, *e.g.*—

$$PbO + C = Pb + CO \text{ (carbon monoxide).}$$
$$CuO + C = Cu + CO.$$
$$Fe_2O_3 + 3C = 2Fe + 3CO.$$
$$ZnO + C = Zn + CO.$$

In such reductions carbon dioxide may be formed instead of, or as well as, carbon monoxide.

It will also combine directly with sulphur, if heated in a stream of sulphur vapour. The product is *carbon disulphide*, CS_2 (p. 345)—

$$C + S_2 = CS_2.$$

Most acids have no action upon it. It will, however, reduce hot concentrated sulphuric acid to sulphur dioxide—

$$C + 2H_2SO_4 = CO_2 + 2SO_2 + 2H_2O.$$

It will not react directly with the halogens, but if carbon is heated in a stream of hydrogen under certain conditions combination may occur between the two elements, the product being *methane* (CH_4) or *acetylene* (C_2H_2).

Alkalis have no action upon carbon.

Carbon will not dissolve in any common solvent, but can be dissolved in molten iron.

Compounds of Carbon.

Oxides of Carbon.—The principal oxides of carbon are *carbon monoxide*, CO (in which the carbon is bivalent) and *carbon dioxide*, CO_2.

Carbon dioxide, CO_2.—Carbon dioxide is by far the most important compound of carbon. It is a gas, and was discovered by the great chemist of the Netherlands, van Helmont (1577–1644), who called it *gas sylvestre* (" the wild gas of the woods "). Before van Helmont's time chemists had not troubled much about gases, regarding them merely as impure forms of ordinary air. Van Helmont, however, recognized their importance, and, in fact, invented the word " gas " to describe them. Carbon dioxide was rediscovered in 1754 by Joseph Black (p. 449), who called it "*fixed air*," and showed that it was liberated from chalk by the action of dilute acid.

Carbon dioxide is always present in the atmosphere, of which it forms about 0·03–0·04 per cent. by volume. Millions of tons of it are thrown into the air every day, since it is formed by the combustion of coal, petrol, wood, and any substance containing carbon, as well as in the breathing of animals and plants. We might expect, therefore, that its percentage in the air would increase, but in practice it is found that this does not happen. One reason is that carbon dioxide is the chief food of green plants, and is therefore *removed* from the air in vast quantities. (See p. 353.)

Besides occurring in the atmosphere, carbon dioxide is found dissolved in practically all natural waters, and occurs also in wells, caves, and grottos, especially in volcanic regions. Being much heavier than air, it collects in these low-lying places, and often renders the atmosphere there quite unfit to breathe. As carbon dioxide will not support combustion, a lighted lamp is used as a test for it in cellars, etc. If the lamp is extinguished the air is so rich in carbon dioxide that it would suffocate a man, while if it goes on burning he may enter the cellar safely. This test was known to the ancients, and is described by PLINY (died A.D. 79) in his *Natural History*.

PREPARATION.—Although carbon dioxide is formed when carbon is burnt in air or oxygen, it is usually prepared in the laboratory by the action of a dilute acid upon a carbonate (salt of *carbonic acid*, H_2CO_3). Any carbonate and any acid will do, but marble and dilute hydrochloric acid are generally employed. The marble is placed in a Woulfe bottle and the gas, which comes off without the application of heat, is dried by passing through concentrated sulphuric acid and collected by downward displacement (or over mercury)—

$$CaCO_3 + 2HCl = CaCl_2 + H_2O + CO_2.$$

We see from this equation that 100 grms. (the G.M.W.) of marble (calcium carbonate) yield 22·4 litres of dry carbon dioxide at N.T.P. To get carbon dioxide quickly in the laboratory, we generally keep a Kipp's apparatus (Fig. 88) at hand, containing marble and hydrochloric acid.

Dr. Joseph Black.

(From a contemporary caricature.)

Some equations for the action of various dilute acids upon carbonates are given below:

$$Na_2CO_3 + H_2SO_4 = Na_2SO_4 + H_2O + CO_2.$$
$$Na_2CO_3 + 2HNO_3 = 2NaNO_3 + H_2O + CO_2.$$
$$Na_2CO_3 + 2HCl = 2NaCl + H_2O + CO_2.$$
$$MgCO_3 + 2HCl = MgCl_2 + H_2O + CO_2.$$
$$K_2CO_3 + H_2SO_4 = K_2SO_4 + H_2O + CO_2.$$
$$MnCO_3 + 2HNO_3 = Mn(NO_3)_2 + H_2O + CO_2.$$
$$CaCO_3 + H_2SO_4 = CaSO_4 + H_2O + CO_2.$$

The last action, that of dilute sulphuric acid upon marble, starts quite vigorously but soon slows down and finally stops altogether. This is because the calcium sulphate, $CaSO_4$, which is formed, is insoluble in water and forms a protective coating over the surface of the remaining marble, thus preventing the acid from getting at it.

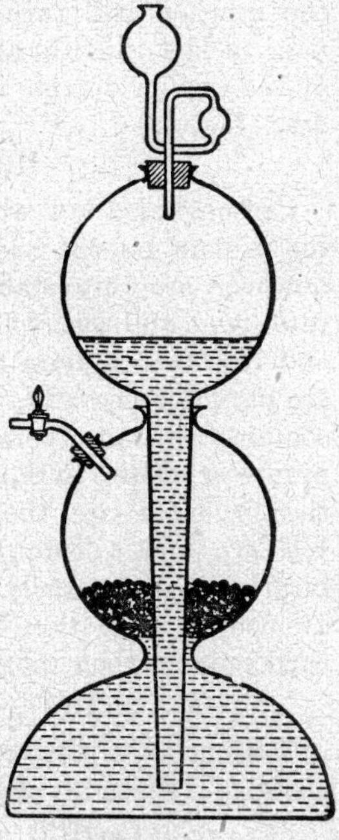

FIG. 88.—Kipp's Apparatus.

Carbon dioxide may also be formed by strongly heating the carbonates of all common metals except sodium and potassium. Thus when zinc or calcium carbonate is strongly heated carbon dioxide is given off and the oxide of the metal left—

$$ZnCO_3 = ZnO + CO_2.$$
$$CaCO_3 = CaO + CO_2.$$

Commercially, carbon dioxide is made by fermenting sugar solution with yeast. For details about this process see below, p. 341. Another commercial process consists in heating limestone, $CaCO_3$ (p. 390), in special lime-kilns, constructed in such a way that the carbon dioxide which is evolved can be collected.

PROPERTIES.—Vapour Density, 22. Molecular Weight, 44.

Carbon dioxide is a colourless gas with a faint but quite distinct smell. It will not burn and will not support combustion or life. It is much heavier than air (V.D. of air = 14·4), and is easily liquefied. It is slightly soluble in water at ordinary pressure and more so under increased pressure. The solution in water is known as soda-water. Carbon dioxide is, indeed, the gas in all mineral and aërated water as well as in sparkling wines. Solid carbon dioxide, sometimes known as " dry ice," is used as a refrigerant, *e.g.* by ice-cream manufacturers.

Carbonic acid.—When carbon dioxide is dissolved in water the solution will turn blue litmus a purplish-red colour—it is, in fact, slightly acid. This is due to the fact that part of the carbon dioxide combines with water forming *carbonic acid*, H_2CO_3—

$$H_2O + CO_2 = H_2CO_3.$$

Carbonic acid is a weak acid, and is very unstable ; up to the present no one has succeeded in isolating it. Its salts, however, are quite stable and are well known. They are the *carbonates* and *bicarbonates*, *e.g.* Na_2CO_3, sodium carbonate, and $NaHCO_3$, sodium bi-carbonate. Most of the carbonates are insoluble in water, the chief exceptions to this rule being sodium carbonate, potassium carbonate (K_2CO_3) and ammonium carbonate $(NH_4)_2CO_3$. *All* bicarbonates are soluble ; the principal are those of sodium, $NaHCO_3$, potassium, $KHCO_3$, and calcium, $Ca(HCO_3)_2$. Sodium and potassium bicarbonates can easily be obtained in the solid state. They are neutral in solution, and on heating split up into the normal carbonate, carbon dioxide and water—

$$2KHCO_3 = K_2CO_3 + H_2O + CO_2.$$

Calcium bicarbonate is soluble in water and also very unstable ; it readily decomposes according to the equation—

$$Ca(HCO_3)_2 = CaCO_3 + H_2O + CO_2.$$

It can, however, be obtained in the solid state.

All carbonates and bicarbonates effervesce when a dilute acid is added to them, carbon dioxide being evolved and the corresponding salt of the metal left. This, therefore, forms a convenient way of making a given salt of a metal. Suppose, for instance, we wanted to prepare calcium nitrate. We could dissolve calcium carbonate in dilute nitric acid, adding so much that a little was left undissolved. We could then filter off the excess and evaporate the clear solution—

$$CaCO_3 + 2HNO_3 = Ca(NO_3)_2 + H_2O + CO_2.$$

The carbonates of sodium, potassium and ammonium are *alkaline* in solution, since carbonic acid is such a weak acid.

To prepare carbonates, we can pass carbon dioxide into a solution of the metallic hydroxide if this is soluble, *e.g.*—

$$2NaOH + CO_2 = Na_2CO_3 + H_2O,$$

or, if the desired carbonate is insoluble, we can precipitate it by adding a solution of sodium carbonate to a solution of a soluble salt of the metal concerned, *e.g.*—

$$BaCl_2 + Na_2CO_3 = BaCO_3 \downarrow + 2NaCl.$$

Sodium and potassium bicarbonates can be made by passing carbon dioxide into a solution of the corresponding carbonate—

$$K_2CO_3 + H_2O + CO_2 = 2KHCO_3.$$

For calcium bicarbonate, see below.

Action of Carbon Dioxide on Lime-water.—We have just seen that carbon dioxide is absorbed by caustic soda or potash solution, with which it forms either the carbonate or bicarbonate according to the amount of carbon dioxide passed. A similar reaction occurs with lime-water, which is a solution of calcium hydroxide, $Ca(OH)_2$. In this case, however, the carbonate which is first formed is insoluble and comes down as a white precipitate, thus "turning the lime-water milky"—

$$Ca(OH)_2 + CO_2 = CaCO_3 \downarrow + H_2O.$$

This reaction, which is very characteristic, is used as a *test for carbon dioxide.*

Further passage of carbon dioxide turns the milky liquid clear again, owing to the formation of calcium *bicarbonate*, which is soluble—

$$CaCO_3 + H_2O + CO_2 = Ca(HCO_3)_2.$$

On boiling this clear solution, the bicarbonate is decomposed and the carbonate re-precipitated, thus turning the liquid milky again—

$$Ca(HCO_3)_2 = CaCO_3 \downarrow + H_2O + CO_2.$$

Here we have an example of a *reversible reaction,* that is, one which will go either way according to the conditions. (For other examples of reversible action, see p. 152.) In this connection it may be mentioned that the dissociation of calcium carbonate into quicklime and carbon dioxide is also reversible, for when carbon dioxide is passed over quicklime calcium carbonate is formed—

$$CaCO_3 \rightleftharpoons CaO + CO_2.$$

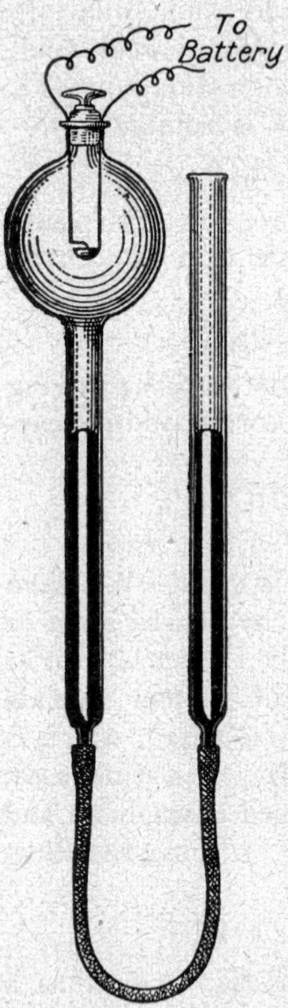

FIG. 89.—Composition of Carbon Dioxide.

If calcium carbonate is heated *in a closed vessel* so that the carbon dioxide cannot escape, it is found that an equilibrium between the two reactions is set up, and that at a given temperature there is always a definite pressure of carbon dioxide.

COMPOSITION OF CARBON DIOXIDE.—If a weighed quantity of carbon is burnt in oxygen and the weight of carbon dioxide produced is found, by absorbing the gas in a weighed bulb containing caustic soda solution and finding the increase in weight, the composition of carbon dioxide by weight can be calculated. Experiments on these lines have shown that the ratio of carbon to oxygen in carbon dioxide is exactly 3 : 8. The vapour density of the gas is 22, ∴ its molecular weight is 44. The atomic weight of carbon is 12 and that of oxygen is 16. Hence the formula for the gas must be CO_2.

Volumetrically the composition of carbon dioxide may be determined by burning a piece of carbon in a measured volume of oxygen. The apparatus employed is shown in Fig. 89. Oxygen is enclosed in the bulb and part of the left limb of the tube, and its pressure is adjusted to the atmospheric pressure by altering the position of the right limb until the mercury is at the same level in both limbs. The carbon, which is on the spoon on the bulb, is ignited by passing an electric current through a platinum wire which just touches it. The wire becomes red-hot and fires the carbon. After the reaction is over, the apparatus is allowed to cool, and the mercury again adjusted so that the pressure of the residual gas is atmospheric.

It is found that there is *no change in volume.* Hence—
1 volume of oxygen produces 1 volume of carbon dioxide, or
1 volume of oxygen is contained in 1 volume of carbon dioxide.
∴ By Avogadro's Hypothesis (equal volumes of all gases under the same conditions of temperature and pressure contain equal numbers of molecules)—

1 molecule of oxygen is contained in 1 molecule of carbon dioxide.

But the formula for the molecule of oxygen is O_2.

∴ the formula for the molecule of carbon dioxide is C_xO_2.

To get x, we find the V.D. This is 22; therefore the M.W. is 44.

But of these 44 parts we know that 32 are oxygen.

∴ 12 parts are carbon.

But the Atomic Weight of carbon is 12, ∴ $x = 1$, and the formula is CO_2.

Carbon Dioxide in the Air.—For an account of the important part played in plant and animal life by the carbon dioxide in the air, see p. 353.

Carbon monoxide, CO.—When carbon dioxide is passed through a tube containing red-hot carbon (*e.g.* coke), the following reaction occurs—

$$C + CO_2 = 2CO.$$

The product, carbon monoxide, is a colourless gas, which will burn with a blue non-luminous flame. As it is insoluble in water it may be collected at the pneumatic trough. To make sure that it is free from any traces of carbon dioxide which might be carried over, it can be passed first through a Drechsel bottle containing caustic soda (Fig. 90).

In the laboratory we generally make carbon monoxide by acting upon *formic acid* (H_2CO_2 or H.COOH) or *oxalic acid* $\left(H_2C_2O_4 \text{ or } \begin{array}{l}COOH\\|\\COOH\end{array}\right)$ with concentrated sulphuric acid. The latter is such a powerful reagent that it splits up the formic acid or oxalic acid molecules, and possesses itself of the water

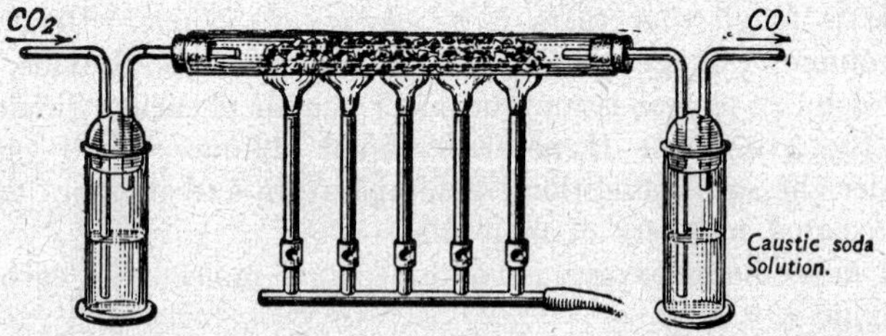

FIG. 90.—Preparation of Carbon Monoxide from Carbon Dioxide.

which is one of the products in each case. The residue of the formic acid is carbon monoxide, and of the oxalic acid a mixture of carbon monoxide and carbon dioxide in equal volumes—

$$\text{(i)} \quad H_2CO_2 = H_2O + CO.$$
$$\text{(ii)} \quad H_2C_2O_4 = H_2O + CO + CO_2.$$

An apparatus suitable for small scale work is shown in Fig. 91.

Concentrated sulphuric acid is placed in the tap-funnel, and the oxalic or formic acid in the flask. On running in the sulphuric acid and heating the flask, the gas is evolved. In the case of oxalic acid, it is necessary to insert a Drechsel bottle containing caustic soda solution to absorb the carbon dioxide which is evolved. The carbon monoxide is then collected over water or, if required dry, over mercury. It cannot be collected by displacement of air since its V.D. is 14, i.e. $\left(\frac{12 + 16}{2}\right)$, which is too close to that of air (14·4).

Carbon monoxide is also formed when a metallic oxide is reduced with carbon, and (mixed with an equal volume of hydrogen) when steam is passed over white-hot coke—

e.g. (i) $ZnO + C = Zn + CO$.
(ii) $H_2O + C = CO + H_2$.

The mixture of carbon monoxide and hydrogen obtained in the second of these reactions is known as *water-gas*, and is used as a fuel (p. 348).

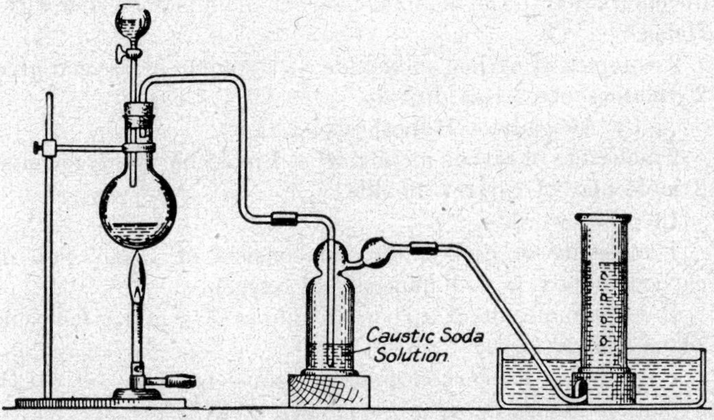

FIG. 91.—Preparation of Carbon Monoxide from Oxalic Acid.

PROPERTIES.—Carbon monoxide is a colourless gas with no taste or smell. It is insoluble in water, and burns with a characteristic blue lambent (" licking ") flame, forming carbon dioxide—

$$2CO + O_2 = 2CO_2.$$

It is extremely poisonous, as it puts the blood out of action, and thus causes death by a kind of suffocation. It is insoluble in caustic soda solution and will not turn lime-water milky.

Owing to its inflammability it may easily be mistaken in the laboratory for hydrogen, from which, however, it may readily be distinguished (*a*) by the fact that it is scarcely lighter than air, and (*b*) by burning it and testing for carbon dioxide afterwards with lime-water.

Since carbon monoxide can take up oxygen to pass into carbon dioxide, it is a *reducing agent*, and can be made to reduce metallic oxides to the metal.

COMPOSITION OF CARBON MONOXIDE.—If a mixture of 2 volumes of carbon monoxide and 1 volume of oxygen is placed in a eudiometer over mercury and sparked, an explosion takes place and carbon dioxide is formed. On allowing the apparatus to regain the original temperature and pressure, it is found that the volume of carbon dioxide produced is equal to the volume of carbon monoxide started with. Hence—

2 volumes of carbon monoxide + 1 volume of oxygen give 2 volumes of carbon dioxide.

∴ by Avogadro's Hypothesis—

2 molecules of carbon monoxide + 1 molecule of oxygen give 2 molecules of carbon dioxide.

In other words—

1 molecule of carbon dioxide consists of 1 molecule of carbon monoxide + $\frac{1}{2}$ molecule of oxygen.

But the molecule of carbon dioxide is CO_2, and $\frac{1}{2}$ molecule of oxygen is O.

∴ Formula for carbon monoxide must be $CO_2 - O = CO$.

Carbon Monoxide as a Fuel.—See p. 348.

Hydrocarbons (Compounds consisting of Carbon and Hydrogen only).—Many hydrocarbons, such as petroleum and "natural gas," are found naturally occurring in the earth's crust, and others, such as acetylene, are known to exist in the atmosphere of some of the cooler stars. Marsh-gas, or methane, CH_4, is formed by the decay of vegetable matter in absence of air, and therefore occurs under water in marshy places and stagnant ponds and backwaters. It is found also in coal-mines, where it is called *fire-damp*. Other hydrocarbons such as *benzene*, C_6H_6, are obtained by the distillation of coal (p. 317). Hydrocarbons are extraordinarily important compounds, both chemically and commercially.

Altogether there are thousands and thousands of them, but in this book we shall deal with only a few of the chief ones, *viz.* methane, ethylene, acetylene, petrol and petroleum, and benzene.

Methane or Marsh-gas, CH_4.—The occurrence in nature of this compound has already been mentioned. It is found also as one of the constituents of the gases from certain gas-wells. Occasionally the bubbles of marsh-gas which come off in bogs and marshes take fire, thus producing the phenomenon known as *will-o'-the-wisp*.

In the laboratory, methane is generally prepared by heating a mixture of sodium acetate with caustic soda. Ordinary

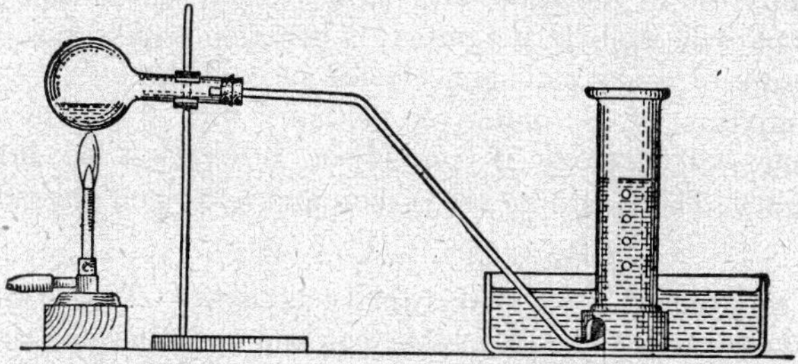

FIG. 92.—Preparation of Methane.

sodium acetate crystals contain water of crystallization ($C_2H_3O_2Na.3H_2O$); this is removed by heating before the acetate is used for the preparation of methane, the *anhydrous* salt, $C_2H_3O_2Na$, being left. Instead of pure caustic soda, it is customary to use *soda-lime*, which is lime that has been stirred up with melted caustic soda, the mixture then being allowed to cool. In a reaction it behaves like caustic soda, but it has two great advantages—(1) it is not deliquescent, and (2) it does not melt easily. Caustic soda is very deliquescent and readily melts, and molten caustic soda quickly attacks glass.

The equation for the action is—

$$C_2H_3O_2Na + NaOH = Na_2CO_3 + CH_4.$$

The apparatus used is shown in Fig. 92. Methane is insoluble in water, and hence may be collected at the pneumatic trough. If required dry it may be bubbled through concentrated sulphuric acid and collected over mercury.

Methane may also be conveniently prepared by the action of water (or dilute hydrochloric acid) upon aluminium carbide, Al_4C_3—

$$Al_4C_3 + 12H_2O = 4Al(OH)_3 + 3CH_4.$$

PROPERTIES.—Methane is a colourless gas with no taste or smell. It is difficult to liquefy, but liquefaction has been carried out. Methane is insoluble in water, and burns with a practically non-luminous flame, forming carbon dioxide and water—

$$CH_4 + 2O_2 = CO_2 + 2H_2O.$$

A mixture of methane with air or oxygen in certain proportions will explode if ignited—a reaction which has been the cause of many serious accidents in coal-mines.

A mixture of 1 volume of methane with 2 volumes of chlorine will explode if ignited or if exposed to bright sunlight. The products are carbon and hydrogen chloride—

$$CH_4 + 2Cl_2 = C + 4HCl.$$

Slow reaction takes place in ordinary daylight. The products in this case are *methyl chloride* (a gas) and hydrogen chloride—

$$CH_4 + Cl_2 = \underset{\text{Methyl chloride.}}{CH_3Cl} + HCl.$$

Under suitable conditions, this *substitution* process may be continued until *all* the hydrogen of the methane has been replaced by chlorine—

(i) $CH_4 + Cl_2 = HCl + CH_3Cl$, *monochloromethane* or *methyl chloride.*

(ii) $CH_3Cl + Cl_2 = HCl + CH_2Cl_2$, *dichloromethane.*

(iii) $CH_2Cl_2 + Cl_2 = HCl + CHCl_3$, *trichloromethane* or *chloroform.*

(iv) $CHCl_3 + Cl_2 = HCl + CCl_4$, *tetrachloromethane* or *carbon tetrachloride.*

Methane is a very stable compound, and not very reactive. It forms a constituent of coal-gas (see p. 317).

COMPOSITION OF METHANE.—The composition of methane

may be determined by eudiometry. By taking a known volume of methane, adding an excess of oxygen, exploding, and measuring the volumes of oxygen left and carbon dioxide formed, we can obtain sufficient data to enable us to calculate the formula. Thus, in an experiment—

27·5 c.c. of methane were mixed with 60 c.c. of oxygen, and the mixture exploded. After the apparatus had regained the original temperature and pressure it was found that the residual gases occupied 32·5 c.c. These gases were the carbon dioxide formed, together with the unused oxygen. On addition of caustic soda solution a decrease in volume occurred, due to absorption of the carbon dioxide. The residual gas, namely, the excess of oxygen, occupied 5 c.c. [As the experiment was done at ordinary temperature, the water vapour produced condensed to liquid water, whose volume, in comparison with that of the gases, is so small that it may be left out of account.] From these figures we can calculate the formula of methane.

The residual oxygen + carbon dioxide formed	= 32·5 c.c.
But residual oxygen	= 5·0 c.c.
∴ vol. of carbon dioxide formed	= 27·5 c.c.

Hence, 27·5 c.c. of methane gave 27·5 c.c. of carbon dioxide, or 1 volume of methane would give 1 volume of carbon dioxide.

∴ by Avogadro's Hypothesis, 1 molecule of methane would give 1 molecule of carbon dioxide. But 1 molecule of carbon dioxide contains 1 atom of carbon, ∴ 1 molecule of methane contains 1 atom of carbon.

Now 60 c.c. of oxygen were taken and 5 c.c. were left; hence 55 c.c. must have been used. But 27·5 c.c. of methane would require only 27·5 c.c. of oxygen to convert the carbon in it to carbon dioxide (from above). ∴ 55 – 27·5, *i.e.* 27·5 c.c. of oxygen must have been used to burn the hydrogen. In other words, 1 volume of methane requires 1 volume of oxygen to convert the hydrogen in it into water.

∴ by Avogadro's Hypothesis—

1 molecule of methane requires 1 molecule of oxygen to

burn its hydrogen. But the molecule of oxygen is O_2, and each oxygen atom will combine with 2 hydrogen atoms.

∴ 1 molecule of oxygen will burn 4 atoms of hydrogen.

Thus we see that 1 molecule of methane contains 1 atom of carbon and 4 atoms of hydrogen.

∴ Formula for methane = CH_4.

Ethylene, C_2H_4.—This gas does not occur free in nature, but is contained in small proportion in coal-gas (see p. 318). It is prepared in the laboratory by heating alcohol (p. 343) with concentrated sulphuric acid. As we saw when dealing with carbon monoxide (p. 330), sulphuric acid often causes great perturbation in organic compounds and causes them to split up. With alcohol—a typical organic compound—this is just what takes place. The alcohol decomposes into ethylene and water and the sulphuric acid greedily seizes the latter. It is, of course, quite wrong to say that the sulphuric acid "takes water out of the alcohol," for pure alcohol contains no water. It contains hydrogen and oxygen, but that is a different matter.

The equation for the action is

$$\underset{\text{Alcohol.}}{C_2H_6O} = \underset{\text{Ethylene.}}{C_2H_4} + H_2O.$$

It appears, therefore, that a small quantity of sulphuric acid should be able to convert quite a large quantity of alcohol into ethylene and water, and this conclusion is borne out in practice.

The apparatus employed for the reaction is shown in Fig. 93. A mixture of alcohol and sulphuric acid is placed in the flask, and more alcohol can be run in, as desired, from the tap-funnel. The gas may be collected over water. As it usually contains sulphur dioxide and carbon dioxide as impurities, it is well to pass it through a Drechsel bottle containing caustic soda solution before collecting it.

To dry ethylene it should be passed through a calcium chloride tube and *not* through concentrated sulphuric acid, which, when cold, slowly absorbs it.

PROPERTIES.—Ethylene is a colourless gas with a sweetish taste and smell. It burns with a luminous flame, and yields an explosive mixture with air or oxygen. One of its most characteristic properties is that it will combine directly with bromine or chlorine, forming colourless oils, *ethylene dibromide* and *ethylene dichloride*—

(i) $C_2H_4 + Br_2 = C_2H_4Br_2$. (ii) $C_2H_4 + Cl_2 = C_2H_4Cl_2$.

(Contrast action of chlorine upon methane, p. 334.)

These substances are called *addition compounds*. Compounds, like ethylene, which will form addition compounds, are called *unsaturated* (*e.g.* ammonia, which "adds on" hydrochloric acid—$NH_3 + HCl = NH_4Cl$. See p. 267).

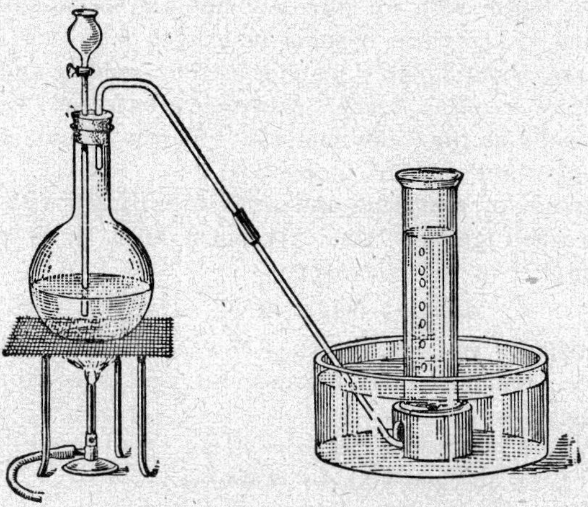

FIG. 93.—Preparation of Ethylene.

COMPOSITION OF ETHYLENE.—The composition of ethylene like that of methane, can be found by eudiometry. Calculate the formula for ethylene from the following data—

(i) Vol. of ethylene taken = 30 c.c.
(ii) ,, ,, ,, + oxygen added = 131 c.c.
(iii) ,, after explosion,
i.e. vol. of carbon dioxide + excess of oxygen = 71 c.c.
(iv) Vol. after addition of caustic soda solution,
i.e. vol. of oxygen left over = 11 c.c.

(Volume of water formed may be neglected.)

Acetylene, C_2H_2.—This is the well-known gas made by the action of water upon calcium carbide—

$$CaC_2 + 2H_2O = Ca(OH)_2 + C_2H_2.$$

Prepared in this way it is slightly impure. When pure it has a sweetish smell, not unlike that of ethylene and not at all objectionable.

Acetylene is a colourless gas, insoluble in water. It burns with a very smoky flame unless special burners are used, designed to supply plenty of air to the flame. From these burners it is delivered either as a fine jet or as a thin sheet, and then burns with an intensely hot and brilliant flame. The flame of acetylene burning in oxygen is as hot as the electric arc (about 3,500° C.), and is used for welding and steel-cutting (*oxy-acetylene flame*). Acetylene is extremely valuable commercially as the " raw material " for the manufacture of many important carbon compounds.

A mixture of acetylene and oxygen explodes with great violence when ignited: this experiment must *on no account* be attempted in the laboratory—

$$2C_2H_2 + 5O_2 = 4CO_2 + 2H_2O.$$

COMPOSITION OF ACETYLENE.—This is determined by eudiometry. Calculate the formula for acetylene from the following data—

(i) Vol. of acetylene taken = 10 c.c.
(ii) ,, ,, oxygen added = 33 c.c.
(iii) Vol. of gases left after explosion,
i.e. carbon dioxide + unused oxygen = 28 c.c.
(iv) Vol. after addition of caustic soda solution,
i.e. vol. of unused oxygen = 8 c.c.

(Volume of water formed may be neglected.)

Petrol and Petroleum are liquid hydrocarbons very similar to methane in their chemical properties. Unlike ethylene (and acetylene) they will not form addition compounds. Petroleum is supposed to have been formed by the decay, under great pressure, of the bodies of countless myriads of minute sea-organisms. It is a mixture of many hydrocarbons which, as they have different boiling-points, can be separated by distilling the petroleum and collecting the distillate in various fractions. The low boiling-point fractions are *petrol*, the middle ones *paraffin oil*, and the high boiling-point fractions include *vaseline*, etc. The importance of petrol and paraffin as fuels for motors and other engines need not be emphasized here. When burnt, they are converted into carbon dioxide and water.

Benzene (known to the public as "benzol" and not to be confused with "benzine" which consists of liquid hydrocarbons similar to methane) has the formula C_6H_6, and is obtained by the distillation of coal-tar, of which it forms one of the principal constituents. It is a colourless volatile liquid which burns with a smoky flame, and is extensively used as a solvent and as a fuel for motors. It is also employed on the large scale for conversion into *aniline* ($C_6H_5.NH_2$), which is the parent substance of thousands of beautiful dyes.

Starch, Sugar, Alcohol and Soap.—These are four common and important organic compounds with which every one is (or should be !) familiar. Their chemistry is rather complicated; even the most expert chemists do not yet know the composition of the starch molecule. However, we can gather some simple information about them, quite enough for our present purpose.

Starch.—Starch is the chief reserve food-material of green plants. It is usually obtained from potatoes, but it is found in large quantities in artichokes, wheat, barley, rye, oats, peas, beans, and other plants. It is present in the plant cells in the form of small grains (see Fig. 94), and the process of extracting it consists merely in crushing or cutting up the tissues of the plant so as to break the cell-walls.

The pulp so obtained is mixed with water and the mixture filtered through sieves whose mesh is large enough to allow the starch granules to pass through but sufficiently small to retain the débris of the plants. On allowing the turbid liquid to settle, the starch forms a layer at the bottom from which the bulk of the water can be poured or siphoned off. The starch is then dried at a gentle heat, and when dry is broken up into small pieces.

When heated with water, starch forms a kind of solution,

which is employed for "starching" linen, and also as a *test for free iodine*, with which it gives a characteristic *deep blue coloration.*

Starch is an important food. When taken into the mouth, it is attacked by an enzyme (p. 342) called *ptyalin*, which converts it into a sugar and thus renders it truly soluble in water. Since all food has to pass through the walls of the small intestine, and must therefore be dissolved (for solid substances cannot pass through a membrane) it is clear that unless starch was converted into a soluble substance like sugar it could not be absorbed by the body.

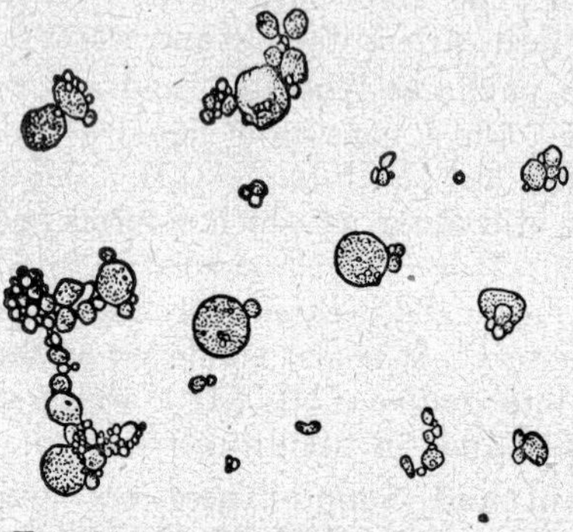

FIG. 94.—Starch Grains under the Microscope.

For the formation of starch in plants see p. 354.

The empirical formula for starch is $C_6H_{10}O_5$. Its true formula is not yet known.

Sugar.—Sugar is the name for a whole class of compounds, of which the chief are *cane-sugar*, $C_{12}H_{22}O_{11}$, and *grape-sugar*, $C_6H_{12}O_6$. Cane-sugar is extracted from the sugar-cane and sugar-beet. It is a white crystalline solid with a sweet taste, and, like starch, it is an important food substance. Young people require more sugar than older ones, hence we find that the child's fondness for sweets gradually diminishes as he grows up—though some of us retain a "sweet tooth" till our second childhood.

When sugar is treated with concentrated sulphuric acid a reaction takes place which (it is said) made the fortune of a well-known firm of boot-polish manufacturers. The sulphuric acid, as usual, splits up the sugar and combines with the water so formed, leaving a black mass of carbon—

$$C_{12}H_{22}O_{11} = 11H_2O + 12C.$$

This carbon is in a very fine state of division, and, after it has been washed free from sulphuric acid and dried, may be made up into a paste with oil. This paste is the old-fashioned "blacking," with which some of us in our schooldays had laboriously to try to get a polish on our boots.

The empirical formula for sugar may be determined by taking a known weight of it, burning it, and weighing the carbon dioxide and water formed. The weight of carbon dioxide is found by absorbing it in a weighed bulb containing caustic soda solution, and that of the water by absorbing it in a weighed calcium chloride tube. If we know that sugar consists of carbon, hydrogen and oxygen only, we can then calculate its *empirical* formula. To get its *true* formula we have, of course, to find its molecular weight, *e.g.* cryoscopically.

Alcoholic Fermentation.—Yeast is a tiny plant. An ordinary lump of yeast is composed of thousands and thousands of yeast plants, each of which consists of a single cell. A single yeast plant, which is oval in shape, is far too small to be seen with the naked eye, but it may be observed under the microscope. Fig. 95 shows you what yeast looks like when very much magnified.

One thing about yeast that will strike you at once is that

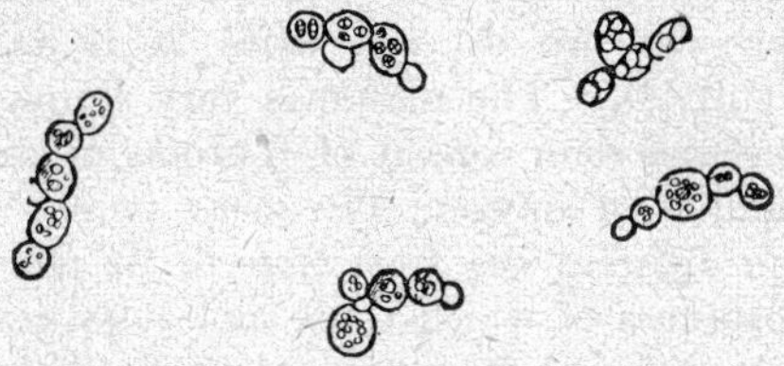

FIG. 95.—Yeast Cells.

it is not green. We shall see later (pp. 351–357) that ordinary green plants feed on the carbon dioxide in the air, which, using the energy of sunlight, they are able to build up into sugar and starch. You will find that the green colouring matter, *chlorophyll*, is essential to this process—plants which do not possess it cannot feed on carbon dioxide, but require ready-made food, as animals do.

When yeast is put into a solution of sugar, it multiplies exceedingly, and at the same time carbon dioxide comes off and alcohol is left in the solution. Now, in order to grow in this way, yeast requires energy. Most animals and plants get their energy by the slow oxidation of their tissues, which are replenished by the food they consume. The yeast plant, however, has to some extent solved the problem in another way. It contains complicated and mysterious substances called *enzymes* (the word *enzyme* is derived from the Greek, and means "in yeast": it was given to these substances because the first known examples were found in yeast, although we know now that enzymes occur in all living organisms), and by means of these enzymes it acts upon the sugar in a very peculiar way. Enzymes are in some respects very similar to the *catalysts* with which many chemical reactions are speeded up or slowed down: they are left unchanged at the end of the action, and so do not appear in the equation.

The first action that takes place when yeast is put into sugar solution is as follows—

$$C_{12}H_{22}O_{11} + H_2O = C_6H_{12}O_6 + C_6H_{12}O_6,$$

i.e. each molecule of sugar takes up a molecule of water and is converted into two molecules of the formula $C_6H_{12}O_6$. You may wonder why we do not write $2C_6H_{12}O_6$ instead of $C_6H_{12}O_6 + C_6H_{12}O_6$. The reason is very simple. Although the two molecules each consist of 6 atoms of carbon, 12 of hydrogen, and 6 of oxygen, *the atoms in one molecule are arranged in a different way from those in the other*, and hence the two substances of which these molecules are representative are quite different from one another. This is a phenomenon with which you have not met before, but it is not difficult to understand. We could write the formula for a house $B_{10,000}\ St_{2,000}\ S_{500}$, where B = bricks, St = stones and S = slates, but it is easy to see that such a formula would not give you any idea of the actual shape of the house, and that it might, in fact, correspond to several different houses of very different form and arrangement. It is exactly the same with atoms in a molecule. The properties of a substance depend not only upon the numbers and kinds of atoms in its molecule, but also upon the way in which they are arranged.

When cane-sugar is acted upon by yeast, then, the first reaction is—

$$\text{cane-sugar} + \text{water} = \text{grape-sugar} + \text{fruit-sugar}.$$
$$C_{12}H_{22}O_{11} + H_2O = C_6H_{12}O_6 + C_6H_{12}O_6.$$

The product is a mixture of two simpler sugars, grape-sugar and fruit-sugar, in equal weights. Grape-sugar or glucose is the sugar found in grapes and in honey, while fruit-sugar occurs in various fruits. The enzyme which brings about this change is called *invertase.* After it has accomplished its task the work is taken up by a second enzyme, called *zymase*, which converts both the grape-sugar and the fruit-sugar into alcohol (C_2H_6O) and carbon dioxide—

$$C_6H_{12}O_6 = 2C_2H_6O + 2CO_2.$$

The important point about this reaction happens to be one of those things which an ordinary chemical equation does not show. It is this—that the conversion of grape- or fruit-sugar into alcohol and carbon dioxide is accompanied by the *liberation of large quantities of energy.* This energy the yeast plant is able to use in order to grow.

You will see, however, that the yeast is not *feeding* upon the sugar. Hence the *dry weight* of the yeast grown in a pure sugar solution does not increase at all, although the *number* of yeast cells does. In order that the yeast may grow and increase in weight it must be supplied with food, though it does not require very much, since it obtains its main supply of energy in the way just described.

The fermentation of liquids containing sugars is important in industry, since it is used in the manufacture of beer, wines and spirits, and also for the production of alcohol on a commercial scale.

Alcohol, C_2H_6O, is made from potato-starch. This is (in one method) treated with dilute sulphuric acid, which converts it into grape-sugar—

$$(C_6H_{10}O_5)_n + nH_2O = nC_6H_{12}O_6.$$

The liquid is then neutralized with lime and fermented by means of yeast. After the fermentation is over, the liquid is filtered and the clear filtrate distilled. Alcohol has a lower boiling-point (78°) than water, so it boils off first, though it always carries a little water with it.

Alcohol is a colourless volatile liquid with a characteristic "winy" smell. It is very difficult to solidify by cold, and is therefore sometimes used in thermometers in cold countries. When pure, it is a powerful poison, but it is not so harmful if diluted: even dilute alcohol, however, may produce intoxication (*i.e.* poisoning).

Alcohol burns with a hot, practically non-luminous, flame. When it can be produced cheaply enough it will form an excellent fuel for motors. Indeed, when the world's supply of petrol is exhausted, we shall probably have to grow vast quantities of plants simply in order to provide starch from which we may obtain the necessary motor-spirit. The products of combustion of alcohol are carbon dioxide and water—

$$C_2H_6O + 3O_2 = 2CO_2 + 3H_2O.$$

Composition of Alcohol.—The percentage composition, determined by burning a known weight of alcohol and weighing the water and carbon dioxide formed, is $C = 52{\cdot}2$; $H = 13{\cdot}0$; $O = 34{\cdot}8$. Hence the empirical formula is C_2H_6O.

A Victor Meyer vapour density determination gives the value 23 for the V.D. of alcohol. Hence the M.W. is 46. This corresponds to C_2H_6O $(2 \times 12 + 6 + 16)$, $\therefore$ true formula is C_2H_6O.

Methylated Spirit.—In order to make alcohol unfit for drinking, it is mixed with various poisonous liquids such as *wood naphtha* or "methyl alcohol" (*methanol*). The mixture is called *methylated spirit*, while pure alcohol is sometimes called *spirit of wine.*

Soap.—Ordinary soap is the sodium salt of an organic acid called stearic acid, $C_{17}H_{35}.COOH$. Its formula is $C_{17}H_{35}.COONa$. It is made from mutton fat by boiling it with caustic soda solution. Mutton fat is a compound of stearic acid with glycerol (or to give it its common name, *glycerine*), so that we may write an equation for the action as follows—

mutton fat (glyceryl stearate) + sodium hydroxide
= soap (sodium stearate) + glycerol.

The glycerol of commerce, then, is a by-product in the manufacture of soap.

For the action of soap on hard water, see p. 198.

Carbon disulphide, CS_2, is formed by passing sulphur vapour over red-hot coke—

$$C + S_2 = CS_2.$$

It is a colourless, volatile, and very inflammable liquid which has a pleasant, sweetish odour when pure. It generally contains impurities, however, which give it a very evil smell. It is used as a solvent (*e.g.* it dissolves sulphur and phosphorus) and also for killing rats and insects, as it is very poisonous.

Flame, Combustion and Fuel

By a *flame* we mean a region in which a chemical reaction between gases is going on so vigorously that the gases glow and give out light.

The structure of a flame varies according to the nature of the substances burning, and is also affected by the shape of the burner, etc. In order to get some idea of the nature of typical flames we shall consider those of (*a*) a candle, and (*b*) the Bunsen burner.

Candle Flame.—When a candle burns, the wax of which it is composed melts, and the molten wax is then sucked up the wick into the region of the flame, where it is vaporized. Wax consists of hydrocarbons (p. 313), so that the products of combustion are carbon dioxide and water. Examination of the flame shows that it consists of three zones, (i) an inner dark zone, (ii) a larger luminous zone, and (iii) on the outside, an enveloping zone which is non-luminous, and is therefore only dimly visible (Fig. 96).

The inner zone consists of unburnt wax-vapour, as can easily be shown by putting into it a short piece of glass tubing, which conducts away some of the vapour. The latter can indeed be lit at the mouth of the tube (Fig. 97).

The luminous zone contains particles of carbon which are heated white-hot. We may, perhaps, imagine that in this zone the hydrogen of the wax is burning, and the flame of the

FIG. 96.—Candle Flame.

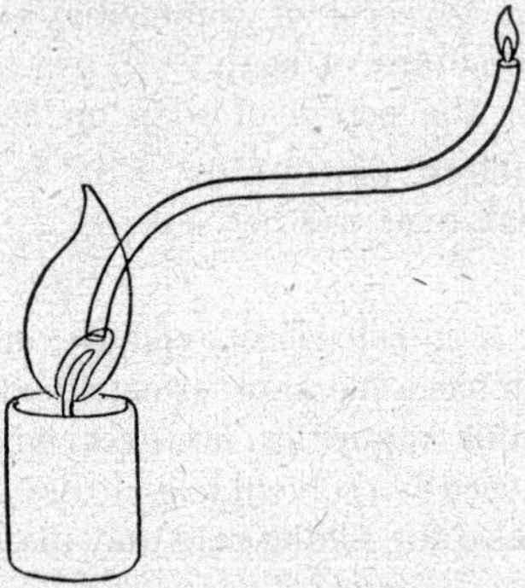

FIG. 97.—Drawing off Wax-vapour from a Candle Flame.

burning hydrogen heats the carbon to incandescence. This was Faraday's explanation, and is not quite accurate. To show that this zone contains carbon, a piece of cold porcelain may be held in it, when the porcelain will become covered with soot (carbon).

In the outermost zone, combustion is completed.

Bunsen Flame.—If the holes at the bottom of the burner are closed, we get a flame similar in all essentials to that of the candle. That the central zone consists of unburnt gas may be shown by drawing off the gas from this region with a piece of glass-tubing as before, or by sticking a pin through a match, resting it in the Bunsen tube, and then lighting the gas. It will be noticed that the match takes fire only after a considerable time, showing that the central cone is quite cool.

Why does the gas in the central region not burn? The answer is plain: there is no air there to burn it. If, however, we open the holes at the bottom, we shall supply more air and can reduce the size of the inner cone, while the luminous cone will disappear altogether. There is now sufficient air to burn up all the carbon straight away, so that the luminous, white-hot particles are no longer formed. What does the inner cone consist of now? Clearly of a mixture of air and gas. Why then is it not burning, and why doesn't the mixture burn right down in the tube? These questions, which may be puzzling at first sight, are answered when we know that, if a mixture of gases is lit, the wave of flame travels through the mixture at a perfectly definite rate. The Bunsen burner is so constructed that, with the ordinary pressure of town gas, the rush of air and gas out of the tube is going faster than a flame-wave travels back in the mixture. If, however, you turn the gas partly off, you will be able to lessen the rush, and the flame may then "strike back."

The wider you open the holes at the base of the burner, the more air can get in. Hence, at the top, the gas has not to spread itself out so much in order to burn, and the flame is therefore smaller. It follows, that, since the gas is now burnt in a smaller space, the heat will be more concentrated and therefore the flame will be hotter. The Bunsen burner, in fact, gives three types of flame—

(1) With a luminous zone. Fairly cool. No air enters at bottom.

(2) A quiet, non-luminous flame. Hot. Some air enters at bottom.

(3) A roaring, non-luminous flame. Very hot. Much air enters at bottom.

With the same supply of gas, No. 1 is the largest and No. 3 the smallest, No. 2 being intermediate. No. 1 is used for bending glass tubing, etc., No. 2 for ordinary purposes, and No. 3 for glass-blowing or in other cases where a very high temperature is required. The highest temperature obtainable with a Bunsen burner is probably about 1,800°; the ordinary flame (hottest part, *i.e.* $\frac{1}{2}$ inch or so above top of central cone) is about 1,200–1,500°.

Fuel.—The chief fuels are coal, coke, coal-gas, hydrocarbons (petrol, paraffin, benzene, etc.) and wood. They are all carbon or carbonaceous substances, and their use depends upon the fact that when they are burnt, forming carbon dioxide, water, etc., large amounts of heat are liberated. Thus, when 12 grams of amorphous carbon are burnt to carbon dioxide, 96,960 calories are evolved, a fact which can be expressed by the equation—

$$C + O_2 = CO_2 + 96{,}960 \text{ cals.}$$

Different fuels are used for different purposes, the choice being of course governed by considerations of (*a*) convenience, and (*b*) price. The uses of ordinary fuels are so well-known that we need not consider them here. We shall, however, deal briefly with some gaseous fuels which are of great importance in commerce, but which are not so well-known to the average man.

Producer-gas is a mixture of carbon monoxide (30 per cent.) and nitrogen (62 per cent.) made by sending a blast of air through red-hot coke. It is used very largely in chemical works.

Water-gas is the name given to a mixture of hydrogen and carbon monoxide, made by passing steam over white-hot coke—

$$C + H_2O = CO + H_2.$$

In the reaction, heat is absorbed.

Water-gas is often made at gas-works and mixed with the coal-gas. The disadvantages of this practice, from the consumers' point of view, are that the gas is thereby made much more dangerously poisonous, and that the heat given out by the combustion of the gas is much less than that given out by the combustion of an equal volume of pure coal-gas. The latter disadvantage is practically overcome by the new method of charging for gas not by volume but by its heating capacity (*i.e.* by the therm instead of by the cubic foot. See p. 318).

SILICON

Symbol: Si; *Atomic Weight:* 28; *Valency:* 4; *Specific Gravity:* 2·5.

Occurrence.—Silicon is very widely distributed, and forms more of the earth's crust than any other element except oxygen. It is always found as its oxide, *silica*, SiO_2. This may occur in the free state as *quartz* and *sand*, or combined with basic metallic oxides as *silicates*. Clay, for example, is largely composed of aluminium silicate. Flints, opals, amethysts and many other similar stones are composed of silica. The word *silica* is derived from the Latin *silex*, a flint.

Preparation.—Silicon may be obtained from silica by heating it with magnesium—

$$SiO_2 + 2Mg = Si + 2MgO.$$

Properties.—Silicon exists in two forms—an amorphous brown powder and a yellow or brown *crystalline* form. It is not very reactive, although it will burn in air if strongly heated, forming silica, SiO_2. It is insoluble in acids.

COMPOUNDS.

As a non-metallic quadrivalent element, like carbon, it forms compounds which in many ways, especially that of constitution, resemble the corresponding compounds of carbon.

Silicon di-oxide, SiO_2.—Silica is an *acidic* oxide, like carbon dioxide, but it is a solid. Of late years it has become very important in the manufacture of "quartz glass"; when silica is heated it becomes soft and can be made into tubes, basins, crucibles, etc., and since silica has a very low coefficient of expansion, quartz-glass vessels can withstand great and sudden changes of temperature without cracking. A silica basin, for example, may be made red-hot and cooled under the tap. Fused silica may also be drawn out into very fine threads used in mirror-galvanometers, etc.

Vitreosil is an opalescent form of quartz glass, made by passing a powerful electric current through a rod or plate of carbon packed in sand. It is cheaper than the transparent form, but equally good for most purposes, although of course it does not look so attractive.

Since it is an acidic oxide, silica will combine with basic oxides to form salts, the *silicates*, which are salts of *silicic acid*. The main constituent of clay is an *alumino-silicic acid*.

It has the formula $H_4Al_2Si_2O_9$, roughly. *Sodium silicate*, Na_2SiO_3, made by dissolving silica in caustic soda, is soluble in water. The commercial product is called *water-glass*, and contains more silica than corresponds to the above formula; it is used in solution as a preservative for eggs, since it clogs up the pores of the shell with calcium silicate and thus prevents the ingress of air and bacteria. It has also been successfully employed in preserving certain of the wooden boats and other objects excavated from the Glastonbury Lake Village, etc.

Glass is a mixture of the silicates of calcium and sodium or potassium. Ordinary *soda-glass* is made by fusing a mixture of sand, limestone, and soda-ash; *hard-glass* is made in a similar way except that potash is used instead of soda; while *flint glass* is made from sand, limestone, litharge and soda or potash. Flint-glass is more highly refractive than soda- or potash-glass, and is therefore used for making lenses; it is, however, soft and easily scratched, therefore microscope objectives, etc., should always be cleaned with silk or chamois leather and not with the rougher cotton or linen cloths.

Coloured glass is made by adding certain metallic oxides to the original mixture or preferably to the glass after fusion. *Blue* glass is made by adding cobalt oxide; *amethyst* or *purple*, from manganese dioxide; *opalescent*, from bone-ash.

Glass is not a solid but a very viscous liquid, cooled so far below its freezing-point that it crystallizes only very slowly. This phenomenon of "super-cooling" is quite common; all supercooled liquids crystallize after a time, and in the case of glass this process is called *devitrification*. Soda-glass devitrifies more quickly than the other kinds. Devitrified glass is brittle and useless.

Silicic acid itself, H_2SiO_3, comes down as a white gelatinous precipitate (but cf. pp. 360–1) when hydrochloric acid is added to a solution of sodium silicate—

$$Na_2SiO_3 + 2HCl = 2NaCl + H_2SiO_3.$$

On heating, it loses water, and is converted into silica—

$$H_2SiO_3 = H_2O + SiO_2.$$

(Compare and contrast carbonic acid, p. 326.)

Silicon hydride or **silicomethane,** SiH_4, is a colourless gas made by the action of hydrochloric acid upon magnesium silicide (prepared by heating silica with magnesium)—

$$Mg_2Si + 4HCl = SiH_4 + 2MgCl_2.$$

It readily takes fire in the air, and, as generally prepared, is spontaneously inflammable. The products of combustion are silica and water—

$$SiH_4 + 2O_2 = SiO_2 + 2H_2O.$$

(Cf. methane, p. 333.)

Silicomethane reacts with chlorine to form silicon tetrachloride and hydrochloric acid—

$$SiH_4 + 4Cl_2 = SiCl_4 + 4HCl.$$

(Cf. methane, p. 334.)

Silicon carbide, or **carborundum,** SiC, is made by heating a mixture of sand and excess of powdered coke in the electric furnace—

$$SiO_2 + 3C = SiC + 2CO.$$

It is an extremely hard crystalline solid, colourless when pure, but black as usually prepared. It is used instead of emery for grinding and polishing, etc.

Relation between the Atmosphere and Plant and Animal Life

The existence of all animal and plant life is intimately bound up with the atmosphere. Two of the principal factors in life are feeding or *assimilation* and breathing or *respiration*, and we shall see that the breathing of animals, and both the breathing and feeding of plants, depend upon exchange of gases between the living organism and the surrounding air.

Respiration and Assimilation.—Just as a steam-engine requires a supply of energy if it is to carry out the purposes for which it is designed, so all living things need energy to grow and move and work. In the case of a steam-engine, the energy is derived from the heat given out when carbon (coal) or oil (a carbon compound) is burnt, and ultimately depends upon the conversion of carbon into carbon dioxide by means of the oxygen of the air. Respiration is at bottom a very similar process, for during breathing carbonaceous substances in the living tissues of a plant or animal are oxidized by atmospheric oxygen and are converted into carbon dioxide and other products. This change results in the setting free of energy, which the organism uses for its life-processes. The actual living matter of plants and animals is a colourless jelly-like substance called *protoplasm*, and it is in the protoplasm that the actual oxidation occurs. The substances which are oxidized are very complex, but their constitution need not worry us here, for it is quite sufficient if we know that they are compounds of carbon and that during respiration their carbon is converted into carbon dioxide.

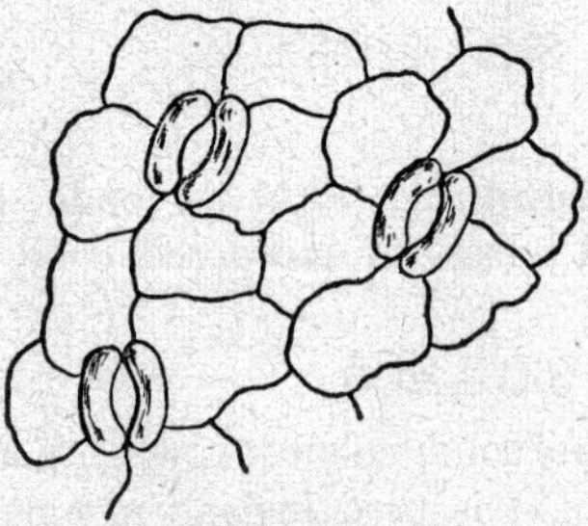

FIG. 98.—Stomata.

During respiration, then, the plant or animal takes in air, in order to get oxygen for this oxidation. Small organisms breathe in air over the surface of their whole body, but larger plants and animals take it in through special openings—mouth and nose, etc., in animals, and little holes, called *stomata* [1] (Fig. 98), on the under surfaces of the leaves, in plants. Thence it is distributed over the body, dissolved in the blood in animals, and dissolved in the sap (and in other ways) in plants.

The essential part of respiration, then (*viz.* oxidation of carbonaceous material) goes on *all over* the body. You must not imagine that you respire mainly with your lungs. The lungs are merely the apparatus used for effecting the exchange of gases between your body and the air ; *you breathe throughout your whole body.*

When living things breathe, therefore, they take in air, for the sake of the oxygen it contains, and they throw back into

[1] Singular *stoma* (Greek, a mouth).

the atmosphere the nitrogen, the unused oxygen, and the carbon dioxide which has been produced. The air, as you know, consists chiefly of oxygen (21 per cent. by volume) and nitrogen (79 per cent.), with a small proportion (3 or 4 litres in 10,000 or 0·03–0·04 per cent.) of carbon dioxide. The air a man breathes *out* from his lungs contains a slightly lower percentage of oxygen and a slightly higher percentage of carbon dioxide. You should not make the error of supposing that expired breath consists *chiefly* of carbon dioxide and contains no oxygen: air does not remain in the lungs long enough for its composition to change very much. Still, ordinary air contains so little carbon dioxide that it takes a long time for it to turn lime-water milky, whereas expired air will turn it milky at once.

Like animals, plants also use up oxygen during breathing, and convert it into carbon dioxide, which they send out into the air. It seems, therefore, that the percentage of carbon dioxide in the atmosphere ought to be steadily increasing, for all living things are breathing it out, and it is, of course, formed in large quantities when coal, oil and wood are burnt. Each ton of coal you burn in your grates, for example, means that about 3 tons of carbon dioxide are thrown into the air. About 2,000,000 tons of coal are used in Great Britain every week, hence in a year, by this operation alone, some 320,000,000 tons of carbon dioxide are sent out into the atmosphere!

How is it, therefore, that the percentage of carbon dioxide in the atmosphere is found by chemists to remain practically constant? Well, there are two reasons. In the first place, carbon dioxide is soluble in water, and the sea therefore takes up a great deal. Secondly, it is a remarkable fact that *carbon dioxide forms the chief food of green plants.* If we analyse the stuff of which plants are made, we find that a great deal of it is water (about 80 per cent.). The rest, which is solid matter, consists chiefly of carbon, together with smaller quantities of hydrogen, oxygen, and nitrogen, and traces of sulphur, phosphorus, chlorine, silicon, magnesium, iron, and various other elements. That carbon is the principal constituent of the solid matter of plants is obvious when one thinks of what happens when a log of wood is heated. At first, the log sizzles and splutters owing to the moisture which is being driven off; then it goes black, and is converted into *charcoal*, which, as we have already seen, is mainly carbon. If you reflect on the enormous mass of vegetation which covers the surface of the globe, you will realize what a vast quantity of carbon dioxide must have been taken from the air and decomposed by plants in order to build up their tissues. Hence you will be able to understand why the percentage of carbon dioxide in the air does not increase.

Plants feed, then, in this way. Water they obtain from the soil, sucking it up through their roots by means of the very fine *root-hairs* which you can see very well on the roots of young mustard seedlings. From the roots the water passes up through the stems into the leaves, where it gradually turns into vapour, and much of it escapes through the stomata. Through the stomata, air enters the leaves. Here carbon dioxide and water react together, forming—probably—in the first instance, oxygen and a substance called *formaldehyde*, CH_2O—

$$CO_2 + H_2O = CH_2O + O_2.$$

The oxygen is sent back into the air as a waste product; you will see from the equation (by Avogadro's Hypothesis) that the volume of oxygen liberated is equal to the volume of carbon dioxide taken in. The formaldehyde does not remain as such in the leaves; several molecules of it combine together to form a sugar, $C_6H_{12}O_6$—

$$6CH_2O = C_6H_{12}O_6, \text{ a sugar.}$$

From sugars, the plant can form starches, in a way we do not understand, and which we cannot yet imitate in the laboratory, but which we can represent by the equation—

$$nC_6H_{12}O_6 = \underset{\text{Starch.}}{(C_6H_{10}O_5)_n} + nH_2O.$$

Starches and sugars, then, are the chief food substances in plants, and they are made from water and from the carbon dioxide of the air.

Now the action $CO_2 + H_2O = CH_2O + O_2$ is not one which will take place spontaneously, since during the action *a great deal of energy is used up.* Where does this energy come from? We can get a clue to this problem by testing the leaves of a plant for starch at various times of the day and night, when we find that *no starch is present at night.* This indicates that *light* is necessary for starch-formation—a conclusion which is confirmed by growing plants in a dark cupboard, when it is found that they form no starch and also become very unhealthy. Under these circumstances, too, *they lose their green colour*—a fact which all of you must have noticed when you have lifted up from the lawn a box which has been left there a day or two. Another significant fact in this connection is that if you test for starch a variegated leaf, that is, a leaf parts of which are green and parts not green, you will find starch only in the green parts. From these and similar considerations it follows that the building-up of starch from carbon dioxide and water can take place only—

(i) in presence of light, and

(ii) when the green colouring-matter is present.

This green colouring-matter, which can be extracted from leaves by boiling them first with water (to kill them) and then with alcohol (or, better, acetone), in which the green substance dissolves, is called *chlorophyll* (Greek, the green of the leaf). It is a very complicated magnesium compound,[1] rather similar in constitution to the red colouring-matter of the blood, *hæmoglobin*, except that the latter is an iron compound, and contains no magnesium.

We believe, then, that the energy necessary to bring about the reaction—

$$CO_2 + H_2O = CH_2O \text{ (formaldehyde)} + O_2$$

is obtained by plants from sunlight, and that the agent which the plant uses for the purpose is chlorophyll. Since ordinary

[1] To give you some idea of the complexity of this substance, it may be stated that Professor Willstätter has shown that it probably is a mixture of two compounds to which he assigns the formulæ—

$[MgN_3C_{31}H_{29}]$ (NH.CO) $(COOCH_3)$ $COOC_{20}H_{39}$)—chlorophyll α.

$[MgN_4C_{32}H_{28}O_2]$ $(COOCH_3)$ $(COOC_{20}H_{39})$—chlorophyll β.

white light is composed of lights of different wave lengths (as can be shown by splitting it up by means of a prism), and since chlorophyll is green, it is obvious that the *green* part of the light is *not* used by the plants, for they reflect it back again and do not absorb it. As a matter of fact, it is the *red* light which is most active in this respect. Plants will grow quite well under red glass, which allows the red light to pass through, but they will not grow under green glass which stops the red rays from passing. This use of red light will probably surprise us when we remember that the most active rays in the majority of chemical reactions are the violet ones, *i.e.* those at the extreme opposite end of the spectrum to the red.

We have seen, therefore, that in plants the main feeding-process (*carbon assimilation*) consists in the absorption of carbon dioxide from the air and the building-up of it into sugars and starches by means of the energy of sunlight which is harnessed by the chlorophyll. Oxygen is a waste product. This process, which is a "building-up by means of light," is therefore called "*photo-synthesis.*"

If we cast our minds back to the breathing-process of plants we shall recollect that, in this case, oxygen is taken in and carbon dioxide is a waste product. Hence, in daylight, two opposing processes are going on—

Breathing.—Oxygen used, carbon dioxide sent out.

Feeding.—Carbon dioxide used, oxygen sent out.

Now plants are not energetic organisms; they do not jump and skip like young lambs. Hence they do not have to *breathe* very much. On the other hand, they may often grow to a considerable size, and they generally grow very quickly, hence they *feed* voraciously. The result is that in daylight the breathing-process is entirely masked by the feeding-process, and if we want to show that plants breathe in the ordinary way, we have to test them at night, or in the dark, when they cannot feed.

We arrive, then, at the following conclusions:

(i) *All living things breathe, by using oxygen to oxidize carbonaceous material. Carbon dioxide is a waste product of this process.*

(ii) *Green plants* FEED *on carbon dioxide, which, in sunlight, they can make to react with water and form sugars and starches.*

You will now be able to understand what a foolish mistake it is to say that plants " breathe in carbon dioxide and breathe out oxygen " ! It is equivalent to saying that a man breathes in porridge, bacon and eggs and toast and marmalade.

Carbonaceous Food of Animals.—Animals do not possess the power of feeding on carbon dioxide. The carbonaceous food which they require must be supplied in the form of starches or sugars or other complex carbon compounds. Hence all animal life is ultimately dependent upon plant life, for though some animals feed on other animals, these must finally obtain their carbonaceous food from plants or plant remains.

Water and Life.—Life cannot exist without water. It has already been mentioned that about 80 per cent. by weight of plants, on the average, consists of water. In the case of animals the percentage is lower, but it is still high. In plants, water plays many parts, but it is a *food*, just as it is for animals. Water leaves a plant through the stomata, in the form of water-vapour. Now there is always water-vapour in the air, though the amount varies. If the humidity of the air is high, evaporation of water from plants will be slow, while if the air is very dry evaporation will go on rapidly. In the latter event, a plant might quickly become dried up and withered ; we therefore find that plants have elaborate arrangements to control the rate of evaporation. They can, for example, close their stomata if the supply of water is running short.

Nitrogen and other Elements.—The elements mentioned on p. 353, as constituents of plants, are also constituents of animal bodies, with the exception of magnesium, which animals are apparently able to do without. Plants obtain their supplies of these elements from the soil, in which they are present in the form of compounds. These compounds dissolve in the soil-water, and the solution is taken up through the roots. In the plant they are worked up into complex substances, which may serve as the food of animals. The chief of these substances with which we have to deal are the *proteins*.

These are nitrogenous bodies which form an essential food of animals. Nitrogen is, indeed, a constant constituent of all living tissue. Plants require it to be presented to them in the form of *nitrates*, which they take up in solution, through their roots, from the soil. In the course of the life-process of the plant, the nitrogen of the nitrates becomes converted into proteins. The fate of these proteins is twofold. The plant may die, in which case the proteins it contains are returned to the soil; or it may be eaten by an animal, when the protein is digested and becomes a part of the animal body. During the life of the animal, proteins are continually being used up, and the nitrogen is excreted in the form of less complicated substances such as *urea* (man) or *hippuric acid* (horses, etc.). If, therefore, dead plants and the excreta and dead bodies of animals are returned to the soil, the latter will not become impoverished of nitrogen, but the nitrogen returned in this way will be of no direct use to plants, which must have it in the form of nitrates. Luckily there is an agency at work which converts organic nitrogenous compounds in the soil into nitrates. This agency is the *bacterial flora*. The soil swarms with bacteria, which cause "decay" of nitrogenous organic matter. The first product is ammonia; by the aid of the oxygen of the air one class of bacteria (the nitrite-forming bacteria) converts the nitrogen of this ammonia into *nitrites*, and a second kind converts the nitrites into nitrates. (These two classes of bacteria are called the *nitrifying bacteria*.) In this way the cycle of changes undergone by the nitrogen in nature is complete (Fig. 99).

There are, however, several factors which modify this simple "nitrogen cycle." In the first place, there are certain species of soil bacteria which convert nitrates into *nitrogen*, which escapes into the air and is therefore lost; these are the *denitrifying bacteria*. Secondly, a great deal of nitrogen is taken from the soil and never replaced, owing to our wasteful system of turning sewage into the sea whenever possible. Thirdly, in order to get sufficiently large crops to feed the population of the world, large quantities of nitrates or ammonium salts have to be added to the soil, as artificial manures.

Fourthly, certain plants, such as peas, beans, and clover, have the power of making direct use of atmospheric nitrogen, by means of peculiar bacteria which live in nodules on their roots ; but the enrichment of the soil brought about in this way and by the production of nitric acid in the air during thunder-storms is not sufficient to make up for the annual drain on the nitrogen content of the soil caused by growing and removing a crop.

In other words, for the establishment of a true equilibrium in the nitrogen cycle, at present much nitrogen has to be

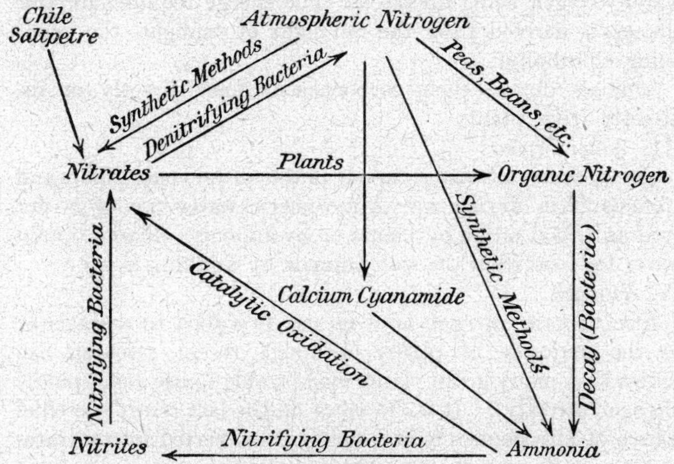

FIG. 99.

added to the soil, by man, in the form of nitrates or ammonium salts. The production of ammonium salts in the manufacture of coal-gas is far too little to supply the need, and the beds of Chile saltpetre will in time become exhausted. Hence the great importance of the recently-perfected methods of building up nitric acid and ammonia from the nitrogen of the air, a problem to which the attention of chemists was fortunately directed in good time by the foresight of the late SIR WILLIAM CROOKES.

The Nitrogen Cycle may be represented by Fig. 99.

Summary of Relation between Air and Plant and Animal Life

I. *Respiration or Breathing.*

Plants and animals use atmospheric oxygen to oxidize carbonaceous materials in their bodies, thus obtaining the necessary energy for their life. Carbon dioxide is thrown back into the air.

II. *Feeding.*

In sunlight, green plants use carbon dioxide for food. They build up sugars and starches from carbon dioxide and water, oxygen being liberated. The energy required for this change is derived from the red light of sunlight, the agent being chlorophyll.

Animals obtain their carbonaceous food directly or indirectly from plants.

III. *Water-vapour.*

The presence of water-vapour in the air prevents plants and animals from drying up. Atmospheric water-vapour is not used as a food either by plants or by animals. Plants obtain water for food from the soil, animals by drinking it.

IV. *Nitrogen.*

Atmospheric nitrogen is of no use as a food to animals or to the majority of plants (although recent research has shown that many green plants *may* be able to use atmospheric nitrogen directly). It is, however, in the last resort the chief source of nitrogenous food, since it is converted into nitrates and ammonia, which are used as manures.

Dialysis

In the middle of the nineteenth century Graham showed that if a solution of salt was placed in a parchment drum floating in a vessel of water, the salt gradually passed through the membrane into the surrounding water; glue, however, if made up into a solution and treated in the same way, would not pass through the membrane. Further investigation showed that most crystalline substances behaved in the same way as salt, while silicic acid, gum, starch, albumen and caramel, and certain other substances, behaved like glue. The latter bodies Graham therefore called *colloids*, because they were " like glue " (Greek, *kolla*, glue); those which readily pass through a membrane he called crystalloids. It follows that if we have a mixture of a colloid and a crystalloid in solution, the two may be separated by floating the solution in a parchment drum in a vessel of pure water, when the crystalloid will slowly pass through while the colloid remains. This process Graham called *dialysis*.

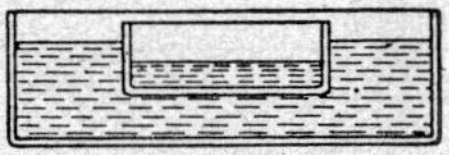

FIG. 100.—Graham's Dialyser.

Recent work has shown that this classification of substances into colloids and crystalloids is unsound; *any* substance may be obtained as a colloid under suitable conditions, and it is therefore preferable to talk of a *colloidal state* of matter, into which some substances pass more readily than others.

In a *colloidal solution* of a solid in a liquid, the particles of the solid are so fine that they will not settle to the bottom, and yet are not so fine that the substance can be regarded as in a " true " solution. In practically all colloidal solutions the particles of the colloidal substance can be observed either directly or indirectly by means of the microscope or ultramicroscope.

QUESTIONS

1. For what reasons are carbon and silicon classified together?
2. What is *organic* chemistry?
3. How does carbon occur in nature?
4. What is meant by allotropy? Illustrate your answer by reference to oxygen and carbon.
5. What are *dolomite, limestone, chalk* and *petrol*?
6. How would you show that amorphous carbon, graphite and diamond all consist of nothing but carbon?
7. How is graphite obtained commercially?
8. Write a short account of the distillation of coal.
9. Why is gas sold by the *therm* and not by the cubic foot? What is a therm?
10. Describe the chemical properties of carbon.
11. Who discovered carbon dioxide, and when?
12. Describe the preparation and properties of carbon dioxide. How may this gas (*a*) be dried, and (*b*) be separated from carbon monoxide?

13. What is the action of carbon dioxide upon (*a*) lime-water, (*b*) caustic soda solution, (*c*) sodium carbonate solution ?

14. Write equations for the action of each of the three mineral acids upon (*a*) sodium carbonate, (*b*) marble, (*c*) zinc carbonate, (*d*) copper carbonate, (*e*) potassium bicarbonate.

15. How would you estimate the strength of a solution of sodium carbonate ?

16. Upon what evidence is the formula CO_2 assigned to carbon dioxide ?

17. Describe the preparation and properties of carbon monoxide.

18. How could you distinguish between carbon monoxide and hydrogen ?

19. Upon what evidence is the formula CO given to carbon monoxide ?

20. What are *hydrocarbons* ? Give three examples.

21. How is methane prepared ? What are its properties ?

22. Give an account of the evidence which leads us to assign the formulæ CH_4, C_2H_4 and C_2H_2 to methane, ethylene and acetylene respectively.

23. Write the formulæ for (*a*) chloroform, (*b*) ethylene dibromide, (*c*) calcium carbide. What is the action of water on the last ?

24. How is ethylene prepared ? In what important respects does its chemical behaviour differ from that of methane ?

25. Describe the preparation and properties of acetylene.

26. What is the empirical formula for starch ?

27. How is starch obtained commercially ?

28. Describe a test for starch.

29. Whence is sugar obtained ? What is its formula ?

30. Describe the action of yeast upon a solution of sugar.

31. What is an *enzyme* ? Give examples.

32. What is the formula for alcohol ? How is alcohol obtained on the large scale ? What is *methylated spirit* ?

33. What is the composition of soap ? How is soap made ? What is its action on hard water ?

34. What is a flame ? Describe the flames of (*a*) a candle and (*b*) a Bunsen burner.

35. How is *water-gas* made ? What is it used for ?

36. How does silicon occur in nature ?

37. What is water-glass ? What is its action in preserving eggs ?

38. State shortly how the following substances may be prepared —*silicon, silicic acid, sodium silicate, silicomethane, carborundum.*

39. What part is played by carbon dioxide in the life of plants and animals ?

40. Write a short account of the circulation of nitrogen in nature.

41. What do you mean by *photosynthesis* ?

42. What part does chlorophyll take in the feeding-process of plants ?

CHAPTER XIX

THE METALS

The elements of which the universe is composed may be classified into two groups. One group consists of the *metals*, while the other includes all those elements which are not metals—the "*non-metals*." You have already studied some of the chief non-metals, such as oxygen, hydrogen, sulphur, phosphorus and carbon, and you have also some acquaintance with common metals, for example, tin, magnesium, copper, zinc, and aluminium. You would probably not have much difficulty in deciding whether a given substance was a metal or not, but perhaps you have never asked yourself what characteristics you go by in making your decision. Let us therefore consider this question, and see if we can frame a *definition* of a metal by finding out what properties all metals possess but non-metals do not.

Properties of Metals.

1. They have a peculiar lustre, which is so characteristic that we usually describe it by calling it simply "metallic."
2. They can usually be very highly polished.
3. They are generally "heavy"—that is, they have a high specific gravity.
4. At ordinary temperatures and pressures they are all solids—with the exception of mercury.
5. Electricity and heat can pass through them very readily, *i.e.* they are good *conductors* of electricity and heat.
6. They have, as a rule, high melting-points and boiling-points.

7. They can be hammered out into thin sheets, *i.e.* they are *malleable*.
8. They can be drawn out into wire, *i.e.* they are *ductile*.
9. They will usually stand a pretty strong pull before they break, *i.e.* they have great *tensile* strength.
10. Their normal oxides are usually *basic* (p. 178), *i.e.* they react with an acid to form a salt + water.
11. Their chlorides are true salts and are not decomposed by water.

If we compare these properties with those of non-metals, we shall find that there are important differences.

Properties of Non-Metals.

1. They do not have a metallic lustre.
2. They cannot be highly polished.
3. Their specific gravities are usually low.
4. At ordinary temperatures, many of them are gases.
5. They are poor conductors of heat and electricity.
6. Generally they have low melting-points and boiling-points.
7. They are not malleable.
8. They are not ductile.
9. They have but little tensile strength.
10. Their normal oxides are usually acidic (p. 178), *i.e.* when dissolved in water they form acids.
11. Their chlorides are not salts, and very often are decomposed by water (*e.g.* phosphorus pentachloride and water, p. 284).

Another point in which metals differ from non-metals is that the former are generally "sonorous"—that is, a sheet or bell of metal when struck emits a musical note. Non-metals are not sonorous.

Mixtures of metals, such as brass (p. 409), bronze (p. 409), etc., are called *alloys*.

If an element shows all the properties which have been mentioned above as characteristic of metals, we can describe it with certainty as a metal. Similarly, any element which shows all the above properties of non-metals is certainly a non-metal. We often find, however, that an element shows some of the properties of metals and some of the properties of non-metals. In cases of this sort, we have to decide which properties are the more important, and decide on these grounds. Otherwise, as in cases of special difficulty, we call such elements *metalloids*, to indicate that while they are "like metals" they cannot definitely be regarded as true metals. Examples of metalloids are arsenic and antimony.

In elementary work, no real difficulty arises. We shall, however, find that *sodium*, the first metal we shall study, is soft, has a low melting-point, and a low specific gravity, and very little tensile strength. Still, it has a metallic lustre, it can be made to take a high polish, it is malleable and ductile, it is a good conductor of heat and electricity, it forms a basic oxide and its chloride is a true salt. There is therefore no doubt about its being a metal.

What are the *most important* properties of metals from this point of view of classification? In practice, if an element forms a basic oxide and a chloride which is a true salt, we can be quite certain that it is justifiable to call the element a metal. As a matter of fact, if it has the two properties just mentioned, it will usually have the others as well. Difficulty arises when an element shows some of the other properties but not these two. We see, in fact, that the distinction between metals and non-metals is one made by man for his own convenience. Nature does not recognize our schemes of classification, and cares not at all for the limitations of our intelligence.

Action of Metals upon Water.—Certain metals have an action upon water. It generally results in the liberation of hydrogen and the formation of the oxide or hydroxide of the metal. The conditions under which the action occurs vary with different metals. Thus metallic *potassium* (a metal like sodium) acts upon water in the cold. Heat is given out and hydrogen is evolved. Potassium is lighter than water, and therefore floats. It is melted by the heat of the reaction, and runs about on the surface of the water as a molten globule. The hydrogen which comes off is ignited by the high temperature produced, and burns with a flame which, instead of being blue, is coloured lilac owing to the fact that part of the potassium burns as well. The solution left has a slimy feel, will turn red litmus blue, and contains *potassium hydroxide*, KOH—

$$2K + 2H_2O = 2KOH + H_2.$$

With *sodium*, a similar reaction occurs. The heat evolved is sufficient to melt the sodium, which runs about as a molten globule, but not to ignite the hydrogen unless hot water is used (or unless the sodium is dropped on filter-paper floating on water), when the hydrogen burns with a flame coloured golden yellow by the sodium in it—

$$2Na + 2H_2O = 2NaOH + H_2.$$

The solution left contains *sodium hydroxide*, NaOH, which closely resembles potassium hydroxide (see p. 378).

Metallic *calcium* also acts upon cold water, but its specific gravity is greater than 1, so it sinks to the bottom. Hydrogen comes off, and the calcium is converted into calcium hydroxide (slaked lime), part of which dissolves in the water, forming lime-water—

$$Ca + 2H_2O = \underset{\text{Calcium hydroxide.}}{Ca(OH)_2} + H_2.$$

Magnesium has no appreciable action on cold water, but it slowly attacks boiling water, and burns readily in steam, forming *magnesium oxide*, MgO (not *hydroxide*), and liberating hydrogen—

$$Mg + H_2O = MgO + H_2.$$

Fig. 101 shows a piece of magnesium ribbon burning in steam. Water is boiled in the flask, and the spiral of ribbon is ignited and then plunged into the steam. The magnesium burns brilliantly and hydrogen is evolved, which may be collected over water as shown.

Copper has no action on either water or steam. *Iron* has no action on pure water, but if heated in a current of steam it is converted into an iron oxide, Fe_3O_4 (*magnetic oxide of iron*), while hydrogen is liberated—

$$3Fe + 4H_2O = Fe_3O_4 + 4H_2.$$

A remarkable feature of this reaction is that it is reversed if hydrogen is passed over heated iron oxide, iron and steam being formed—

$$Fe_3O_4 + 4H_2 = 3Fe + 4H_2O.$$

This may appear rather strange at first, but we can explain it in the following way. Suppose that we had 300,000 men

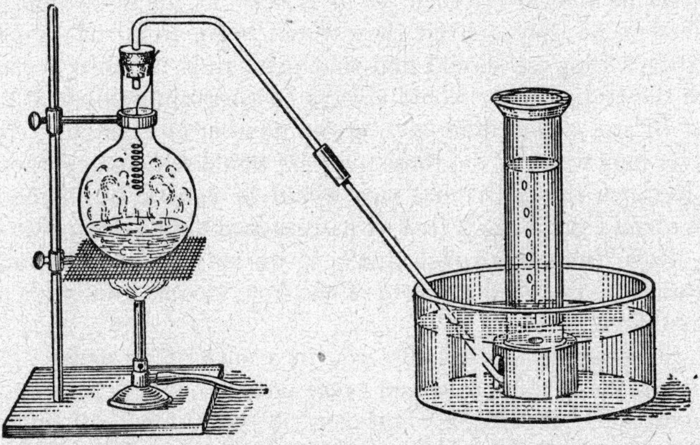

FIG. 101.—Action of Magnesium upon Steam.

at Bristol and we wanted to transport them to London by rail. The rate at which we could do so (which we may measure by counting the number of men deposited in London in 1 hour) would obviously depend upon (*a*) the number of trains we had at our disposal, and (*b*) the speed at which they moved. Suppose, in addition, that the men on arrival in London were anxious to get back to Bristol. If we swept them out of Paddington so that they could get no trains, and if no other means of locomotion were available, they would not be able to manage it.

On the other hand, suppose we let them stay freely at Paddington, cut off all the trains *from* Bristol, and put on several trains *to* Bristol. It is clear that the men could then get back quite easily, but that no more could come up.

A little thought will show us that there is a third possibility. Suppose we had similar trains running each way at the same speed, but twice as many *towards* London as *away* from it. Suppose also that the men, on arrival at either London or Bristol, immediately took the next train back again and so on. If we started with 300,000 men at Bristol, what would happen ? Well, as soon as the first trains arrived at London, men would begin to come back to Bristol again. We should *never* be able to get them *all* at London at the same time, for as soon as they arrived they would begin to go back again. After a time we should find that (excluding the men actually in the trains) there would always be a certain number of men at Bristol and a (different) certain number at London. However long we went on, these *numbers* would not change, though of course the individual *men* would be constantly changing. We could say, in fact, that we had reached a *state of equilibrium*.

Now, from this rough analogy, we may be able to understand the puzzling problem of the iron, steam, iron oxide and hydrogen.

Suppose we are heating iron in a current of steam. The iron attacks the steam and takes out its oxygen, leaving the hydrogen. Hydrogen, however, is very fond of oxygen, and is not likely to give it up without a fight. We may imagine that it would attack the iron oxide if it had the chance and try to get the oxygen back. But it never has this chance, for the stream of steam sweeps it away as soon as it is formed. It is like the men who arrived at London and were turned out of the station as soon as they arrived so that they had no chance of getting back. Hence after a time all the iron has been converted into iron oxide.

Suppose, now, we take iron oxide and heat it in a current of hydrogen. In these circumstances, the hydrogen is able to get its own back. It begins to combine with the oxygen of the oxide, forming steam and setting the iron free. The steam has no chance to retaliate, as it is swept away by the current of hydrogen.

Lastly, suppose we were to heat some iron and steam in a *closed* vessel. What would happen then? Well, the iron and steam would react to form iron oxide and hydrogen, but as soon as these were formed they would act upon one another to give iron and steam, and so on. At first, when there was a large excess of the iron and steam, the rate at which iron oxide and hydrogen were formed would be very great, but the rate of the reverse action would be slow. However, the more iron oxide and hydrogen there became, the greater would be the rate at which they could react to form iron and steam.

Hence, the rate of formation of iron oxide and hydrogen gradually diminishes from the start, while the rate of formation of iron and steam gradually increases. At length these two rates become equal. In other words, just as much iron oxide will be *formed* in a given time as is split up in that time. At this stage, therefore, there will be no apparent change taking place, since the relative proportions of iron, iron oxide, steam and hydrogen will remain constant. An equilibrium will, in fact, have been set up. Of course, the molecules of iron oxide present at one instant are not all the *same* molecules of iron oxide which were there at the previous instant, but there is the same *number* of them, and hence for all practical purposes the composition of the mixture remains constant when equilibrium has been set up.

You will find more about reversible reactions in Chapter XII.

Action of Acids upon Metals.—An important part of any course in elementary chemistry is the investigation of the action of the three mineral acids, sulphuric, hydrochloric, and nitric, upon metals. We may regard as *typical* the reaction which occurs when a metal dissolves in a dilute acid, yielding a salt of the metal and liberating hydrogen, *e.g.*—

$$Mg + H_2SO_4 = MgSO_4 + H_2.$$

Common metals which dissolve in cold dilute sulphuric acid or hydrochloric acid in this way are magnesium, zinc, and iron—

$$Mg + 2HCl = MgCl_2 + H_2.$$
$$Zn + H_2SO_4 = ZnSO_4 + H_2.$$
$$Zn + 2HCl = ZnCl_2 + H_2.$$
$$Fe + H_2SO_4 = FeSO_4 + H_2.$$
$$Fe + 2HCl = FeCl_2 + H_2.$$

Tin is insoluble in dilute sulphuric acid and also in *cold* dilute hydrochloric acid. It will, however, dissolve in *hot* hydrochloric acid, hydrogen and tin chloride (*stannous chloride*, $SnCl_2$) being formed—

$$Sn + 2HCl = SnCl_2 + H_2.$$

Concentrated sulphuric acid will, as a rule, not dissolve metals in the cold. On heating, however, vigorous action may occur, but the gas evolved is not hydrogen—it is *sulphur dioxide*, SO_2. We may imagine that hydrogen is first formed, in the usual way, but that it then *reduces* the hot concentrated acid to sulphur dioxide, being itself oxidized to water—

$$H_2 + H_2SO_4 = 2H_2O + SO_2.$$

Certain metals, such as copper and mercury, which are not attacked by the cold dilute acid, are readily dissolved by the hot concentrated acid—

$$Cu + 2H_2SO_4 = CuSO_4 + 2H_2O + SO_2.$$
$$Hg + 2H_2SO_4 = HgSO_4 + 2H_2O + SO_2.$$
$$\text{Also } Zn + 2H_2SO_4 = ZnSO_4 + 2H_2O + SO_2.$$

The action of concentrated sulphuric acid upon copper is made use of in the preparation of sulphur dioxide in the laboratory (p. 300).

Nitric Acid.—For an account of the action of nitric acid upon metals, see p. 272. Owing to the fact that nitric acid is such a powerful oxidizing agent, the hydrogen which is perhaps liberated in the first instance is immediately oxidized to water, the nitric acid therefore being reduced to one or more of its many reduction products—oxides of nitrogen, nitrogen itself, or even ammonia.

Metallic Salts.—See p. 186, also revision notes, p. 442.

Oxidation of Metals.—All metals form oxides—even the

noble metals gold and silver. Many metallic oxides can be obtained by direct combination of the metal with oxygen, that is, by heating the metal in a stream of oxygen or air. In other cases, they have to be prepared by an indirect method.

Magnesium.—Magnesium is a silvery-white metal which rusts slowly in damp air, being converted into its oxide, MgO. This is a white powder, which can be obtained much more readily by heating magnesium in air or oxygen. The magnesium takes fire and burns with a very brilliant flame, leaving the oxide as a white ash—

$$2Mg + O_2 = 2MgO.$$

We see from the equation that 48 grams of magnesium would require 32 grams (or 22·4 litres at N.T.P.) of oxygen (or, of course, about 5 times that quantity of air).

Zinc.—Zinc is fairly stable in the air, and rusts only extremely slowly. For this reason it is used to coat iron objects ("galvanized iron"). When zinc is exposed to the action of moist air for a long time it is converted into a white rust, which is a mixture (or compound) of zinc oxide, ZnO, with zinc carbonate ($ZnCO_3$).

If heated strongly in the air, zinc takes fire and burns with a greenish-blue flame, forming clouds of the very light zinc oxide, known as *philosophers' wool*—

$$2Zn + O_2 = 2ZnO.$$

Iron.—The fact that iron rusts when exposed to the air is known to every one. Investigation has shown that both air and moisture are necessary for rusting to occur. Thus, when bright iron is exposed to *dry* air (*e.g.* in a desiccator), it remains bright indefinitely, while if it is sealed up with water in a flask from which all air has been extracted, again no rusting occurs. The essential action in rusting is the combination of iron with oxygen to form iron oxide, Fe_2O_3 (ferric oxide); but a film of *liquid* water is said to be essential as well. At any rate, the brown powder into which iron crumbles when it is exposed to ordinary damp air consists mainly of ferric oxide loosely combined with more or less water—$Fe_2O_3.xH_2O$.

When iron is strongly heated in air, it quickly oxidizes to a different oxide, namely, *magnetic* oxide of iron, Fe_3O_4—

$$3Fe + 2O_2 = Fe_3O_4.$$

When formed in this way, the magnetic oxide of iron is sometimes known as "smithy scales." Its chemical name is *ferroso-ferric oxide*, since it is regarded as a compound of ferrous oxide, FeO, with ferric oxide, Fe_2O_3 ($Fe_3O_4 = FeO.Fe_2O_3$). The same oxide is formed in INGEN-HOUSZ's experiment, that is, the burning of iron in oxygen.

Copper.—Copper is unchanged in dry air, but in moist air it gradually becomes converted into a green mass composed of copper sulphate or chloride and copper hydroxide, $Cu(OH)_2$. (It should, however, be stated that the surface of ordinary copper, which is brownish, is due to the fact that the copper has become coated with a thin film of the oxide, which protects the rest of the metal from oxidation. A clean surface of *pure* copper has a rosy colour, and quickly tarnishes in the air, owing to the formation of the film of oxide.)

When copper is strongly heated in the air, it is oxidized. On the surface, oxidation proceeds as far as the black *cupric oxide*, CuO, while inside it usually goes no farther than the reddish-brown *cuprous oxide*, Cu_2O. Only by *very prolonged* heating in air is copper *completely* converted into cupric oxide, hence, if you are asked how to determine the equivalent of copper, *do not* say "by taking a known weight of copper, heating it in air, and weighing the cupric oxide formed." Life is too short.

Lead.—Lead, which, when pure, is a silvery-white metal, is unattacked by dry air. In moist air it rapidly rusts, *but on the surface only.* The film of rust which is formed (consisting of lead hydroxide, $Pb(OH)_2$, and lead carbonate, $PbCO_3$) protects the underlying metal from further action.

When lead is heated in air it melts (327°), and the molten metal soon becomes covered with a greyish powder. On further heating and stirring, the whole of the metal is quickly converted into a yellow powder known as *massicot* (PbO). This can be melted by increasing the temperature ; on cooling it solidifies to a solid which, when powdered, is known as *litharge*—it is still lead monoxide, PbO.

If litharge is roasted in a current of air at about 400° it is converted into a red crystalline powder known as *red lead* or minium. Minium, which has the formula Pb_3O_4, has been used from very remote times as a red pigment—whence our word *miniature* (Italian *miniare*, to paint in minium)—

$$6PbO + O_2 = 2Pb_3O_4.$$

When heated to nearly 500°, red lead splits up again into litharge and oxygen, so that the above reaction is reversible—

$$2Pb_3O_4 \rightleftharpoons 6PbO + O_2.$$

Red lead may be regarded as a compound of litharge with lead peroxide or dioxide, PbO_2 ($Pb_3O_4 = PbO_2.2PbO$). When it is acted upon by concentrated nitric acid it yields lead nitrate, while the dioxide is left—

$$Pb_3O_4 + 4HNO_3 = 2Pb(NO_3)_2 + 2H_2O + PbO_2.$$

Since lead nitrate is soluble in water, it can be dissolved, and the dioxide, which is insoluble, can be filtered off, washed and dried.

Lead dioxide, PbO_2, is a powerful oxidizing agent.

Mercury.—When mercury is heated in air to a temperature just below its boiling-point it is slowly converted into *mercuric oxide*, HgO—

$$2Hg + O_2 = 2HgO.$$

This reaction was probably known to Zosimus (third or fourth century, A.D.), and is clearly described by the Arab who wrote a text-book of chemistry, called *The Sage's Step*, in Spain, in the twelfth century.

When mercuric oxide is heated further, its red colour changes to black and it splits up again into mercury and oxygen—

$$2HgO = 2Hg + O_2.$$

(Cf. Lavoisier's work, p. 167.)

Sodium

Symbol: Na; *Atomic Weight:* 23; *Valency:* 1; *Melting-point:* 96°; *Specific Gravity:* 0·97.

History and Occurrence.—Sodium is very chemically active, hence it is not found free in nature. In the form of its chloride, NaCl, *common salt,* it is widely distributed in large quantities. Vast deposits of salt occur in England, Germany, Austria, and many other countries, while in solution it is found in the sea and in salt-lakes and salt-springs. Large beds of sodium nitrate, $NaNO_3$, or *Chile saltpetre,* are found in Chile and other parts of South America. Sodium carbonate or *natron,* Na_2CO_3, occurs in Egypt, East Africa, and Australia. Sodium was first prepared in 1807 by Sir Humphry Davy. You may have heard the lines (not the author's)—

"*Sir Humphry Davy*
Abominated gravy.
He lived in the odium
Of having discovered sodium."

Davy obtained sodium by melting some caustic soda (NaOH) in a platinum crucible, connected to the positive pole of a battery, and then inserting into the fused mass a platinum wire connected with the negative pole of the battery. The caustic soda was thus electrolysed, and split up into oxygen (at the anode) and sodium and hydrogen (at the cathode). Small metallic globules of molten sodium rose to the surface of the caustic soda, and took fire on reaching the air, burning with a golden-yellow flame.

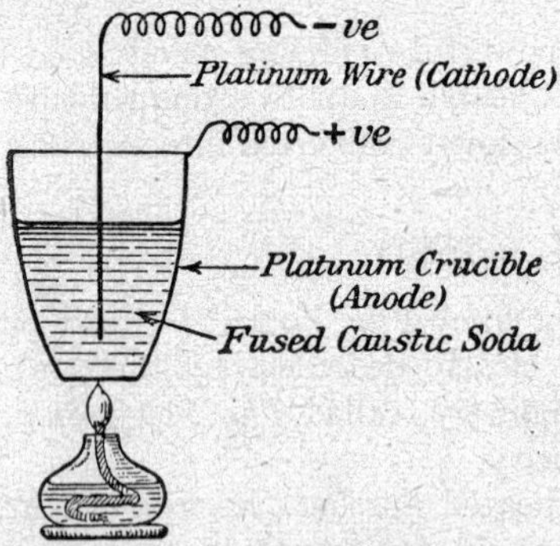

Fig. 102.—Davy's Apparatus for obtaining Sodium.

Manufacture.—Davy's method is that still employed

Sir Humphry Davy.

commercially for obtaining sodium, except that the apparatus is of course much larger and different in detail. The current, too, is derived from a generator, and not from a battery. The caustic soda is placed in a large iron pot, through the bottom of which an iron rod sticks up. This rod is the cathode. Surrounding (but of course not touching) the cathode is a nickel tube which is made the anode.

The oxygen and hydrogen which are obtained as by-products are in themselves quite valuable, and help to make the process pay. Most of the sodium of commerce is converted into sodium cyanide, NaCN, which is used in the extraction of gold.

Properties.—Sodium is a soft, silvery metal which can easily be moulded between the fingers. It is readily attacked by moist air, a freshly-cut surface—which at first has a bright metallic lustre—rapidly rusting over and becoming dull. This is due to the formation of a film of *sodium monoxide*, Na_2O, which is afterwards converted, by the moisture and carbon dioxide of the air, into *sodium hydroxide*, and then *sodium carbonate*—

$$\text{(i)} \quad 4Na + O_2 = 2Na_2O.$$
$$\text{(ii)} \quad Na_2O + H_2O = 2NaOH.$$
$$\text{(iii)} \quad 2NaOH + CO_2 = Na_2CO_3 + H_2O.$$

Sodium is therefore kept in air-tight tins, the lids of which have been soldered on, or—in smaller quantities, as in the laboratory—in petroleum, which contains no oxygen.

When heated in air or oxygen, sodium first melts (96°) and then takes fire, burning with a bright yellow flame and forming *sodium peroxide*, Na_2O_2—

$$2Na + O_2 = Na_2O_2.$$

For the action of sodium on water, see p. 366.

Sodium amalgam.—Sodium amalgam (written Na/Hg) is a solution of sodium in mercury. It is made by pressing sodium under mercury. When added to water it sinks to the bottom, and a steady stream of bubbles of hydrogen comes off, the sodium reacting with the water and leaving the mercury unchanged.

Compounds of Sodium.—The principal compounds of

sodium are the *peroxide, hydroxide, chloride, carbonate, sulphate,* and *nitrate.*

Sodium peroxide, Na_2O_2, is made by burning sodium in dry air from which all carbon dioxide has been removed—

$$2Na + O_2 = Na_2O_2.$$

It is a yellowish solid, and is a powerful oxidizing agent. Even in the cold, it reacts vigorously with water, forming oxygen and sodium hydroxide—

$$2Na_2O_2 + 2H_2O = 4NaOH = O_2.$$

This forms a convenient method of preparing oxygen in the laboratory.

Sodium hydroxide, NaOH, is alternatively known as caustic soda. It is one of the commonest and most important chemicals in the laboratory, and is a white, crystalline, deliquescent solid which dissolves in water to form a strongly alkaline solution. The solution turns red litmus blue, pink methyl orange yellow, and colourless phenolphthalein pink. Some of its chief properties have been discussed already (p. 186).

Caustic soda can be made in the laboratory by boiling a 10 per cent. solution of sodium carbonate with excess of lime—

$$Na_2CO_3 + Ca(OH)_2 \rightleftharpoons CaCO_3 \downarrow + 2NaOH.$$

The action is *reversible,* that is, under certain conditions, sodium hydroxide will act upon calcium carbonate, giving sodium carbonate and lime. Hence the experiment has to be so arranged as to prevent the backward reaction as far as possible. This is done by using an *excess* of lime—much more than is required by the equation—and also by keeping the liquid hot, since the backward reaction proceeds best in the cold.

The calcium carbonate, which is precipitated, is filtered off together with the excess of lime, and the clear filtrate is evaporated. On concentration, any lime which has dissolved separates out, and can be removed by a second filtration. The filtrate of caustic soda solution is then heated in iron pots until all the water is driven off. This requires a temperature higher than that of the melting-point of caustic soda, and the latter is therefore left as a liquid. It is run off and either sealed up in metal drums or cast, in moulds, into the thin sticks or pellets so familiar in the laboratory.

Other manufacturing processes are *electrolytic*, and it is by these that most of the caustic soda of commerce is made at the present day. Generally a concentrated solution of common salt is electrolysed in a cell of special form (cf. p. 222). Chlorine is evolved at the anode, which is made of carbon, and sodium is liberated at the cathode. The sodium, however, immediately attacks the water present, and forms caustic soda, with liberation of hydrogen—

$$2Na + 2H_2O = 2NaOH + H_2.$$

The hydrogen is led off through a pipe, dried, compressed, and stored in steel cylinders. The solution of caustic soda is evaporated and the caustic soda obtained as described above. It should be noted that *all* the products of this electrolytic operation are valuable, for the chlorine is used for bleaching, etc. (p. 215), and the hydrogen is used for making margarine or for other purposes. Only by making all their by-products commercially useful in some way can chemical manufacturers make their processes pay and at the same time keep prices low.

In the laboratory, caustic soda can be made in the first way described, or by adding little pellets of sodium carefully to distilled water.

PROPERTIES.—That caustic soda is crystalline can be seen by snapping a stick of it and looking at the broken surfaces. If caustic soda is left exposed to the air it deliquesces (p. 197), but after a time the liquid so formed goes solid again, owing to the absorption of carbon dioxide from the air, resulting in the formation of sodium carbonate—

$$2NaOH + CO_2 = Na_2CO_3 + H_2O.$$

Caustic soda is very soluble in water, heat being evolved during the dissolution. The solution is strongly alkaline, and has a slimy feel owing to the fact that it dissolves the outer layers of the skin. When caustic soda solution is added to solutions of salts of metals which form insoluble hydroxides, the latter are precipitated, *e.g.*—

$$CuSO_4 + 2NaOH = Na_2SO_4 + Cu(OH)_2 \downarrow \text{ (blue ppt.)}$$
$$Pb(NO_3)_2 + 2NaOH = 2NaNO_3 + Pb(OH)_2 \downarrow \text{ (white ppt.)}$$
$$FeCl_3 + 3NaOH = 3NaCl + Fe(OH)_3 \downarrow \text{ (red-brown ppt.)}.$$

In the case of silver, which does not form a hydroxide, the *oxide* is precipitated—

$$2AgNO_3 + 2NaOH = 2NaNO_3 + H_2O + Ag_2O \downarrow \text{ (brown ppt.)}.$$

If heated with an ammonium salt, caustic soda liberates ammonia, *e.g.*—

$$NH_4Cl + NaOH = NaCl + H_2O + NH_3.$$

Caustic soda is used in the laboratory for preparing metallic hydroxides, for absorbing carbon dioxide and sulphur dioxide, for the titration of acids in volumetric analysis, for preparing ammonia and marsh-gas, and for many other purposes. Commercially it is used in making soap, which, together with glycerol, is obtained when mutton-fat is boiled with caustic soda solution. Mutton-fat is a compound of glycerol with an acid called *stearic acid*. When boiled with caustic soda solution, it is split up, the glycerol being liberated and the stearic acid being left as *sodium stearate*, $C_{17}H_{35}.COONa$, which is ordinary "hard" soap. "Soft" soap—formerly much more widely used than at present—is *potassium* stearate.

Caustic soda is also used (*a*) in the manufacture of glass, (*b*) in the dye industry, and (*c*) in the artificial silk industry, as well as for many other purposes.

Sodium chloride or **common salt,** NaCl, is well-known to every one. It is a white solid, crystallizing in cubes, and has no water of crystallization. It is obtained commercially by evaporating brine, or sea-water, as well as by direct mining. In the laboratory it can be made by (*a*) burning sodium in a stream of chlorine, $2Na + Cl_2 = 2NaCl$, or (*b*) by neutralizing caustic soda with hydrochloric acid, $NaOH + HCl =$

$NaCl + H_2O$, or (*c*) by acting upon sodium carbonate with hydrochloric acid—

$$Na_2CO_3 + 2HCl = 2NaCl + H_2O + CO_2.$$

Salt can be purified by making a cold saturated solution of it and passing a stream of hydrogen chloride into the solution, when pure sodium chloride is precipitated.

Many uses of salt are common knowledge. It is, in addition, the starting-point for the production of practically all the sodium and chlorine compounds (except sodium nitrate) used in commerce.

Sodium carbonate, Na_2CO_3.—Ordinary washing-soda is sodium carbonate *decahydrate,* $Na_2CO_3.10H_2O$. By the action of heat, the water of crystallization may be driven off, when a white powder, anhydrous sodium carbonate, Na_2CO_3, is left. This is sometimes known as *soda-ash.* Washing-soda crystals, if their faces are perfect, remain unchanged in the air, but if they are scratched the crystals *effloresce* (p. 197), and gradually fall to a white powder, which is not the anhydrous salt but the *mono*-hydrate, $Na_2CO_3.H_2O$.

In solution, sodium carbonate reacts alkaline, since carbonic acid is such a weak acid. Dilute acids act upon sodium carbonate, causing liberation of carbon dioxide and formation of the sodium salt of the acid employed, *e.g.*—

$$Na_2CO_3 + 2HCl = 2NaCl + H_2O + CO_2.$$
$$Na_2CO_3 + 2HNO_3 = 2NaNO_3 + H_2O + CO_2.$$
$$Na_2CO_3 + H_2SO_4 = Na_2SO_4 + H_2O + CO_2.$$

Since sodium carbonate is alkaline, it can be estimated in solution by titration with a standard acid, if an indicator unaffected by carbon dioxide (e.g. methyl orange) is used. Litmus itself may be used if the solution is boiled, so as to drive off the carbon dioxide and thus prevent its action on the litmus. From the above equations it is clear that the equivalent of anhydrous sodium carbonate is $\frac{46 + 12 + 48}{2} = 53$; that of washing soda will of course be $\frac{46 + 12 + 48 + 180}{2} = 146$.

Sodium carbonate is manufactured by saturating a concentrated solution of salt with ammonia and then allowing it to flow down a tower up which a stream of carbon dioxide is blown. In this way, sodium bicarbonate and ammonium chloride are formed. The equation is quite easy to remember, as only 1 molecule of each substance is required—

$$NH_3 + H_2O + NaCl + CO_2 = NH_4Cl + NaHCO_3.$$

The sodium bicarbonate is not very soluble, and thus separates out. It is filtered off and heated, when it decomposes into sodium carbonate, water, and carbon dioxide—

$$2NaHCO_3 = Na_2CO_3 + H_2O + CO_2.$$

From the soda-ash thus obtained, washing-soda can be made, if desired, by dissolving it in water and evaporating the solution to the point of crystallization.

One of the chief points of interest in this process (which is known as the SOLVAY or *Ammonia-Soda* process) is its self-contained nature. Thus, the carbon dioxide is prepared by heating lime-stone in a lime-kiln—

$$CaCO_3 = CaO + CO_2,$$

and the other product, lime, is used to regenerate the ammonia from the ammonium chloride formed—

$$CaO + 2NH_4Cl = CaCl_2 + 2NH_3 + H_2O.$$

The carbon dioxide evolved when the sodium bicarbonate is heated is of course used again; the equations show that, in a single operation, half the original amount of carbon dioxide is converted into sodium carbonate and the other half regained as gas.

The only waste product is therefore calcium chloride.

Formerly, much sodium carbonate was prepared by a process, now obsolete, invented by the Frenchman, LEBLANC (1742–1806). This consisted in heating salt with sulphuric acid, to form sodium sulphate, and then heating the sodium sulphate with carbon (coke) and limestone ($CaCO_3$). The carbon reduced the sodium sulphate to sodium sulphide, Na_2S, and this then reacted with the limestone to form sodium carbonate and calcium sulphide. As the latter is insoluble, the sodium carbonate could be obtained from the mixture by extraction with water. The equations for the various actions are as follows:

$$\text{I.}\left\{\begin{array}{lll}\text{(i)} & NaCl + H_2SO_4 & = NaHSO_4 + HCl. \\ \text{(ii)} & NaHSO_4 + NaCl & = Na_2SO_4 + HCl.\end{array}\right.$$

$$\text{II.}\left\{\begin{array}{lll}\text{(i)} & Na_2SO_4 + 2C & = Na_2S + 2CO_2. \\ \text{(ii)} & Na_2S + CaCO_3 & = Na_2CO_3 + CaS.\end{array}\right.$$

The process was kept alive long after sodium carbonate could be made more cheaply by the Ammonia-Soda process by the facts (*a*) that the hydrochloric acid is an extremely valuable by-product, and (*b*) that nitric acid manufacturers produce thousands of tons of sodium bisulphate, which found a ready market in the Leblanc process (cf. Equation I. (ii)).

Sodium bicarbonate, $NaHCO_3$.—When carbon dioxide is passed into caustic soda solution, it is absorbed. First of all, sodium carbonate is formed—

$$2NaOH + CO_2 = Na_2CO_3 + H_2O.$$

Further action of carbon dioxide results in the formation of sodium *bi*carbonate—

$$Na_2CO_3 + H_2O + CO_2 = 2NaHCO_3.$$

Sodium bicarbonate is a white crystalline solid with a neutral reaction in solution. It is used as a baking-powder, since on heating it loses carbon dioxide, which makes the dough "rise"—

$$2NaHCO_3 = Na_2CO_3 + H_2O + CO_2.$$

The reaction represented by this equation affords a convenient means of preparing pure anhydrous sodium carbonate for analytical work in the laboratory.

Dilute acids act upon sodium bicarbonate, carbon dioxide being evolved—

$$NaHCO_3 + HCl = NaCl + H_2O + CO_2.$$

If treated in solution with the calculated quantity of caustic soda, it is converted into the normal carbonate—

$$NaHCO_3 + NaOH = Na_2CO_3 + H_2O.$$

Sodium sulphate, Na_2SO_4, may be made by any of the general methods used for preparing salts (p. 442), but is generally obtained by strongly heating salt with concentrated sulphuric acid. At a lower temperature, only the *bi*-sulphate, $NaHSO_4$, is obtained—

High temp.	$2NaCl + H_2SO_4 = Na_2SO_4 + 2HCl.$
Lower temp.	$NaCl + H_2SO_4 = NaHSO_4 + HCl.$

When crystallized out from its solution in water, sodium sulphate separates as its deca-hydrate, $Na_2SO_4.10H_2O$. This is known as GLAUBER'S salt, after its discoverer, JOHN RUDOLPH GLAUBER (1604–68). He called it *sal mirabile,* and ascribed to it all kinds of wonderful healing properties. It is still widely used as a purgative, though the habit of taking it—or any similar salt or mixture of salts—regularly is a very pernicious one, and may lead to a very different sort of feeling from that which is so widely advertised.

Sodium nitrate, $NaNO_3$, occurs naturally as Chile saltpetre (p. 374). The crude nitrate, known locally as *caliche,* contains sodium iodate (p. 241) from which it is purified by fractional crystallization from water. The sodium iodate remains in the mother-liquors, and is used as a source of iodine.

Sodium nitrate is very largely used (about 4,000,000 tons *per annum*) as a fertilizer for plants (*e.g.* sugar-cane, banana, cereals). It is applied to the growing crop as a top-dressing in the spring; its effects last for one year only, since it is so soluble that it is all leached out of the soil by the winter rains. It is also used in the manufacture of nitric acid and potassium nitrate.

Sodium nitrate is a white deliquescent crystalline solid. When strongly heated it loses oxygen, and is converted into *sodium nitrite,* $NaNO_2$—

$$2NaNO_3 = 2NaNO_2 + O_2.$$

Sodium nitrite is a pale yellow crystalline solid, readily soluble in water. Dilute acids act upon it, causing evolution of oxides of nitrogen. It is chiefly employed in the manufacture of aniline dyes.

Potassium

Symbol: K; *Atomic Weight:* 39; *Valency:* 1; *Melting-point:* 62°; *Specific Gravity:* 0·87.

The Arab chemists of the early Middle Ages obtained a white crystalline solid by burning plants, stirring up the residue with water, filtering, and evaporating. This solid, now known as potassium carbonate, they called *al-qali*, " the ash," whence our word alkali (which should really be *alqali*) and the Latinized name *kalium* for potassium. The mystery of the symbol K for 1 atom of potassium, which may have puzzled you, is thus explained. The word *potash* comes from the custom of concentrating the solution of the ash in *pots*.

In most of its chemical and physical properties, potassium is closely similar to sodium, and this similarity extends also to the compounds of the two elements. One striking difference, however, is that sodium and its compounds colour a Bunsen flame *golden-yellow*, whereas potassium and its compounds give a *lilac* coloration.

The principal sources of potassium and potassium salts are the vast saline deposits at Stassfurt in North Germany. These deposits are considered by geologists to consist of the salts left by the drying-up of an inland sea. The chief potassium compound in them is *carnallite*, $KCl.MgCl_2.6H_2O$, from which most of the world's supply of potassium and its compounds is made.

Potassium hydroxide, chloride, carbonate and bicarbonate are very similar to the corresponding sodium compounds, except that *potassium carbonate* is deliquescent, and forms a *mono*-hydrate instead of a deca-hydrate, while *potassium bicarbonate* is much more soluble than sodium bicarbonate.

Potassium nitrate, KNO_3, or *nitre* or *saltpetre,* is found in the soil of certain tropical countries, such as India (" Indian saltpetre "). It is made by the bacterial oxidation of nitrogenous animal refuse in the presence of wood-ashes; this process is a regular industry in India.

It is also manufactured from Chile saltpetre, $NaNO_3$, by adding this compound to a hot concentrated solution of potassium chloride, when "double decomposition" occurs—

$$NaNO_3 + KCl = KNO_3 + NaCl.$$

By regulating the concentrations, the comparatively sparingly-soluble sodium chloride can be made to separate practically completely. After removal of the salt the solution is allowed to cool, when the potassium nitrate crystallizes out.

Potassium nitrate forms white anhydrous crystals which are soluble in water but are not deliquescent and therefore can be used in the manufacture of gunpowder; sodium nitrate, on the other hand, is very deliquescent, and is, naturally, useless for this purpose.

When potassium nitrate is strongly heated it loses oxygen and is converted into *potassium nitrite*—

$$2KNO_3 = 2KNO_2 + O_2.$$

Owing to the ease with which it loses this oxygen, it is a good *oxidizing agent.*

The solubility curve of potassium nitrate is given on p. 138.

Potassium chlorate, $KClO_3$, is manufactured by the electrolysis of a hot concentrated solution of potassium chloride. The caustic potash formed at the cathode reacts with the chlorine liberated at the anode, according to the equation—

$$6KOH + 3Cl_2 = 5KCl + KClO_3 + 3H_2O.$$

Potassium chlorate is a white anhydrous crystalline solid. It is a strong oxidizing agent, and is commonly used in the laboratory as a source of oxygen. Its oxidizing powers render it a good germicide; it is therefore sometimes made up into "chlorate lozenges" for the cure of sore throat. Mixtures of potassium chlorate and sulphur or red phosphorus explode very violently when rubbed or struck.

Questions

1. Who discovered sodium, and when?
2. How does sodium occur in nature?
3. How is sodium obtained commercially?
4. Write the formulæ for the following compounds of sodium—chloride, carbonate, bicarbonate, sulphate, nitrate, hydroxide, peroxide, salt, natron, Chile saltpetre, Glauber's salt.
5. Write equations for the following actions:

   Sodium on water.
   Sodium peroxide on water.
   Carbon dioxide on caustic soda solution.
   Heat on sodium bicarbonate.
   Caustic soda on copper sulphate solution.

6. How would you prepare caustic soda in the laboratory?
7. How is caustic soda obtained commercially?
8. What is soap? How is it made?
9. For what purposes is caustic soda used?
10. Write equations for the action of (*a*) hydrochloric acid, (*b*) nitric acid, (*c*) sulphuric acid upon (i) sodium carbonate, (ii) sodium bicarbonate, (iii) caustic soda.
11. What weight of sodium carbonate could be obtained from 10 kilograms of caustic soda, and what volume of carbon dioxide (at N.T.P.) would be required for the purpose?
12. What volume of carbon dioxide, at 27° C. and 380 mm. pressure, could be obtained by heating 42 grams of sodium bicarbonate?
13. How is sodium carbonate manufactured?
14. Given sodium carbonate and the necessary reagents (but no other sodium compound), how could you make (*a*) sodium bicarbonate, (*b*) sodium hydroxide, (*c*) sodium sulphate, (*d*) sodium nitrate, (*e*) sodium nitrite? What is the action of hydrochloric acid upon (*a*)?
15. How is potassium chlorate manufactured? What is the action of heat upon it?
16. How could you distinguish between potassium chloride and sodium chloride?
17. What are the chief characteristics of metals?
18. How may metals be distinguished from non-metals?
19. Explain the terms *malleable, ductile, conductor, tensile strength, basic oxide, alloy, metalloid.*
20. Write a short account of the action of metals upon water.
21. Describe the actions which occur between (*a*) steam and iron, (*b*) iron oxide and hydrogen.
22. What do you mean by a *reversible reaction*? Give an example.
23. Write a short essay on "The action of the mineral acids upon some common metals."

24. Write a brief account of the action of air and oxygen upon magnesium, zinc, iron, copper, lead and mercury.

25. Write the formulæ for (*a*) cuprous oxide, (*b*) litharge, (*c*) minium, (*d*) massicot, (*e*) red-lead, (*f*) ferroso-ferric oxide, (*g*) lead monoxide, (*h*) smithy scales, (*k*) cupric oxide, (*l*) magnetic oxide of iron, (*m*) ferric oxide, (*n*) ferrous oxide, (*o*) mercuric oxide, (*p*) lead dioxide, (*q*) magnesium oxide, (*r*) philosophers' wool.

CHAPTER XX

CALCIUM, MAGNESIUM, ZINC, COPPER, IRON, LEAD

CALCIUM

Symbol: Ca; *Valency:* 2; *Atomic Weight:* 40; *Melting-point:* 800°; *Specific Gravity:* 1·52.

History and Occurrence.—Metallic calcium is very chemically active, hence the element is not found free in nature. It was first isolated by SIR HUMPHRY DAVY in 1808, and was obtained pure by MOISSAN in 1898. Moissan made it by heating calcium iodide with excess of sodium—

$$CaI_2 + 2Na = Ca + 2NaI \text{ (\textit{sodium iodide})}.$$

Compounds of calcium, such as gypsum, quicklime, slaked lime and limestone, have of course been known and used for thousands of years, since many of them occur naturally in large quantities.

Calcium carbonate, $CaCO_3$, is the chief calcium mineral. This is found amorphous as *limestone* and *chalk*, and in various crystalline forms as *calcite, aragonite, marble, Iceland spar*, etc. *Dolomite*, a constituent of many rocks, is a mixture of calcium carbonate and magnesium carbonate, $MgCO_3$.

Calcium is also found in the form of its sulphate. *Gypsum* and *alabaster* are $CaSO_4.2H_2O$, calcium sulphate *dihydrate*, while *anhydrite* is anhydrous calcium sulphate, $CaSO_4$. Calcium *phosphate*, $Ca_3(PO_4)_2$, occurs naturally in large quantity.

Calcium is widely distributed in the soil (chiefly as its carbonate), and is found in all plants and animals. Eggshells consist largely of calcium carbonate, and calcium salts are found in the blood.

Preparation.—Calcium is becoming of importance in technical chemistry, and is therefore prepared on a large scale by the electrolysis of fused anhydrous calcium chloride, $CaCl_2$. Chlorine is evolved from the anode, and calcium is deposited on the cathode, which is made of an iron rod.

Properties.—Calcium is a hard silvery-white metal with a slight tinge of yellow. It is not affected by dry air, but in moist air it slowly oxidizes, forming *calcium hydroxide*, $Ca(OH)_2$, "slaked lime"—

$$2Ca + O_2 + 2H_2O = 2Ca(OH)_2.$$

Calcium attacks water in the cold, with evolution of hydrogen and formation of calcium hydroxide—

$$Ca + 2H_2O = Ca(OH)_2 + H_2.$$

It has a specific gravity of 1·52 and melts at 800° C. If heated in air or oxygen it burns with a reddish flame, forming *calcium oxide*, CaO (quicklime).

It will dissolve readily in dilute acids, the corresponding calcium salt being obtained, *e.g.*—

$$Ca + 2HCl = CaCl_2 + H_2.$$
$$Ca + H_2SO_4 = CaSO_4 + H_2.$$

COMPOUNDS OF CALCIUM.

Calcium oxide or **quicklime,** CaO, is formed when the metal burns in air or oxygen—

$$2Ca + O_2 = 2CaO,$$

and when the carbonate or nitrate is strongly heated—

$$CaCO_3 = CaO + CO_2.$$
$$2Ca(NO_3)_2 = 2CaO + 4NO_2 + O_2.$$

Commercially it is made by heating limestone (mineral amorphous calcium carbonate) in a lime-kiln.[1]

The limestone is crushed and mixed with coal or coke. The kiln is filled with the mixture which is then lit at the bottom. The lime, in the form of a powder or in small lumps, is removed from the kiln and fresh mixture added at the top. Once the

[1] Note that this word is more properly pronounced *kill* than *kiln*.

kiln is lit it is kept going until it wears out, a period which may be as much as ten years. Lime prepared in this way contains the ashes of the coal or coke used, but these are rarely harmful, and are often beneficial in lime which is used for commercial purposes. In kilns of more modern type, the heating is effected by the combustion of producer-gas (p. 348), and the quicklime is then obtained free from ash.

Calcium oxide is a white amorphous substance very difficult to melt. It will melt, however, in the electric furnace, and can even be boiled! The temperature of the oxyhydrogen flame (p. 162) does not melt it, but merely makes it white-hot. White-hot quicklime gives out a very brilliant light, called the *limelight*, which is used in lanterns, and was formerly employed in theatres for illuminating the actors (hence the phrase "*in the limelight*").

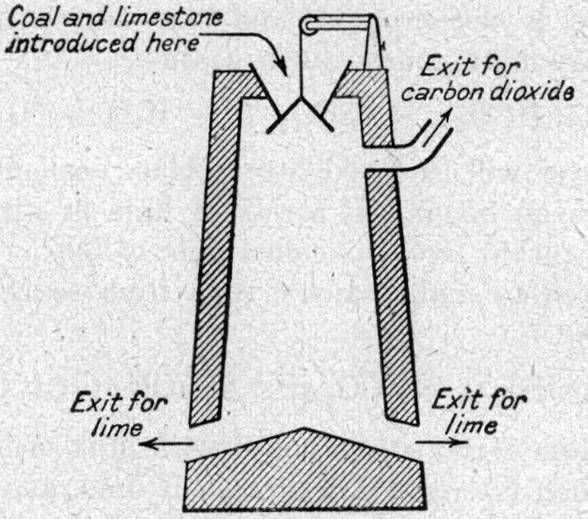

FIG. 103.—Lime-kiln.

Calcium oxide will dissolve in dilute acids, yielding the corresponding calcium salt, and water—

$$CaO + H_2SO_4 = CaSO_4 + H_2O.$$
$$CaO + 2HCl = CaCl_2 + H_2O.$$
$$CaO + 2HNO_3 = Ca(NO_3)_2 + H_2O.$$

When water is added to quicklime, the lime gets very hot,

and **calcium hydroxide or slaked lime,** $Ca(OH)_2$, is formed. If the quicklime is in lumps, these will fall to pieces, and the slaked lime will be obtained as a white powder. Calcium hydroxide is slightly soluble in water; the solution is called *lime-water*, and is used as a test for carbon dioxide and as a mouth-wash for infants.

When carbon dioxide is passed into lime-water, a white precipitate of calcium carbonate (chalk) is formed—

$$Ca(OH)_2 + CO_2 = CaCO_3 \downarrow + H_2O.$$

Further passage of carbon dioxide causes the calcium carbonate to dissolve, hence the "milky" lime-water becomes clear again. This is due to the formation of *calcium bicarbonate*, which is soluble in water—

$$CaCO_3 + H_2O + CO_2 = Ca(HCO_3)_2.$$

If the clear solution of calcium bicarbonate is boiled, the bicarbonate is decomposed, and the white precipitate of calcium carbonate comes down again—

$$Ca(HCO_3)_2 = CaCO_3 \downarrow + H_2O + CO_2 \uparrow.$$

Lime-water will turn red litmus blue; calcium hydroxide is therefore an *alkali*. If *excess* of lime is stirred up with water, the turbid liquid is called *milk of lime*. Milk of lime is often used to make caustic soda from sodium carbonate (see p. 378)—

$$Ca(OH)_2 + Na_2CO_3 \rightleftharpoons 2NaOH + CaCO_3 \downarrow.$$

The sodium carbonate is boiled with milk of lime, and the liquid is then filtered. The excess of lime, and the precipitated calcium carbonate, are left on the filter, and the filtrate is a solution of caustic soda.

Lime (quick or slaked) finds many uses both in the laboratory and in various industries. It is employed in the purification of coal-gas, in the manufacture of washing-soda (p. 382), in tanning, in glass-making (p. 350); in the manufacture of bleaching-powder (p. 217), in the refinement of sugar, and for many other purposes. It is also the principal constituent of *mortar* and *cement*.

Mortar consists of a pasty mixture of slaked lime, sand, and water. The "setting" of mortar is due chiefly to the loss of moisture by evaporation, but the lime slowly changes into *calcium carbonate* by combining with the carbon dioxide of the air—

$$Ca(OH)_2 + CO_2 = CaCO_3 + H_2O.$$

Part of it, too, may combine with the sand (SiO_2, silicon dioxide, p. 349), forming *calcium silicate*, $CaSiO_3$—

$$Ca(OH)_2 + SiO_2 = CaSiO_3 + H_2O.$$

You can easily show that old mortar contains calcium carbonate by adding a little dilute hydrochloric acid, when an effervescence will take place—

$$CaCO_3 + 2HCl = CaCl_2 + H_2O + CO_2.$$

Portland cement is made by strongly heating a mixture of limestone or chalk ($CaCO_3$), and clay. The product is then finely powdered and is ready for use. When mixed thoroughly with water it quickly sets to a hard mass.

Concrete is a mixture of Portland cement and small gravel or finely broken bricks. It is now extensively used in the construction of buildings. Reinforced concrete consists of concrete that has been allowed to set around a steel framework or skeleton. It is less liable to crack than concrete not so reinforced.

Calcium carbonate, $CaCO_3$.—As previously mentioned, calcium carbonate exists naturally in many different forms. Vast quantities are found in the amorphous state as *limestone* and *chalk*, of which hills and even whole mountain ranges may be formed. Chalk is partly composed of the skeletons of countless minute sea-animals, though the main bulk was probably formed by precipitation from sea-water.

Precipitated chalk is calcium carbonate which has been precipitated either by passing carbon dioxide through lime-water, or by adding sodium carbonate to a solution of calcium chloride—

$$Ca(OH)_2 + CO_2 = CaCO_3 \downarrow + H_2O,$$
$$\text{or } CaCl_2 + Na_2CO_3 = CaCO_3 \downarrow + 2NaCl.$$

Calcium carbonate can also be made by passing carbon dioxide over warm lime.

Calcium carbonate is insoluble in water, but it dissolves in dilute acids with evolution of carbon dioxide. It is also soluble in water containing carbon dioxide (see above, under *lime-water*)—

$$CaCO_3 + H_2O + CO_2 \rightleftharpoons Ca(HCO_3)_2 \text{ (calcium bicarbonate).}$$

This reaction is reversible, since when the solution of calcium bicarbonate is heated, the calcium carbonate is reprecipitated—

$$Ca(HCO_3)_2 = CaCO_3 \downarrow + H_2O + CO_2.$$

[For the effect of the presence of calcium bicarbonate in water, see *Hardness of Water*, p. 199.]

The equations for the action of the dilute mineral acids upon calcium carbonate are as follow:

$$CaCO_3 + 2HCl = CaCl_2 + H_2O + CO_2.$$
$$CaCO_3 + 2HNO_3 = Ca(NO_3)_2 + H_2O + CO_2.$$
$$CaCO_3 + H_2SO_4 = CaSO_4 + H_2O + CO_2.$$

With sulphuric acid, the action ceases after awhile, if the carbonate is in lumps (*e.g.* marble). This is because the calcium sulphate, which is practically insoluble in water, forms a coating on the lump and thus prevents the acid from getting through to the inside. Calcium chloride and nitrate, on the other hand, are soluble, hence the action in these cases goes on to completion.

Calcium bicarbonate, $Ca(HCO_3)_2$, the formation of which has been described above, is usually met with only in solution. It can, however, be made, as a white powder which decomposes on heating, by adding a concentrated solution of potassium bicarbonate to a cold concentrated solution of calcium chloride—

$$CaCl_2 + 2KHCO_3 = Ca(HCO_3)_2 + 2KCl.$$

It is, of course, soluble in water.

Calcium sulphate, $CaSO_4$.—The naturally occurring forms of this substance have already been mentioned, p. 389.

When *gypsum*, $CaSO_4.2H_2O$ (calcium sulphate dihydrate) is carefully heated to 120–130°, it loses part of its water of crystallization, and is converted into *Plaster of Paris*, which has the formula $(CaSO_4)_2H_2O$, or $CaSO_4.\frac{1}{2}H_2O$, and is chemically known as *calcium sulphate hemi-hydrate.* When Plaster of Paris is made into a thick paste with water it rapidly becomes converted into a solid mass of gypsum. The gypsum takes up slightly more room than the paste of the plaster, and hence if the latter is allowed to set in moulds, sharp casts of the moulds may be obtained. Plaster of Paris is also used in surgery, for forming moulds round broken limbs and thus keeping the bones in place. Its use for this purpose was first described by a Persian doctor, called ABU MANSUR MUWAFFAK, in the tenth century.

Calcium sulphate is only very slightly soluble in water, hence it can be prepared by mixing concentrated solutions of calcium chloride and sodium sulphate—

$$CaCl_2 + Na_2SO_4 = CaSO_4 \downarrow + 2NaCl.$$

It is, however, sufficiently soluble to make water *hard*. (See p. 199.) The hardness is "permanent."

Calcium nitrate, $Ca(NO_3)_2$.—Calcium nitrate can be made by dissolving calcium, or its oxide, hydroxide or carbonate, in dilute nitric acid, and evaporating the solution to crystallization—

$$e.g.\ CaO + 2HNO_3 = Ca(NO_3)_2 + H_2O.$$

The crystals obtained have 4 molecules of water of crystallization in them—$Ca(NO_3)_2.4H_2O$. They are deliquescent.

When strongly heated, calcium nitrate splits up into quicklime, oxygen and nitrogen peroxide—

$$2Ca(NO_3)_2 = 2CaO + 2NO_2 + O_2.$$

[*Compare* zinc nitrate and copper nitrate, and *contrast* potassium nitrate, sodium nitrate and ammonium nitrate.]

Basic calcium nitrate, i.e. calcium nitrate combined with lime, $Ca(NO_3)_2.xCa(OH)_2$, is used as an artificial manure. (See p. 271.)

Calcium chloride, $CaCl_2$, can be made by the action of chlorine upon heated calcium—

$$Ca + Cl_2 = CaCl_2,$$

or by dissolving calcium or its oxide, hydroxide or carbonate in dilute hydrochloric acid—

$$Ca + 2HCl = CaCl_2 + H_2.$$
$$CaO + 2HCl = CaCl_2 + H_2O.$$
$$Ca(OH)_2 + 2HCl = CaCl_2 + 2H_2O.$$
$$CaCO_3 + 2HCl = CaCl_2 + H_2O + CO_2.$$

On evaporating the solution, the salt separates out in the form of colourless, extremely deliquescent crystals of the *hexahydrate*, $CaCl_2.6H_2O$. If these are strongly heated, they lose their water of crystallization, and the *anhydrous* salt, $CaCl_2$, is left. This can be fused and granulated, and in the granular form is used for drying gases, etc.; it is the substance so familiar in desiccators. [*Note* that it cannot be used for drying *ammonia*, since it combines with this gas, forming the compound $CaCl_2.8NH_3$.] Calcium chloride is obtained commercially as a by-product in the manufacture of sodium carbonate by the ammonia-soda process (p. 382).

Calcium carbide, CaC_2, is made by heating a mixture of quicklime and powdered coke in the electric furnace—

$$CaO + 3C = CaC_2 + CO.$$

When pure it is a white crystalline solid, but as generally prepared it is grey, owing to the presence in it of particles of carbon. It is decomposed by water, with evolution of acetylene—

$$CaC_2 + 2H_2O = Ca(OH)_2 + C_2H_2 \text{ (acetylene)}.$$

This reaction is of great commercial importance, since acetylene is readily converted into acetic acid and other organic compounds.

Calcium phosphate, $Ca_3(PO_4)_2$.—See p. 279. A form of calcium phosphate known as "*superphosphate*" (p. 287) is used as an artificial manure.

Bleaching-powder, $Ca(OCl)Cl$ or $CaOCl_2$, is sometimes regarded as a hybrid compound, half-way between calcium chloride and calcium hypochlorite—

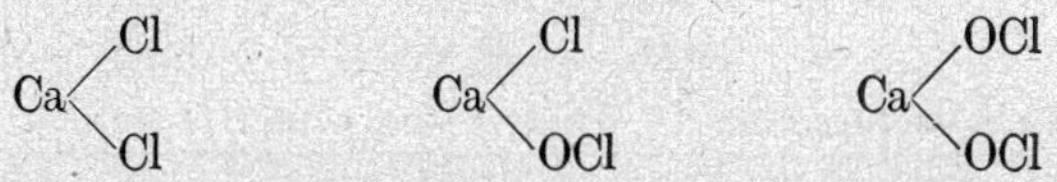

Its actual composition still remains unknown.

It is made by passing chlorine slowly over a layer of dry slaked lime on the floor of a series of chambers made of stone or lined with lead. The reaction which occurs can be represented as follows—

$$Ca(OH)_2 + Cl_2 = Ca(OCl)Cl + H_2O.$$

Bleaching-powder is a white solid which smells of chlorine. It is acted upon by all dilute acids, and chlorine is evolved—

$$CaOCl_2 + H_2SO_4 = CaSO_4 + H_2O + Cl_2.$$
$$CaOCl_2 + 2HCl = CaCl_2 + H_2O + Cl_2.$$
$$CaOCl_2 + 2HNO_3 = Ca(NO_3)_2 + H_2O + Cl_2.$$

It is used for bleaching, and as a disinfectant. Another name for it is chloride of lime. For more about it see p. 217.

Equivalent of Calcium.—The equivalent of calcium can be determined by dissolving a known weight of the metal in dilute hydrochloric acid and measuring the volume of hydrogen evolved.

Questions

1. What are the chief minerals in which calcium is found ?
2. Write the formulæ for (*a*) quicklime, (*b*) alabaster, (*c*) Plaster of Paris, (*d*) gypsum, (*e*) marble, (*f*) limestone, (*g*) calcium bicarbonate.
3. Write a short account of the commercial preparation and uses of quicklime.
4. What are (*a*) mortar, (*b*) Portland cement, (*c*) concrete ? What happens when mortar " sets " ?
5. What is *bleaching-powder* ? How is it made ? What is it used for ? What is the action of dilute hydrochloric acid upon it ?
6. Write the formulæ for (*a*) calcium chloride hexahydrate, (*b*) anhydrous calcium chloride, (*c*) calcium hypochlorite, (*d*) calcium carbide.
7. How is calcium carbide made ? What is the action of water upon it ?
8. Describe in detail how you would determine the equivalent of calcium.

9. Complete the following equations:

(i) $CaOCl_2 + 2HNO_3 =$
(ii) $CaCO_3 + 2HCl =$
(iii) $2Ca(NO_3)_2 =$
(iv) $CaCO_3 + H_2O + CO_2 =$

10. What is *lime-water*? What is the action of carbon dioxide upon it? What is the action of chlorine upon it? (See p. 217.)

11. Write a short account of the *Hardness of Water*. How may hard water be softened? (See p. 198.)

12. What are the properties of metallic calcium? How is the element isolated?

13. Starting with calcium oxide, how could you prepare (*a*) calcium carbonate, (*b*) calcium sulphate, (*c*) bleaching-powder, (*d*) anhydrous calcium chloride?

14. Compare the properties of calcium and its compounds with those of zinc and its compounds.

MAGNESIUM

Symbol: Mg; *Valency:* 2; *Atomic Weight:* 24·32; *Melting-point:* 650°; *Specific Gravity:* 1·74.

History and Occurrence.—Magnesium sulphate ("Epsom salt") was obtained in 1695 by NEHEMIAH GREW, from the water of a spring at Epsom. From the sulphate, BLACK in 1755 obtained the oxide, magnesia, from which in turn, in 1800, DAVY succeeded in isolating metallic magnesium.

Magnesium occurs chiefly as its carbonate, $MgCO_3$. When it is found unmixed, this compound is called *magnesite*, but it occurs more often in association with calcium carbonate as the mineral *dolomite*, $MgCO_3.CaCO_3$, of which whole mountain ranges (*e.g.* the Dolomitic Alps) are largely built. Magnesium occurs also as the chloride in the mineral *carnallite*, $KCl.MgCl_2.6H_2O$, vast quantities of which occur in the saline deposits at Stassfurt (N. Germany). *Asbestos* is a calcium magnesium silicate, $CaSiO_3.3MgSiO_3$.

Extraction.—Magnesium is obtained commercially by the electrolysis of fused anhydrous carnallite, chlorine being evolved at the anode and magnesium being set free, in a molten condition, at the cathode. The liquid magnesium rises to the surface of the fused carnallite, whence it is run off.

Properties.—Magnesium is a fairly hard metal, with a silvery lustre. It is stable in dry air, but slowly oxidizes in moist air, forming magnesium oxide, MgO. It has a specific gravity of 1·74, melts at 650°, and boils at about 1150°. It is ductile and malleable and is usually met with as magnesium ribbon, wire, turnings or powder. In making magnesium wire the metal has to be heated; ribbon is made from the wire by means of heavy rollers.

When heated in the air or in oxygen, magnesium takes fire and burns with an extremely brilliant flame, rich in the chemically and photographically active rays. In oxygen, the product of combustion is *magnesium oxide*, MgO, but in air this is mixed with a little *magnesium nitride*, Mg_3N_2. Magnesium will burn in steam and, less readily, in carbon dioxide; in each case the oxide of the metal is formed and the other element (hydrogen or carbon) is liberated:

$$Mg + H_2O = MgO + H_2.$$
$$2Mg + CO_2 = 2MgO + C.$$

Magnesium is employed commercially in the preparation of "flashlight powders" for photography, in the firework industry, and as a constituent of the strong, but light, alloy (with aluminium) called *magnalium* (p. 433).

Magnesium is readily soluble in dilute acids, *e.g.*

$$Mg + H_2SO_4 = \underset{\text{Magnesium sulphate.}}{MgSO_4} + H_2,$$

$$Mg + 2HCl = \underset{\text{Magnesium chloride.}}{MgCl_2} + H_2.$$

From very dilute nitric acid, under suitable conditions, magnesium will liberate hydrogen—a very unusual reaction (cf. p. 272). Caustic soda and potash have no action on magnesium.

Compounds of Magnesium.—Magnesium oxide or *magnesia*, MgO, can be obtained by burning magnesium in oxygen (or air, but see above), or by heating the carbonate or nitrate:

$$MgCO_3 = MgO + CO_2.$$
$$2Mg(NO_3)_2 = 2MgO + 4NO_2 + O_2.$$

It is a white powder, very slightly soluble in water, to which it gives an alkaline reaction. It is used in medicine, and also as a "refractory" or heat-resisting substance in electric furnaces.

Magnesium carbonate, $MgCO_3$, is a white powder. Like the oxide it is used in medicine. If suspended in water through

FIG. 104.— Domestic Use of Magnesium Sulphate.

which carbon dioxide is blown, it is converted into the bicarbonate, which dissolves; the water is thus rendered temporarily hard (cf. p. 199):

$$MgCO_3 + CO_2 + H_2O \rightleftharpoons Mg(HCO_3)_2.$$

Magnesium sulphate, $MgSO_4$, can be made by dissolving the metal, the oxide or the carbonate in dilute sulphuric acid:

$$Mg + H_2SO_4 = MgSO_4 + H_2.$$
$$MgO + H_2SO_4 = MgSO_4 + H_2O.$$
$$MgCO_3 + H_2SO_4 = MgSO_4 + H_2O + CO_2.$$

On evaporating the solution, colourless needles of magnesium sulphate *heptahydrate*, $MgSO_4.7H_2O$, separate out; these are commonly known as Epsom salt—a useful purgative.

Questions

1. Describe the occurrence, extraction and properties of magnesium
2. Starting from metallic magnesium, how would you prepare specimens of (*a*) magnesium oxide, (*b*) magnesium sulphate ?
3. Write equations for the action of magnesium upon (*a*) dilute sulphuric acid, (*b*) oxygen, (*c*) nitrogen, (*d*) carbon dioxide, (*e*) dilute hydrochloric acid, (*f*) steam.

Zinc

Symbol: Zn; *Valency:* 2; *Atomic Weight:* 65·4; *Melting-point:* 419°; *Specific Gravity:* 6·9.

History and Occurrence.—Metallic zinc does not occur naturally, and it was not obtained in a pure state until 1720. Its chief ores are *zinc blende* (ZnS, zinc sulphide) and *calamine* ($ZnCO_3$, zinc carbonate). These compounds, and zinc oxide or *tutia*, ZnO, were known to the ancient chemists, who used to prepare *brass*—an alloy of zinc and copper—by heating copper with tutia.

The principal deposits of zinc ores are found in Great Britain, Belgium, Germany, Poland, Australia, and North America.

Extraction.—The zinc ore is strongly heated in air, when (i) zinc blende is oxidized, or (ii) calamine loses carbon dioxide, the product in each case being zinc oxide, ZnO—

$$\text{(i)}\ 2ZnS + 3O_2 = 2ZnO + 2SO_2.$$
$$\text{(ii)}\ ZnCO_3 = ZnO + CO_2.$$

The sulphur dioxide which is given off when zinc blende is used is not wasted, but is converted into sulphuric acid. In this way money is saved, and the price of the zinc is correspondingly lowered.

The zinc oxide obtained in the first operation is then mixed with powdered coal and strongly heated in fireclay retorts, when carbon monoxide is formed and the zinc liberated—

$$ZnO + C = Zn + CO.$$

The reaction is therefore a *reduction* of zinc oxide by carbon.

The zinc vapour which comes over is cooled in receivers, where part of it condenses to a powder ("zinc dust") and part to a liquid, which is allowed to solidify in moulds. Commercially, crude zinc is known as *spelter*.

Properties.—Zinc is a hard and rather brittle bluish-white metal. Its specific gravity is 6·9, its melting-point 419°, and its boiling-point 730°. Zinc is not attacked by dry air, but in moist air it is slowly converted into a white "rust," which consists of basic zinc carbonate, *i.e.* zinc carbonate ($ZnCO_3$) combined with some zinc hydroxide, $Zn(OH)_2$. If heated strongly in air or oxygen, zinc burns with a greenish-blue flame, forming clouds of white zinc oxide ("*philosophers' wool*")—

$$2Zn + O_2 = 2ZnO.$$

Ordinary zinc readily dissolves in acids. Thus with dilute sulphuric acid the following reaction takes place—

$$Zn + H_2SO_4 = \underset{\text{Zinc sulphate.}}{ZnSO_4} + H_2;$$

and with dilute hydrochloric acid—

$$Zn + 2HCl = \underset{\text{Zinc chloride.}}{ZnCl_2} + H_2.$$

Zinc also dissolves readily in dilute nitric acid, yielding a solution of zinc nitrate. Oxides of nitrogen are given off at the same time, and ammonium nitrate may be detected in the solution, so that the action is rather complex. (Cf. under *nitric acid*, p. 272, for the action of this acid on other metals.)

With concentrated sulphuric acid, zinc yields *sulphur dioxide* on heating—

$$Zn + 2H_2SO_4 = ZnSO_4 + 2H_2O + SO_2.$$

Zinc will also dissolve in hot concentrated caustic soda or caustic potash solution, liberating hydrogen. A solution of a peculiar compound called sodium (or potassium) *zincate* is left—

$$Zn + 2NaOH = \underset{\text{Sodium zincate.}}{Na_2ZnO_2} + H_2.$$

It is a strange fact that *pure* zinc will not dissolve in dilute sulphuric acid. Since, owing to improvements in zinc manufacture, the laboratory specimen is often very pure nowadays, you may already have noticed this phenomenon. You can, however, easily get the zinc to dissolve by adding a drop of copper sulphate solution. The copper, which is deposited on the zinc [$CuSO_4 + Zn = ZnSO_4 + Cu$], apparently acts as a catalyst, and the rest of the zinc then rapidly dissolves. It is thought that the action of the copper may be electrical.

Zinc is used in the laboratory for the preparation of hydrogen. For this purpose it is generally *granulated* by pouring the molten metal from a height into a tub of cold water.

Commercially, zinc is chiefly used to coat iron and thus prevent it from rusting. The iron object is first thoroughly cleansed and then dipped into melted zinc, when a thin layer of the latter metal is deposited on the iron. Iron treated in this way is called *galvanized iron*.

Zinc is also used in the preparation of alloys, *e.g.* brass and German silver (p. 409), and also in electric batteries. In a flash-lamp battery, for example, there are three cells. Each cell consists of a zinc cylinder, closed at the bottom, and filled with a paste of sal-ammoniac (NH_4Cl, ammonium chloride, p. 267), manganese dioxide, glycerol, and water. Inserted into this paste is a carbon rod; this forms the positive plate of the cell, while the zinc cylinder forms the negative plate.

COMPOUNDS OF ZINC.

Zinc oxide, ZnO, may be prepared in any of the usual ways, *i.e.* (*a*) by heating the metal in air or oxygen, (*b*) by heating the carbonate, (*c*) by heating the nitrate, (*d*) by heating the hydroxide—

(*a*) $2Zn + O_2 = 2ZnO$.
(*b*) $ZnCO_3 = ZnO + CO_2$.
(*c*) $2Zn(NO_3)_2 = 2ZnO + 4NO_2 + O_2$.
(*d*) $Zn(OH)_2 = ZnO + H_2O$.

It is generally made by burning zinc in air. It is a white amorphous powder, which turns yellow when heated, but goes white again on cooling. It will dissolve readily in dilute acids, yielding zinc salts, *e.g.*—

$$ZnO + H_2SO_4 = ZnSO_4 + H_2O.$$
$$ZnO + 2HCl = ZnCl_2 + H_2O.$$
$$ZnO + 2HNO_3 = Zn(NO_3)_2 + H_2O.$$

Zinc oxide is sometimes used to make white paint for chemical laboratories and other places where hydrogen sulphide is likely to be present in the atmosphere. Ordinary white paint contains lead carbonate ($PbCO_3$), which is turned into black *lead sulphide* by hydrogen sulphide—

$$PbCO_3 + H_2S = PbS + H_2O + CO_2.$$

It would therefore be foolish to use white lead paint in laboratories. *Zinc* sulphide, ZnS, however, is *white*, so that paints made from zinc oxide do not go black when exposed to hydrogen sulphide. A disadvantage of zinc oxide as a paint is that it will not cover so great a surface as the same weight of lead carbonate (" white lead ").

Zinc hydroxide, $Zn(OH)_2$, comes down as a white precipitate when a solution of caustic soda is added to a solution of a zinc salt—

$$ZnSO_4 + 2NaOH = Zn(OH)_2 \downarrow + Na_2SO_4.$$
$$ZnCl_2 + 2NaOH = Zn(OH)_2 \downarrow + 2NaCl.$$
$$Zn(NO_3)_2 + 2NaOH = Zn(OH)_2 \downarrow + 2NaNO_3.$$

It is soluble in excess of caustic soda, forming sodium zincate (p. 402).

Zinc chloride, $ZnCl_2$, can be obtained in the form of its crystalline *monohydrate*, $ZnCl_2.H_2O$, by dissolving zinc, zinc oxide, zinc hydroxide, or zinc carbonate in excess of concentrated hydrochloric acid and evaporating the solution to the point of crystallization. The crystals are deliquescent, and if heated they partly decompose, yielding hydrogen chloride and *zinc oxychloride*—

$$ZnCl_2.H_2O = \underset{\text{Zinc oxychloride.}}{Zn(OH)Cl} + HCl. \uparrow$$

To prepare *anhydrous* zinc chloride, $ZnCl_2$, therefore, it is necessary to proceed in another way, *viz.*, to heat zinc in a stream of hydrogen chloride—

$$Zn + 2HCl = ZnCl_2 + H_2.$$

Zinc sulphate, $ZnSO_4$, is usually met with in the form of its *heptahydrate*, $ZnSO_4.7H_2O$—"zinc sulphate crystals" or *white vitriol*. It can be made by dissolving zinc or its oxide, hydroxide or carbonate in dilute sulphuric acid and evaporating the solution—

$$Zn + H_2SO_4 = ZnSO_4 + H_2.$$
$$ZnO + H_2SO_4 = ZnSO_4 + H_2O.$$
$$Zn(OH)_2 + H_2SO_4 = ZnSO_4 + 2H_2O.$$
$$ZnCO_3 + H_2SO_4 = ZnSO_4 + H_2O + CO_2.$$

It is a very poisonous substance, but a dilute solution of it is sometimes used as an eye-lotion.

Zinc carbonate, $ZnCO_3$, comes down as a white precipitate when a solution of sodium *bi*-carbonate is added to a solution of a zinc salt, *e.g.*—

$$ZnSO_4 + 2NaHCO_3 = ZnCO_3 + Na_2SO_4 + H_2O + CO_2.$$

If sodium *carbonate* is used instead of the bicarbonate, the precipitate consists of a *basic* zinc carbonate [$x Zn(OH)_2 . y ZnCO_3$].

Zinc carbonate easily dissolves in dilute acids, yielding solutions of zinc salts with evolution of carbon dioxide, *e.g.*—

$$ZnCO_3 + 2HNO_3 = Zn(NO_3)_2 + H_2O + CO_2.$$

Zinc sulphide, ZnS, can be obtained as a white precipitate by adding ammonium sulphide to a solution of zinc sulphate—

$$(NH_4)_2S + ZnSO_4 = ZnS \downarrow + (NH_4)_2SO_4.$$

It dissolves in dilute acids, hydrogen sulphide being evolved, *e.g.*—

$$ZnS + 2HCl = ZnCl_2 + H_2S.$$

When not quite pure it is phosphorescent (*i.e.* it shines in the dark) after exposure to light. It also glows when X-rays, or the rays from radium, are allowed to strike it, and for this reason is much used in work in this field.

Equivalent of Zinc.—The equivalent of zinc is usually determined by dissolving a known weight of the metal in dilute sulphuric or hydrochloric acid, and measuring the volume of hydrogen evolved. (See p. 63.)

Questions

1. If you were given some granulated zinc, how could you prepare specimens of (*a*) zinc sulphate, (*b*) zinc oxide, (*c*) anhydrous zinc chloride, (*d*) zinc carbonate ?

2. What is the action of heat upon (*a*) zinc carbonate, (*b*) zinc nitrate, (*c*) zinc chloride crystals, $ZnCl_2.H_2O$?

3. Mention two alloys of which zinc is a constituent.

4. What are the chief ores of zinc ?

5. How is zinc extracted from its ores ?

6. How would you determine the equivalent of zinc ?

7. Compare and contrast the properties of zinc with those of calcium.

8. How is zinc sulphide prepared ? What peculiar properties does this substance possess ?

9. What weight of zinc sulphate crystals could you obtain by dissolving 15 grams of zinc carbonate in dilute sulphuric acid ? What weight of 10 per cent. sulphuric acid would you require for the purpose ? What volume of carbon dioxide, measured dry at N.T.P., would be evolved ?

10. Starting from zinc sulphate, how could you make (*a*) metallic zinc, (*b*) zinc nitrate ?

11. A hydrogen cylinder, of capacity 10 litres, is to be filled with hydrogen at a pressure of 120 atmospheres at 18° C. What weight of zinc would have to be dissolved in dilute hydrochloric acid in order to get the requisite hydrogen, and what would the weight of the latter be ?

12. What is *galvanized iron* ? How is it made ?

13. Describe the preparation and properties of zinc oxide. Why is zinc oxide sometimes used as a paint ?

14. What is the action of hot concentrated caustic soda solution upon zinc ?

Copper

Symbol : Cu ; *Valency :* 1 or 2 ; *Atomic Weight :* 63·6 ; *Melting-point :* 1,083° ; *Specific Gravity :* 8·95.

History and Occurrence.—Copper has been known to man from very remote times, since in some parts of the world it occurs naturally in the metallic state. Moreover, it is fairly easily obtained from some of its ores, so that it was in common use among the nations of the ancient world. The copper used by the Egyptians was mined in the peninsula of Sinai. The Greeks and Romans obtained it largely from the island of Cyprus : in fact, the two words Cyprus and Copper are connected together. It used to be thought that copper was so called because it came from Cyprus, but, on the other hand, some scholars now believe that the Romans borrowed the word copper from a Northern nation, and that Cyprus received its name because it was the "copper island." Cyprus was a favourite resort of Venus, and for this and other reasons copper was often called by the name of the goddess and represented by her sign (circular mirror with a handle), ♀.

Large quantities of native metallic copper have been found near the great lakes in North America, and smaller quantities in other places. The *chief ores* of copper are *copper pyrites*, $CuFeS_2$; *cuprite*, Cu_2O; and *malachite*, $Cu(OH)_2.CuCO_3$.

Extraction.—1. Native copper, when occurring in large boulders, proves rather troublesome to deal with, since it is so tough. In cases of difficulty, huge electrolytic cells have been built around the boulders and filled with acidified copper sulphate solution. A thin sheet of pure copper is made the cathode, and the boulder forms the anode. On passing a current through the "cell," copper passes from the anode to the cathode, where it is deposited. In this way native copper is extracted and refined at the same time.

2. *Cuprite* and *malachite* (oxide and basic carbonate) are heated with powdered coke in a furnace, when the carbonate is converted into oxide, and the oxide then reduced to metallic copper—

(i) *Cuprite.* $Cu_2O + C = 2Cu + CO.$

(ii) *Malachite.* (*a*) $Cu(OH)_2.CuCO_3 = 2CuO + H_2O + CO_2.$

(*b*) $CuO + C = Cu + CO.$

3. Most copper ores, however, contain sulphur, and the extraction of copper from them is a difficult matter. The crushed and purified ore is roasted in a regulated current of air, when the iron is converted into iron oxide and the copper is left as cuprous sulphide—

$$4CuFeS_2 + 9O_2 = 2Cu_2S + 6SO_2 + 2Fe_2O_3.$$

The roasted ore is then further purified, by removal of the iron oxide, and again heated upon the hearth of a furnace.

Part of the cuprous sulphide is converted into cuprous oxide, which then acts upon the remainder of the sulphide to form copper and sulphur dioxide.

$$2Cu_2S + 3O_2 = 2Cu_2O + 2SO_2.$$
$$2Cu_2O + Cu_2S = 6Cu + SO_2.$$

The copper so obtained is rather impure. It is melted, and the molten metal is stirred up with poles of green wood. This reduces any cuprous oxide remaining in the metal to copper.

The crude copper can be refined electrolytically as described in § 1.

Cathode (−) **Anode** (+)

Pure Copper ←—— Pure Copper —— Crude Copper

Crude Copper ↓ Impurities go into solution or fall to the bottom of the cell.

Properties.—Copper is a metal of a characteristic reddish colour. It is *malleable* (*i.e.* it can be beaten into thin sheets) and *ductile* (*i.e.* it can be drawn out into wire). It is an extremely good conductor of electricity, and is therefore widely used in the electrical industry. At a very high temperature (2,320°) it will boil, forming a green vapour.

In dry air, copper is unaffected at ordinary temperatures, but in moist air it is slowly converted into a greenish rust called *verdigris*. This consists of a mixture (or compound) of copper carbonate, $CuCO_3$, with copper hydroxide, $Cu(OH)_2$. If heated in air or oxygen, it is *slowly* converted into black *cupric oxide*, CuO, but it will not burn with a flame. The oxidation is so slow that it is not convenient to determine the equivalent of copper in this way. To determine the equivalent it is better to reduce a known weight of carefully dried cupric oxide in a current of hydrogen or purified coal-gas; or to convert a known weight of copper into its oxide by dissolving in nitric acid, evaporating to dryness, and igniting the residual copper nitrate.

Action of Acids on Copper.

1. *Sulphuric acid.*—The dilute acid has no action on copper. The concentrated acid dissolves copper on heating, yielding sulphur dioxide, copper sulphate and water—

$$Cu + 2H_2SO_4 = CuSO_4 + 2H_2O + SO_2.$$

This reaction is used in the laboratory for the preparation of sulphur dioxide. It will be noticed that the residue is *black*; this is because some black *cuprous sulphide*, Cu_2S, is formed as a by-product. While the equation given above represents fairly accurately the main result, there is little doubt that the actual changes are considerably more complex.

2. *Hydrochloric acid.*—The dilute acid has no action. The hot concentrated acid *slowly* dissolves copper, forming *cuprous chloride*, Cu_2Cl_2, which is oxidized at once if air is present to *cupric chloride*, $CuCl_2$.

3. *Nitric acid.*—Nitric acid readily dissolves copper, with formation of oxides of nitrogen. The actual course of the reaction depends upon the concentration of the acid, etc., but the equation for moderate concentration is—

$$3Cu + 8HNO_3 = 3Cu(NO_3)_2 + 4H_2O + 2NO.$$

This reaction is used in the laboratory for the preparation of nitric oxide (NO). The acid should be diluted with a little water.

Copper finds extensive application in industry and the arts, both as the pure metal and in the form of its *alloys* or mixtures with other metals. The composition of some of the chief copper alloys is shown in the following table—

Alloy.	Approximate Composition in Parts by Weight.		
Brass . .	Copper, 2.	Zinc, 1.	
Bronze . .	Copper, 9.	Tin, 1.	
Bell-metal . .	Copper, 4.	Tin, 1.	
German-silver .	Copper, 3.	Nickel, 1.	Tin, 1.
Phosphor-bronze .	Bronze, 99·5 per cent;	Phosphorus, 0·5 per cent.	

Bronze was extensively made in ancient days at Brindisi [Brundisium], hence, according to some authorities, the name "*bronze*" (= metal from Brundisium).

Compounds of Copper.

Since copper can be both univalent and bivalent, it forms two oxides and two series of salts, the cupr*ous* and the cupr*ic*.

Cuprous Compounds.

In the *cuprous* compounds, copper is univalent. Hence cuprous oxide is Cu_2O, cuprous chloride Cu_2Cl_2, etc.

Cuprous oxide, Cu_2O, occurs naturally as the mineral *cuprite*. It is best prepared by reducing Fehling's solution with grape-sugar. Fehling's solution is made by mixing cupric sulphate and potassium sodium tartrate in solution and adding caustic soda. When heated with grape-sugar it yields a red precipitate of cuprous oxide. Cuprous oxide is a red powder insoluble in water.

Cuprous chloride, Cu_2Cl_2, is generally made by heating a solution of cupric chloride with copper turnings and hydrochloric acid—

$$CuCl_2 + Cu = Cu_2Cl_2.$$

The clear solution so obtained is poured into water, when the cuprous chloride comes down as a white precipitate, rapidly turning blue or green on exposure to air, owing to oxidation to a *cupric* compound.

Cuprous sulphide, Cu_2S, is formed when copper burns in the vapour of sulphur, or when sulphur and copper turnings are heated together. It is a black substance, chiefly of historic interest, since its formation in the above way was observed by the Hindoos of 3,000 years ago, who therefore called sulphur the "enemy of copper"—in their language, Sanskrit, *sulvari*, whence our *sulphur*.

Cupric Compounds.

In these compounds, which are far more common and important than the cuprous compounds, copper is bivalent.

Hence cupric oxide is CuO, cupric sulphate $CuSO_4$, etc. When we talk about "copper nitrate," "copper chloride," and so on, it is understood that we mean the cupr*ic* compounds if we give no further details.

Cupric oxide, CuO, which is formed by strongly heating copper in air or oxygen, is more conveniently made by heating copper nitrate—

$$2Cu(NO_3)_2 = 2CuO + 4NO_2 + O_2.$$

Nitrogen peroxide and oxygen are formed at the same time.

It is a black powder, and has the property of attracting moisture, although it does not *deliquesce* (p. 198). It is said to be *hygroscopic.* If it is to be used in a quantitative experiment, it must be first heated in a crucible and then allowed to cool in a desiccator, so that the moisture it contains may be driven off.

Copper oxide will dissolve readily in dilute acids, giving solutions of cupric salts. Cupric salts are usually blue, and almost always give blue solutions when dissolved in water.

Cupric sulphate, $CuSO_4$, may be obtained by dissolving copper oxide or copper carbonate in dilute sulphuric acid, and evaporating the solution until it crystallizes on cooling. The crystals so obtained are sometimes known as *blue vitriol* or *bluestone*; they have the formula $CuSO_4.5H_2O$, *i.e.* they are *cupric sulphate penta-hydrate.* When they are heated to 100°, they lose some of their water of crystallization and are converted into cupric sulphate *monohydrate*, $CuSO_4.H_2O$. At 230° the monohydrate loses its water, yielding the greyish-white anhydrous salt, $CuSO_4$. This is used as a test for water, with which it goes blue, owing to the formation of the penta-hydrated salt.

Commercially, cupric sulphate is made by blowing air through a hot mixture of scrap copper and dilute sulphuric acid—

$$2Cu + 2H_2SO_4 + O_2 = 2CuSO_4 + 2H_2O.$$

Copper sulphate is a very important article of commerce. It is very poisonous, especially to the lower forms of plant life, and is therefore used as a germicide and fungicide. Potatoes are sprayed with "Bordeaux mixture" (copper sulphate and lime or limestone stirred up with water) to kill the fungus, called *Phytophthora*, which causes potato-disease. Copper sulphate solution is also used to spray vines, wheat, etc., to check the development of moulds. It is used in the dye industry and also in electrolytic copper-plating.

When a solution of copper sulphate is mixed with caustic soda solution, a blue precipitate of *copper hydroxide* is formed—

$$CuSO_4 + 2NaOH = Cu(OH)_2 \downarrow + Na_2SO_4.$$

Cupric sulphate solution with sodium carbonate yields a bluish-green precipitate of **cupric carbonate**—

$$CuSO_4 + Na_2CO_3 = CuCO_3 + Na_2SO_4.$$

The carbonate is, however, impure, being mixed with copper hydroxide or perhaps loosely combined with it. It is called a *basic* carbonate (cf. p. 188).

Cupric chloride, $CuCl_2$, may be made by dissolving copper oxide, hydroxide or carbonate in dilute hydrochloric acid and evaporating the solution to crystallization. The green crystals which form have the formula $CuCl_2.2H_2O$ (cupric chloride *dihydrate*). When gently heated they lose their water of crystallization, and are converted into the anhydrous salt, $CuCl_2$, which is yellowish brown. When strongly heated the anhydrous salt splits up into cuprous chloride and chlorine—

$$2CuCl_2 = Cu_2Cl_2 + Cl_2.$$

Cupric chloride is used as a catalyst in DEACON'S process for the manufacture of chlorine (see p. 220).

When solutions of copper salts are treated with ammonia they give a fine deep-blue colour. This reaction is used as a test for copper salts.

Cupric sulphide, CuS, is obtained as a black precipitate when hydrogen sulphide is passed through a solution of a cupric salt, *e.g.*—

$$CuSO_4 + H_2S = CuS \downarrow + H_2SO_4.$$

Flame Test.—Copper compounds colour the Bunsen flame bluish-green.

Questions

1. Mention the chief ores of copper.
2. Describe the extraction and purification of copper.
3. How does copper react with acids ?
4. Given metallic copper, how could you prepare (*a*) copper sulphate, (*b*) copper hydroxide, (*c*) cuprous oxide, (*d*) cupric oxide ?

Iron

Symbol: Fe ; *Valency:* 2 or 3 ; *Atomic Weight:* 56 ; *Melting-point:* 1,533° ; *Specific Gravity:* 7·9.

History and Occurrence.—Metallic iron is the chief constituent of meteorites, so that it has been known to man from time immemorial. The art of extracting it from its ores was known to the ancient Egyptians, and pieces of iron have been found in the masonry of one of the pyramids. In very early days it was more or less of a curiosity, and was a precious metal, but later it became widely used for making swords and other weapons of war. The alchemists supposed it to be under the influence of the planet Mars, and the sign of the god Mars, ♂ (shield and spear), was often used as a symbol for iron. About 2,500 tons of iron were used in the construction of SOLOMON'S Temple (about 1000 B.C.), and NEBUCHADREZZAR is said to have carried off into captivity in 604 B.C. a thousand blacksmiths from Damascus. Iron was worked in India from about 1000 B.C., and Indian steel was taken by sea to Arabia, where it was used by the Arabs for making their famous sword-blades.

The word *iron* is of Scandinavian origin.

The chief naturally occurring compounds of iron are the oxides, sulphide and carbonate :

Oxides—*Hæmatite,* Fe_2O_3 ; *Magnetite* (lodestone), Fe_3O_4 ; *limonite,* $2Fe_2O_3.3H_2O$.

Sulphide.—*Iron pyrites,* FeS_2.

Carbonate.—*Spathic iron ore,* $FeCO_3$.

Extraction.—The chief ores of iron are hæmatite (Lancashire, Belgium, North America), *magnetite* (Scandinavia, Germany, North America), *limonite* (South Wales), and *spathic iron ore* (mixed with clay as *clay ironstone* in many parts of

Great Britain). *Iron pyrites* is used principally as a source not of iron but of *sulphur*.

To get iron from its ores they are first roasted (heated in a current of air) and the dry iron oxide, Fe_2O_3, so obtained is heated with coke and a flux, *e.g.* limestone, in a blast furnace. The nature of the flux depends on the nature of the impurities (" gangue ") in the ore.

The roasted ore, mixed with coke and (say) limestone ($CaCO_3$), is introduced into the furnace through a cup and cone hopper at the top (see the figure). A blast of hot air is blown in through pipes called *tuyères* (" twyers ") at the bottom, and the coke is thus burnt to carbon monoxide. The carbon monoxide acts upon the iron oxide, reducing it to iron, being itself oxidized to carbon dioxide—

$$Fe_2O_3 + 3CO \rightleftharpoons 2Fe + 3CO_2.$$

The iron melts and sinks to the bottom of the furnace, whence it can be drawn off at will. The earthy impurities in the ore react with the flux, forming a fusible waste material or *slag*. This also sinks to the bottom of the furnace, but as it is lighter than the molten iron it floats on the surface of the latter and is run off through a different opening, as shown in the figure. If the earthy impurities were not removed in this way, they would remain in the furnace and choke it up. By removing them as slag, *all* the material introduced at the top of the furnace is got rid of, and fresh charges can be added without stopping the process, which is, indeed, continued until the furnace is worn out.

The molten iron which flows down to the well of the furnace is run into moulds, where it solidifies, on cooling, into blocks called *pig iron* or *cast iron*. It is very impure, containing as much as 4·5 per cent. of carbon as well as other impurities. To purify it, it is melted in a furnace with a little hæmatite, when the impurities are burned and oxidized away. The pure iron (99 per cent.) is called *wrought iron*. Unlike cast iron, which is brittle and *cannot* be welded, wrought iron is very tough, and *can* be welded, that is, two pieces of it, when red-hot, can be joined together by hammering. It is used chiefly by blacksmiths and for the cores of electro-magnets.

Steel is a mixture of iron and *iron carbide*, Fe_3C. Most of it is made at the present day by the *Siemens-Martin* process. A mixture of cast iron, scrap iron and hæmatite (Fe_2O_3) is placed on an open hearth and strongly heated. The hearth is lined with a mixture of magnesium oxide (MgO) and lime

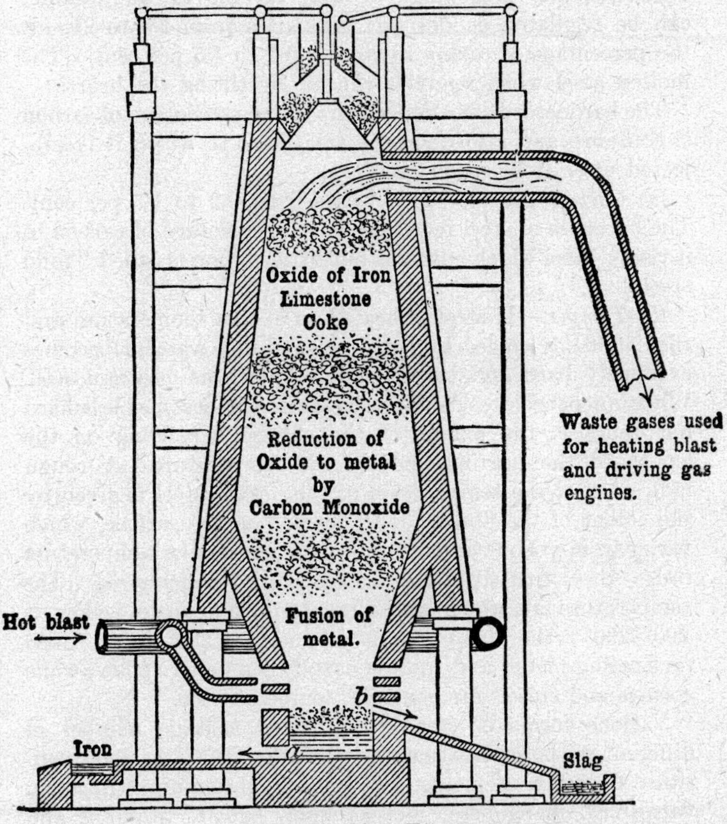

FIG. 105.—Blast Furnace.

(CaO). During the reaction, any phosphorus (often present as impurity in cast iron) is oxidized to phosphorus pentoxide, P_2O_5, which combines with the lining of the hearth, forming magnesium and calcium phosphates, and is therefore removed.

This is important, as the presence of phosphorus in steel is very injurious. The phosphates are used as a fertilizer ("basic slag").

By suitably adjusting the proportions of the cast iron and hæmatite, the percentage of iron carbide in the product can be regulated as desired. It varies from 2·8 to 21, *i.e.* the percentage of *carbon* in steel is 0·2 to 1·5 per cent. The molten steel when ready is run off by tilting the hearth.

The hardness of steel depends upon the percentage of carbon it contains, and also upon the treatment to which it is subjected after it has been made.

(*a*) *Carbon content.*—This varies from 0·2 to 1·5 per cent. The hardness of steel increases as the percentage of carbon in it rises; steel which contains but little carbon is called "mild steel."

(*b*) *Temper.*—If steel is heated to a high temperature and then suddenly cooled by being plunged into water it becomes extremely hard and brittle and is known as *quenched steel.* When quenched steel is carefully heated it becomes less hard but tougher, the extent of the change depending on the length of the heating and on the temperature. A rough indication of the temperature of the heated steel is given by the colour of the film of oxide formed on the surface, which varies from yellow through brown to blue as the temperature rises. Steel treated in this way is said to be *tempered.* The temperature at which the film of oxide is pale yellow is 200°–230°; the blue colour is produced at 290°–300°. Steel for cutting blades and tools is usually tempered yellow, while springs and chisels are generally tempered blue.

Various forms of steel, suitable for a large number of different purposes, are made by the admixture of small quantities of other elements, *e.g.* nickel, chromium, tungsten, vanadium, manganese, molybdenum, cobalt, titanium and silicon. Chromium produces a harder steel, nickel a more elastic, molybdenum a tougher, and so on. Nickel steels, containing 1–5 per cent. of nickel and 0·25–0·45 per cent. of carbon, and nickel-chromium steels (1–4·5 per cent. nickel, 1–2 per cent. chromium) are used for propeller shafts, piston rods, crankshafts, steering-gears, axles, brake-rods, etc. Stainless steel contains about 12–15 per cent. chromium. Silicon steel, or silico-manganese steels (1–2 per cent. silicon, 0·4–1 per cent. manganese, 0·40–0·65 per cent. carbon), are used especially for making springs. Manganese steels containing 12–14 per cent. manganese are used for tramways points and crossing-rails, as they are very hard and tough.

Properties.—Pure iron is a rather soft, shiny, white, magnetic metal. It dissolves in dilute sulphuric and hydrochloric acids, with evolution of hydrogen and formation of *ferrous sulphate* and *ferrous chloride* respectively—

$$Fe + H_2SO_4 = \underset{\text{Ferrous sulphate.}}{FeSO_4} + H_2.$$

$$Fe + 2HCl = \underset{\text{Ferrous chloride.}}{FeCl_2} + H_2.$$

It is also dissolved by cold *dilute* nitric acid, when *ferrous nitrate*, $Fe(NO_3)_2$, is one of the products. *Concentrated* nitric acid, however, has a peculiar effect upon iron: it renders it *passive*. When iron has been made *passive* it will not dissolve even in the ordinary dilute acids which usually dissolve it so readily! Passive iron can be made to lose its passivity by rubbing it with sand-paper or by heating it in a stream of hydrogen. The passivity is due to the formation of a thin coating of iron oxide on the surface of the iron. Some other metals, such as chromium, may be rendered passive by treatment with nitric acid.

In moist air, iron rapidly rusts, forming a brown powder which consists of iron oxide (*ferric* oxide, Fe_2O_3) combined with more or less water—$xFe_2O_3.yH_2O$. It is said that absolutely pure iron will not rust, and it has also been claimed that the presence of carbon dioxide is necessary for the formation of rust. The whole matter is very complicated, and is not yet settled. On reading this, you will probably lose any glow of self-satisfaction you may have felt after "successfully" solving the problem in the laboratory. Still, if you did not find out the necessary conditions under which iron *will* rust, you at least discovered conditions under which it will *not* rust, and that is something. The farther you go in science, the better you will realize how tremendous is the task of explaining fully even that phenomenon which appears simplest.

Iron will combine directly with many non-metallic elements if heated with them. Thus with sulphur it yields *ferrous sulphide*, FeS, while if heated in oxygen it burns brilliantly, forming *magnetic oxide of iron*, Fe_3O_4. The latter reaction is very striking and beautiful; it was discovered by INGEN-HOUSZ somewhere between 1780 and 1782. When heated in chlorine, iron will burn, and *ferric chloride*, $FeCl_3$, is formed—

$$2Fe + 3Cl_2 = 2FeCl_3.$$

COMPOUNDS OF IRON.

Since iron can sometimes be bivalent and at other times tervalent, it forms two series of compounds. Those in which it is bivalent are called *ferrous* compounds, while those in which it is tervalent are called the *ferric* compounds.

Oxides.—Iron forms three oxides, viz. *ferrous oxide*, FeO, which may be regarded as the parent substance of the ferrous compounds; *ferric oxide*, Fe_2O_3, to which correspond the ferric compounds; and *magnetic oxide of iron*, Fe_3O_4, which can be regarded as a compound of ferrous oxide with ferric oxide ($FeO + Fe_2O_3 = Fe_3O_4$) and is therefore sometimes known as *ferroso-ferric oxide*. There are few salts corresponding to this oxide.

Ferr*ous* salts can easily be oxidized to ferr*ic* salts and are therefore *reducing agents*.

Ferrous Compounds.

Ferrous oxide, FeO, can be made by carefully reducing ferric oxide in a current of hydrogen at 300°—

$$Fe_2O_3 + H_2 = H_2O + 2FeO.$$

It can also be made in other ways, but it is not important. It is a black powder which takes fire spontaneously in the air, especially when slightly warm, and burns with incandescence, forming ferric oxide—

$$4FeO + O_2 = 2Fe_2O_3.$$

It readily dissolves in dilute acids, yielding the corresponding ferrous salts, *e.g.*—

$$FeO + H_2SO_4 = \underset{\text{Ferrous sulphate.}}{FeSO_4} + H_2O.$$

Ferrous chloride, $FeCl_2$, may be made by dissolving iron in dilute hydrochloric acid and evaporating the solution to the point of crystallization. On cooling, pale-green crystals of *ferrous chloride tetrahydrate*, $FeCl_2.4H_2O$, separate out. The anhydrous salt, $FeCl_2$, which is a white crystalline solid, is best made by heating iron wire in a current of hydrogen chloride.

Ferrous sulphate or **green vitriol,** $FeSO_4.7H_2O$, may be made by dissolving iron in dilute sulphuric acid—

$$Fe + H_2SO_4 = FeSO_4 + H_2,$$

and evaporating the solution (preferably in the absence of air) until it is concentrated enough to deposit crystals on cooling. The pale-green crystals thus formed are *ferrous sulphate heptahydrate*, $FeSO_4.7H_2O$. If they are cautiously heated in absence of air they lose their water of crystallization, and the anhydrous salt, $FeSO_4$, is left as a white powder.

When ferrous sulphate crystals ($FeSO_4.7H_2O$) are strongly heated they decompose, yielding oxides of sulphur and steam, which come off, and ferric oxide, Fe_2O_3, which is left behind as a red solid. If the gases which are evolved are collected in a receiver they combine in part to form *fuming* sulphuric acid or *oleum*.

Ferrous sulphate solution gradually goes brown on exposure to air, and a reddish-brown precipitate is thrown down in time. These changes are due to oxidation of the ferrous sulphate by atmospheric oxygen; the precipitate contains *ferric hydroxide*, $Fe(OH)_3$, and possibly consists of a basic salt.

Ferrous sulphate solution is largely used in making ink,

which consists of a mixture of a dark blue dye with tannin and ferrous sulphate solution. When fresh, writing in such an ink is blue, the colour of the dye, but it goes black gradually on exposure to air owing to the fact that the oxygen oxidizes the ferrous sulphate which then forms a black insoluble compound with the tannin.

Addition of solutions of caustic alkalis to a solution of ferrous sulphate *in the absence of air* causes the precipitation of a *white* gelatinous solid, *ferrous hydroxide*, $Fe(OH)_2$—

$$FeSO_4 + 2NaOH = Fe(OH)_2 + Na_2SO_4.$$

Under ordinary circumstances, however, when air is present, the precipitate is greenish and finally turns brown. This is due to oxidation. The green precipitate is a compound of ferrous hydroxide with ferric hydroxide, $Fe(OH)_2.2Fe(OH)_3$. The brown compound is ferric hydroxide, $Fe(OH)_3$.

Ferrous sulphide, FeS, is made by heating iron and sulphur together in the proper proportions by weight (56 iron to 32 sulphur)—

$$Fe + S = FeS.$$

It is a black solid, used chiefly for the preparation of hydrogen sulphide, which is evolved freely when a dilute acid is added—

$$FeS + 2HCl = FeCl_2 + H_2S,$$
$$\text{or } FeS + H_2SO_4 = FeSO_4 + H_2S.$$

Ferric Compounds.

Ferric oxide, Fe_2O_3, occurs naturally in the anhydrous state as the important mineral *hæmatite*, Fe_2O_3, and in the hydrated state as the almost equally important *limonite*, $2Fe_2O_3.3H_2O$. It can be made by strongly heating ferric hydroxide, $Fe(OH)_3$ (see next paragraph), or ferrous sulphate (see above). Prepared from ferrous sulphate in this way, it is known as *jeweller's rouge*, and is used as a polishing powder and as a red pigment.

It is soluble in dilute acids, with which it forms ferric salts.

Ferric hydroxide, $Fe(OH)_3$, is formed as a reddish-brown precipitate by adding caustic soda or potash solution, or ammonium hydroxide, to a solution of a ferric salt (*e.g.* ferric chloride, $FeCl_3$)—

$$FeCl_3 + 3NaOH = Fe(OH)_3 + 3NaCl.$$

It is a weak base, and will dissolve in dilute acids forming ferric salts.

Ferric chloride, $FeCl_3$.—Anhydrous ferric chloride can be obtained as a black scaly or crystalline solid by heating iron wire in a stream of chlorine. If dissolved in water it forms a yellow solution from which yellow deliquescent crystals can be obtained by evaporation. These crystals consist of ferric chloride hexahydrate, $FeCl_3.6H_2O$.

Ferric sulphate, $Fe_2(SO_4)_3$, is a white or yellowish powder made by heating ferrous sulphate with a mixture of sulphuric and nitric acids and evaporating the solution—

$$6FeSO_4 + 3H_2SO_4 + 2HNO_3 = 3Fe_2(SO_4)_3 + 4H_2O + 2NO.$$

The ferrous sulphate has been *oxidized.*

OTHER IRON COMPOUNDS.

Ferroso-ferric oxide, Fe_3O_4, occurs naturally as *magnetite* or lodestone. It is formed when iron burns in air or oxygen, and also when iron is heated in a current of steam—

$$3Fe + 4H_2O = Fe_3O_4 + 4H_2.$$

This reaction is reversible, for when magnetic oxide of iron is heated in a current of hydrogen, iron and steam are formed—

$$Fe_3O_4 + 4H_2 = 3Fe + 4H_2O.$$

Iron disulphide, FeS_2, exists naturally in two different crystalline varieties, *iron pyrites* and *marcasite.* Iron pyrites is used in the manufacture of sulphuric acid (see p. 305).

QUESTIONS

1. Mention the chief ores of iron.
2. Describe the extraction of iron from its ores.
3. How could you prepare from metallic iron (*a*) ferrous chloride, (*b*) ferric chloride ?

Lead

Symbol: Pb; *Valency:* 2 or 4; *Atomic Weight:* 207·1; *Melting-point:* 327·4° C.; *Specific Gravity:* 11·35.

History and Occurrence.—Like copper, lead has been known to man for several thousand years. The metal and certain of its compounds were widely used by the Egyptians, Assyrians, Babylonians and other nations of antiquity. The oldest lead object in existence is a small figure now preserved in the British Museum; experts believe it to be about 5,000 years old. In England, lead mines on the Mendips and in Shropshire and Derbyshire were worked as long ago as the days of the Roman occupation, and many pigs of lead stamped with the name of the reigning Caesar have been discovered in these districts. The word *lead* originally meant a weight or plummet, and it is interesting that a modified form of it is found in the "lot" of *pilot*, i.e. "to heave the lead." The symbol Pb is derived from the Latin name of the metal, *plumbum*.

The chief ore of lead is *galena*, lead sulphide, PbS; this is a heavy, black, shiny mineral found to some extent in England but in much larger quantities in the United States, Spain, Germany and Australia. About 1,000,000 tons of lead are produced annually.

Extraction.—Metallic lead occurs in Nature only in very minute traces, but it can very easily be obtained from galena, a fact which explains why the metal was discovered by man so early in the history of civilization. Two methods of extraction are in common use—

i. The galena is roasted in a current of air at a comparatively low temperature, when part is converted into lead oxide, PbO, and part into lead sulphate, $PbSO_4$, while part is left unchanged:

$$(a)\ 2PbS + 3O_2 = 2PbO + 2SO_2$$
$$(b)\ PbS + 2O_2 = PbSO_4.$$

The temperature of the furnace is then raised to about 750° C. and the current of air is cut off. The following reactions then occur between the unchanged galena, the lead oxide and the lead sulphate:

$$(c)\ 2PbO + PbS = 3Pb + SO_2$$
$$(d)\ PbSO_4 + PbS = 2Pb + 2SO_2.$$

The melted lead collects at the bottom of the furnace and is run off from time to time.

ii. In the second process the galena is first roasted and then heated in a blast furnace with limestone and coke. The first roasting converts the galena into lead oxide, PbO, and this is reduced to metallic lead by the carbon monoxide formed by the burning of the coke—

$$2PbS + 3O_2 = 2PbO + 2SO_2$$
$$PbO + CO = Pb + CO_2.$$

The limestone reacts with earthy impurities in the galena to form a fusible slag which can be run off.

The impure lead obtained in these ways is melted and stirred, when the impurities (chiefly antimony, arsenic, bismuth, and tin) are oxidized and collect on the surface of the molten lead as a solid scum which can be scraped off.

Properties. Pure lead is a silvery white metal of specific gravity 11·35; it melts at 327·4° C. and boils at 1,525° C. If carefully purified, lead is only slowly attacked by the air, but ordinary lead rapidly tarnishes, owing to the formation of a film of the oxide, hydroxide and carbonate. This film protects the underlying metal from further corrosion, so that lead finds many applications out-of-doors, as, for instance, in roofing.

Lead is a soft metal and leaves a mark if rubbed across paper. It can be cut with a knife and is readily malleable, while if gently warmed it can be pressed or moulded into pipes and sheets.

Lead is soluble in nitric acid, forming lead nitrate and nitrogen peroxide, nitric oxide, etc.—

$$Pb + 4HNO_3 = Pb(NO_3)_2 + 2H_2O + 2NO_2$$
$$3Pb + 8HNO_3 = Pb(NO_3)_2 + 4H_2O + 2NO.$$

Hot concentrated sulphuric acid rapidly dissolves lead, with formation of lead sulphate, $PbSO_4$, and evolution of sulphur dioxide—

$$Pb + 2H_2SO_4 = PbSO_4 + 2H_2O + SO_2.$$

The dilute acid has no action, neither has hydrochloric acid.

The *equivalent* of lead has been determined by the reduction in hydrogen of a weighed quantity of lead monoxide, PbO.

Oxides of Lead.

Lead forms several oxides, of which the most important are—

PbO, lead monoxide or litharge;
Pb_3O_4, triplumbic tetroxide or red lead (minium);
PbO_2, lead peroxide or dioxide.

Lead monoxide, PbO.—When lead is heated in air it melts (327·4° C.), and the molten metal soon becomes covered with a greyish powder. On further heating and stirring, the whole of the metal is quickly converted into a yellow powder known as *massicot*; this is lead monoxide, PbO. On increasing the temperature the massicot melts, and if the molten substance is allowed to cool it solidifies into a reddish crystalline variety, called *litharge*, since it is obtained in the purification of silver (litharge = "silver stone"). Like massicot, litharge is a form of lead monoxide, PbO.

Lead monoxide is easily reduced to the metal, e.g. by heating it with carbon or in a current of hydrogen—

$$PbO + C = Pb + CO$$
$$PbO + H_2 = Pb + H_2O.$$

It dissolves in dilute acids to give lead salts, *e.g.*—

$$PbO + 2HNO_3 = \underset{\text{Lead nitrate}}{Pb(NO_3)_2} + H_2O.$$

It is used in glass manufacture and as a source of more important compounds of lead such as "red lead" and "white lead" (see below).

Lead hydroxide, $Pb(OH)_2$, is formed as a white precipitate when caustic soda, caustic potash or ammonium hydroxide is added to a solution of a soluble lead salt—

$$Pb(NO_3)_2 + 2NaOH = Pb(OH)_2 \downarrow + 2NaNO_3.$$

It is slightly soluble in water (cf. p. 200).

Red lead or **minium,** Pb_3O_4.—If litharge is roasted in a current of air at about 400–450° C. it is converted into a red crystalline powder known as *red lead* or *minium,* which has already been described on p. 373.

Lead peroxide or **dioxide,** PbO_2.—This is a chocolate brown powder obtained by the action of an oxidizing agent, such as potassium chlorate, upon litharge, but most conveniently prepared from red lead by the reaction described on p. 373. It is used as an oxidizing agent; thus it oxidizes hot hydrochloric acid to chlorine—

$$PbO_2 + 4HCl = PbCl_2 + 2H_2O + Cl_2,$$

and combines with sulphur dioxide, to form lead sulphate, with so much evolution of heat that it becomes incandescent—

$$PbO_2 + SO_2 = PbSO_4.$$

COMPOUNDS OF LEAD.

Lead chloride, $PbCl_2$, may be made by heating lead in chlorine,

$$Pb + Cl_2 = PbCl_2,$$

but is generally made as a white crystalline precipitate by adding a solution of hydrochloric acid or a soluble chloride to a solution of lead nitrate—

$$Pb(NO_3)_2 + 2NaCl = PbCl_2 \downarrow + 2NaNO_3.$$

It is slightly soluble in cold water and more soluble in hot.

Lead carbonate, $PbCO_3$, is obtained as a white precipitate by adding a solution of sodium *bi*carbonate to a solution of lead nitrate. Sodium carbonate precipitates not the normal lead carbonate, $PbCO_3$, but a *basic* carbonate, $2PbCO_3.Pb(OH)_2$, called white lead. This substance is largely used for making paints and is therefore manufactured commercially. The best white lead is made by placing rolls of lead on shelves in barrels or pots, at the bottom of which is a layer of vinegar. The pots are kept warm, and after four to twelve weeks the lead is found to be converted into white lead.

When lead carbonate is heated it splits up into litharge and carbon dioxide—

$$PbCO_3 = PbO + CO_2.$$

It will react with acids to form the corresponding lead salt—

$$PbCO_3 + 2HNO_3 = Pb(NO_3)_2 + H_2O + CO_2.$$

Lead nitrate, $Pb(NO_3)_2$, is formed when lead is dissolved in nitric acid, but is more conveniently prepared in the laboratory by dissolving litharge in dilute nitric acid—

$$PbO + 2HNO_3 = Pb(NO_3)_2 + H_2O.$$

It is a white crystalline solid, soluble in water. When heated, it splits up into litharge, nitrogen peroxide and oxygen—

$$2Pb(NO_3)_2 = 2PbO + 4NO_2 + O_2.$$

The crystals usually fly to pieces with sharp cracks during this reaction ; this phenomenon is known as *decrepitation* and is shown also by potassium chlorate, common salt, etc.

Questions

1. What do you know of the history and occurrence of lead ?
2. Describe the extraction and purification of lead.
3. How does metallic lead react with (*a*) water, (*b*) air, (*c*) acids ?
4. Given metallic lead, how could you prepare specimens of (*a*) litharge, (*b*) red lead, (*c*) white lead ?
5. How is lead nitrate prepared ? What is the action of heat on this substance ?
6. Describe the preparation and chief properties of the oxides of lead.

CHAPTER XXI

NICKEL, CHROMIUM, ALUMINIUM, MERCURY

Nickel

Symbol: Ni; *Valency:* 2; *Atomic Weight:* 59; *Melting-point:* 1,450°; *Specific Gravity:* 8·8.

History and Occurrence.—An ore found in the copper mines of the Harz Mountains, from which, however, no copper could be extracted, was called by the German miners *Kupfer-nickel, i.e.* "false copper." From this ore KRONSTEDT succeeded, in 1751, in isolating a new metal, *nickel*; but it was the celebrated chemist BERGMANN (1774) who first made a close investigation of the metal and of some of its compounds.

Nickel is found chiefly as its sulphide and arsenide, the principal deposits of these minerals occurring in Ontario, Canada. In combination with silicon, oxygen and magnesium, nickel occurs as the mineral *garnierite*, and this ore, though not as important as the Ontario varieties, is mined to some extent in New Caledonia.

Extraction.—After the sulphide ores have received a preliminary treatment, they are sent to a refinery (*e.g.* at Swansea). Here they are roasted in a current of air, when the nickel is oxidized to nickel oxide. Any copper oxide present is now dissolved out by means of dilute sulphuric acid, which, under the conditions selected, does not dissolve the nickel oxide. The latter is then reduced to metal by means of producer-gas (p. 348)—

$$NiO + CO = Ni + CO_2.$$

The crude nickel obtained in this way is heated to about

60° in a stream of carbon monoxide, when a peculiar compound known as *nickel carbonyl*, $Ni(CO)_4$, is produced—

$$Ni + 4CO = Ni(CO)_4.$$

The vapour of this compound is led away and heated to 200°, when it decomposes into its constituents—

$$Ni(CO)_4 = Ni + 4CO.$$

The nickel is deposited in an extremely pure state, and the carbon monoxide is used over and over again.

Properties.—Nickel is a silvery-white, magnetic metal of specific gravity 8·8; it melts at 1,450°. It is stable in dry air, and tarnishes only very slowly in moist air; it is therefore used for *nickel-plating* other metals, on which it is deposited electrolytically.

Nickel is a constituent of many alloys, *e.g.*:

Monel metal, Ni 60; Cu 35; and some Fe; used in various kinds of industrial chemical apparatus;

German silver, Ni 20; Cu 60; Zn 20; used for ornaments, plate, etc.;

Nichrome, Ni 60; Cr 14; Fe 26; used in electrical heating, *e.g.* in "electric fires";

Invar, Ni 35; Fe 65; C and Mn, traces; used in clocks, watches, etc., owing to its very small coefficient of expansion.

Nickel is also widely employed as a catalyst, both in pure chemistry and in chemical industry.

In its ordinary compounds, nickel is bivalent. The sulphate, $NiSO_4$, the chloride, $NiCl_2$, and the carbonate, $NiCO_3$, are green in colour, as are most other nickel salts.

Chromium

Symbol: Cr; *Valency:* 2, 3 or 6; *Atomic Weight:* 52·0; *Melting-point:* 1,920°; *Specific Gravity:* 6·8–7·1.

History and Occurrence.—Chromium was first prepared by Vauquelin in 1797. It is a fairly abundant element, occurring principally as *chromite* or *chrome iron ore*, $Cr_2O_3.FeO$.

Extraction.—The chromite is first treated in such a way as to obtain chromium sesquioxide, Cr_2O_3, from it. The sesquioxide, in charges of two or three hundredweight, is then mixed with a slight excess of aluminium powder, and the mixture fired. Intense heat is evolved, and a mass of molten chromium is left at the bottom of the reaction-crucible—

$$Cr_2O_3 + 2Al = 2Cr + Al_2O_3.$$

In general, however, since chromium is chiefly required for chromium-plating, the chromium sesquioxide is converted into chromium sulphate (or potassium dichromate), solutions of which are used in the plating-baths.

Properties.—Chromium is a hard, greyish-white metal with a silvery lustre. It is extremely stable in moist air at ordinary temperatures, but may be made to burn with a bright flame when strongly heated. It is soluble in dilute hydrochloric and sulphuric acids, even in the cold, forming *chromous* salts, *e.g.* $CrCl_2$; concentrated nitric acid renders it *passive* (p. 417), probably owing to the formation of a thin, but coherent and protective, coating of oxide.

Alloys of chromium with iron, and with iron and nickel, are used industrially for armour-plating and many other purposes. "Chromium steel" is very hard and exceedingly tough, and is extremely resistant to acids. The so-called "stainless steel" is not a true steel, but an alloy containing about 84 per cent. iron, 13 per cent. chromium, and 1 per cent. nickel. "Nichrome" (p. 428) is used in electric fires, etc.

Chromium-plating is carried out by the electrolytic deposition of chromium from a hot solution of chromium trioxide (chromic acid) and chromium sulphate, to which a little chromium carbonate has been added. As the deposit is inclined to be rather porous, it is usual to plate the object with nickel first.

Chromium compounds (*e.g.* chrome alum),

$$K_2SO_4.Cr_2(SO_4)_3.24H_2O,$$

and sodium dichromate, $Na_2Cr_2O_7$, are used in tanning leather, in the manufacture of dyes and pigments, and in the photographic industry.

Chromium Compounds.—The principal compounds of chromium are the *chromates* and *dichromates*. *Sodium dichromate*, $Na_2Cr_2O_7.2H_2O$, is made by fusing chrome iron ore with sodium carbonate and lime in the presence of air—

$$4FeO.Cr_2O_3 + 8Na_2CO_3 + 8CaO + 7O_2 = 2Fe_2O_3 + 8Na_2CrO_4 + 8CaCO_3.$$

After cooling, the fused mass is powdered and treated with a warm dilute solution of sodium carbonate. The insoluble matter is allowed to settle, and the clear liquid is then made very slightly acid with sulphuric acid and evaporated to crystallization—

$$\underset{\text{Sodium chromate.}}{2Na_2CrO_4} + H_2SO_4 = Na_2SO_4 + \underset{\text{Sodium dichromate.}}{Na_2Cr_2O_7} + H_2O.$$

Potassium dichromate, $K_2Cr_2O_7$, is made by mixing a solution of sodium dichromate with potassium chloride—

$$Na_2Cr_2O_7 + 2KCl = 2NaCl + K_2Cr_2O_7.$$

The mixture of salt and potassium dichromate so formed is separated by fractional crystallization.

Potassium dichromate forms orange-red crystals, with no water of crystallization. It dissolves in water, and the acidified solution is used as an oxidizing agent. In the presence of sulphuric acid the oxidizing action may be represented by the equation—

$$K_2Cr_2O_7 + 4H_2SO_4 = \underset{\text{Chromium sulphate.}}{Cr_2(SO_4)_3} + K_2SO_4 + 4H_2O + \underset{\text{(available for oxidation).}}{3O}$$

Sodium dichromate, $Na_2Cr_2O_7.2H_2O$, is cheaper and more soluble than the potassium salt, and is equally good for ordinary oxidations. It is not so convenient for quantitative analysis, since it is deliquescent and therefore cannot be accurately weighed out directly. In the so-called "bichromate" cells, the potassium salt is generally used.

Potassium chromate, K_2CrO_4, may be made by addition of the calculated quantity of potassium hydroxide to a solution of potassium dichromate—

$$K_2Cr_2O_7 + 2KOH = 2K_2CrO_4 + H_2O.$$

On evaporation of the solution the potassium chromate separates in the form of yellow crystals. In solution, potassium chromate is used as a reagent in qualitative analysis, since it gives precipitates of insoluble chromates with certain metals, *e.g.* silver (brick-red), lead (yellow), barium (yellow).

Chrome alum, $K_2SO_4.Cr_2(SO_4)_3.24H_2O$, is a dark purple crystalline substance usually prepared by passing sulphur dioxide into a solution of potassium dichromate acidified with sulphuric acid—

$$K_2Cr_2O_7 + 3SO_2 + H_2SO_4 = K_2SO_4 + Cr_2(SO_4)_3 + H_2O.$$

On evaporation of the solution, chrome alum separates. Its crystals are isomorphous (p. 145) with those of ordinary potash alum, $K_2SO_4.Al_2(SO_4)_3.24H_2O$.

Aluminium

Symbol: Al; *Valency:* 3; *Atomic Weight:* 26·97; *Melting-point:* 659°; *Specific Gravity:* 2·7.

History and Occurrence.—Metallic aluminium does not occur naturally, but aluminium compounds are extremely abundant and are found universally in rocks and clays. Aluminium silicates are the chief constituents of slate, mica, felspar, china and ordinary clays, garnet, topaz and tourmaline; while aluminium oxide, Al_2O_3, occurs in *bauxite* ($Al_2O_3.2H_2O$), corundum and other minerals. Sodium aluminium fluoride occurs as the mineral *cryolite* Na_3AlF_6.

Metallic aluminium was first prepared by the German chemist Wöhler in 1827, but it was not till half a century later that a successful manufacturing process was invented simultaneously by Hall in America and Héroult in France.

Extraction.—Aluminium is now obtained commercially by this process, which uses purified bauxite as the starting-point. Alumina, *i.e.* aluminium oxide, Al_2O_3, is first prepared, and this is then dissolved in melted cryolite. On passing a powerful direct electric current through the solution, the alumina is electrolysed, oxygen coming off from the anode and aluminium being liberated at the cathode. The anode, which consists of rods of carbon, is gradually burned away, and has to be replaced. The metallic aluminium collects in a molten state on the floor of the cell, whence it is tapped off from time to time.

Properties.—Aluminium is a metal of a bluish-white, silvery lustre. It melts at 659°, boils at about 1,800°, and has a specific gravity of 2·7. It can be highly polished, and is malleable and ductile. Its low specific gravity, coupled with its moderate hardness, renders it very useful in the construction of aeroplanes [1] and airships. Aluminium is also employed on a large scale for the manufacture of domestic utensils such as saucepans and kettles, while its good conductivity has led to its use in high-tension cables, *e.g.* in the Grid. The cables have steel cores, to strengthen them.

Aluminium soon tarnishes in moist air, owing to the formation of a thin film of oxide; this film is, however, coherent, so that the underlying metal is protected from further corrosion or "rusting." On heating aluminium in the air, it burns with a brilliant white flame, forming aluminium oxide (with traces of aluminium nitride)—

$$4Al + 3O_2 = 2Al_2O_3.$$
$$[2Al + N_2 = 2AlN.]$$

Nitric acid has no action on it; it dissolves, however, in hot concentrated sulphuric acid, forming aluminium sulphate and sulphur dioxide—

$$2Al + 6H_2SO_4 = Al_2(SO_4)_3 + 6H_2O + 3SO_2.$$

It dissolves easily in concentrated hydrochloric acid, forming the chloride and hydrogen—

$$2Al + 6HCl = 2AlCl_3 + 3H_2.$$

It also dissolves quickly in hot aqueous solutions of caustic soda or potash, forming *aluminates*, with evolution of hydrogen—

$$2H_2O + 2Al + 2NaOH = \underset{\text{Sodium aluminate.}}{2NaAlO_2} + 3H_2.$$

[1] Or "airplanes" as Lord B—rb—k would have us write.

It is therefore undesirable to use much soda in aluminium saucepans.

Aluminium is a powerful reducing agent; in the form of powder it readily reduces metallic oxides with liberation of intense heat. A mixture of ferric oxide and aluminium powder is called *thermit*; when ignited by means of a piece of burning magnesium ribbon the whole mass becomes incandescent and molten iron is left. This reaction is used for welding pieces of iron together *in situ* and also in incendiary bombs. The combustion of a stream of aluminium powder in a current of oxygen gives a flame hotter than that of the oxyhydrogen blowpipe, which, for some engineering purposes, it has replaced.

Many *alloys of aluminium* are better, for various purposes, than the metal itself. The two of most importance are *duralumin* (about 95 per cent. Al, 4·5 per cent. Cu, 0·5 per cent. Mg, 0·5 per cent. Mn) and *magnalium* (aluminium with 1 or 2 per cent. each of magnesium, copper and nickel).

Aluminium Compounds.—The chief compound of aluminium is *alum* ("potash alum," "potassium alum"), $K_2SO_4.Al_2(SO_4)_3.24H_2O$. This is a white crystalline solid made (among other ways) by mixing in solution equi-molecular weights of potassium sulphate, K_2SO_4, and aluminium sulphate, $Al_2(SO_4)_3$, and crystallizing the solution. The crystals are isomorphous with those of chrome alum (p. 431). Alum is used in the dye industry and in tanning, while small quantities find application as a "styptic," *i.e.* a substance to clot blood and so prevent bleeding.

Aluminium sulphate, $Al_2(SO_4)_3.18H_2O$, is made by heating bauxite or kaolin (china-clay) with sulphuric acid, and is put on the market in solid blocks called "alum-cake." It is used in the purification of sewage, and in paper-making.

Aluminium oxide, Al_2O_3, in its natural crystalline form of corundum, is used in making "emery-paper," while the amorphous substance is important as a catalyst in many industrial chemical processes. Much alumina is also used in the manufacture of artificial rubies and sapphires, which consist of aluminium oxide coloured with small quantities of chromium sesquioxide, Cr_2O_3 (ruby), or magnetic oxide of iron and titanium dioxide (sapphire).

Mercury

Symbol: Hg; *Valency:* 1 or 2; *Atomic Weight:* 200·61; *Melting-point:* —39°; *Boiling-point:* 360°; *Specific Gravity:* 13·59.

History and Occurrence.—Mercury has been known from time immemorial, and even the Muslim chemists of the early middle ages recognized that it is a metal. For several centuries it was believed that all other metals were compounds of mercury with sulphur.

Mercury is found in small quantities as the free element. It is, however, obtained chiefly from its ore *cinnabar*, HgS, which is mined in Spain, Mexico, Russia, Peru, China, Japan and several other countries.

Extraction.—Cinnabar (with or without a small admixture of charcoal) is roasted in a current of air, and the mercury vapour and sulphur dioxide so produced are passed through cooled earthenware receivers called *aludels* (p. 242). Here the mercury condenses; if necessary it may be purified by predistillation—

$$HgS + O_2 = Hg + SO_2.$$

If the cinnabar ore is rich, it is mixed with lime and the mixture is strongly heated in cast-iron retorts, when the following reaction occurs—

$$4HgS + 4CaO = 4Hg + CaSO_4 + 3CaS.$$

Properties.—Mercury is the only metallic element liquid at ordinary temperatures. It is usually transported in iron bottles, a " bottle " of mercury containing 75 lb. of the metal. (Try to lift one !)

Mercury is not oxidized in the air at ordinary temperatures, but is gradually converted into the red oxide HgO, if heated in air or oxygen to a temperature just below its boiling-point (360°). It is not dissolved by dilute sulphuric or hydrochloric acid; concentrated sulphuric acid dissolves it, forming mercuric sulphate and sulphur dioxide—

$$Hg + 2H_2SO_4 = HgSO_4 + 2H_2O + SO_2,$$

and so does nitric acid, concentrated or dilute, forming mercur*ous* nitrate, $Hg_2(NO_3)_2$ (cold dilute acid), or mercur*ic* nitrate, $Hg(NO_3)_2$ (hot concentrated acid). Alkalis and most of the common gases (except chlorine, hydrogen sulphide and ozone) have no action upon mercury.

On account of its high density, low specific heat and high boiling-point, it is extremely useful in thermometry; the fact that it does not "wet" glass is an additional advantage. It is also useful for the collection and storage of gases that are soluble in water, while the part it played in the development of the oxygen theory of combustion has already been described (pp. 166–168).

Amalgams.—Many metals will dissolve in mercury, and the solutions so formed are called "amalgams." Sodium amalgam, made by cautiously pressing pieces of sodium into slightly warmed mercury, is used as a reducing agent. Tin amalgam was formerly used in "silvering" mirrors, while amalgams of cadmium, gold, etc., are employed in dentistry for filling teeth.

Compounds of Mercury.—The chief compounds of mercury are mercuric oxide, mercuric chloride and mercurous chloride. In the first two of these compounds the mercury is bivalent, while in the last it is univalent.

Mercuric oxide, HgO, is obtained as a red crystalline powder by heating mercury in the air for several days to a temperature just below its melting-point. It may be prepared as a yellowish precipitate by adding caustic soda solution to a solution of mercuric chloride—

$$HgCl_2 + 2NaOH = HgO + 2NaCl + H_2O.$$

On heating, mercuric oxide blackens, and then splits up into mercury and oxygen—

$$2HgO = 2Hg + O_2.$$

It is soluble in dilute acids, forming mercuric salts.

Mercuric chloride, $HgCl_2$, otherwise known as "corrosive sublimate," is a white crystalline solid made by passing chlorine over heated mercury—

$$Hg + Cl_2 = HgCl_2.$$

It is a white crystalline solid, slightly soluble in cold water and more soluble in hot. It is very poisonous, particularly to microscopic forms of life, and is therefore used as a germicide and antiseptic.

Mercurous chloride, Hg_2Cl_2, sometimes called *calomel*, is made by heating a mixture of mercuric chloride and mercury,

$$HgCl_2 + Hg = Hg_2Cl_2,$$

or by adding hydrochloric acid to a solution of mercurous nitrate—

$$2HCl + Hg_2(NO_3)_2 = Hg_2Cl_2 \downarrow + 2HNO_3.$$

It is a white solid, insoluble in water, and is used in medicine. With ammonia, it yields a substance of a fine black colour—hence its name "calomel" (Greek, *beautiful black*).

Questions

1. How does nickel occur naturally ? How is it extracted, and for what purposes is it used ?

2. Describe the occurrence, extraction and principal properties of chromium.

3. What is potassium dichromate ? How is it made, and for what purposes is it used ? How would you prepare a specimen of potassium chromate from it ?

4. How does aluminium occur naturally ? From what ore is it obtained, and by what method ?

What are the chief properties and uses of aluminium ?

5. Describe the preparation of (*a*) chrome alum, (*b*) potash alum. What is meant by saying that these substances are isomorphous ?

6. Describe the occurrence, extraction and properties of mercury. What is an *amalgam* ?

7. Describe the preparation and properties of mercuric oxide, mercuric chloride and mercurous chloride.

8. Write the formulæ of nickel carbonyl, alumina, chromium sesquioxide, aluminium sulphate, calomel, chrome iron ore, cinnabar and corrosive sublimate.

Appendix I

TABLE OF EXACT ATOMIC WEIGHTS

Element.	Symbol.	Atomic Weight.	Element.	Symbol.	Atomic Weight.
Actinium	Ac	•	Molybdenum	Mo	96·0
Aluminium	Al	26·97	Neodymium	Nd	144·27
Antimony	Sb	121·76	Neon	Ne	20·183
Argon	A	39·94	Nickel	Ni	58·69
Arsenic	As	74·93	Niobium	Nb	93·3
Barium	Ba	137·36	Nitrogen	N	14·008
Beryllium	Be	9·02	Osmium	Os	190·8
Bismuth	Bi	209·0	Oxygen	O	16·00 [Standard]
Boron	B	10·82			
Bromine	Br	79·916	Palladium	Pd	106·7
Cadmium	Cd	112·41	Phosphorus	P	31·02
Caesium	Cs	132·81	Platinum	Pt	195·23
Calcium	Ca	40·07	Polonium	Po	210
Carbon	C	12·00	Potassium	K	39·1
Cerium	Ce	140·13	Praseodymium	Pr	140·92
Chlorine	Cl	35·457	Proto-actinium	Pa	•
Chromium	Cr	52·01	Radium	Ra	225·97
Cobalt	Co	58·94	Radon	Rn	222
Copper	Cu	63·57	Rhenium	Re	186·31
Dysprosium	Ds	162·46	Rhodium	Rh	102·91
Eka-Caesium			Rubidium	Rb	85·44
Erbium	Er	167·64	Ruthenium	Ru	101·7
Europium	Eu	152·0	Samarium	Sa	150·34
Fluorine	F	19·0	Scandium	Sc	45·1
Gadolinium	Gd	157·3	Selenium	Se	79·2
Gallium	Ga	69·72	Silicon	Si	28·06
Germanium	Ge	72·6	Silver	Ag	107·88
Gold	Au	197·2	Sodium	Na	22·997
Hafnium	Hf	178·6	Strontium	Sr	87·63
Helium	He	4·002	Sulphur	S	32·06
Holmium	Ho	163·5	Tantalum	Ta	181·4
Hydrogen	H	1·0078	Tellurium	Te	127·5
Illinium	Il	•	Terbium	Tb	159·2
Indium	In	114·8	Thallium	Tl	204·39
Iodine	I	126·932	Thorium	Th	232·12
Iridium	Ir	193·1	Thulium	Tm	169·4
Iron	Fe	55·84	Tin	Sn	118·7
Krypton	Kr	82·92	Titanium	Ti	47·9
Lanthanum	La	138·9	Tungsten	W	184·0
Lead	Pb	207·22	Uranium	U	238·14
Lithium	Li	6·94	Vanadium	V	50·95
Lutecium	Lu	175·0	Xenon	Xe	130·2
Magnesium	Mg	24·32	Ytterbium	Yb	173·5
Manganese	Mn	54·93	Yttrium	Y	88·92
Manurium	Ma	•	Zinc	Zn	65·38
Mercury	Hg	200·61	Zirconium	Zr	91·22

TABLE OF
APPROXIMATE ATOMIC WEIGHTS

Element.	Symbol.	Atomic Weight.
Aluminium	Al	27
Barium	Ba	137
Boron	B	11
Bromine	Br	80
Calcium	Ca	40
Carbon	C	12
Chlorine	Cl	35·5
Copper	Cu	63·6
Hydrogen	H	1
Iodine	I	127
Iron	Fe	56
Lead	Pb	207
Magnesium	Mg	24
Mercury	Hg	200
Nitrogen	N	14
Oxygen	O	16
Phosphorus	P	31
Potassium	K	39
Silicon	Si	28
Silver	Ag	108
Sodium	Na	23
Sulphur	S	32
Tin	Sn	119
Zinc	Zn	65

Appendix II

REVISION NOTES

1. **Atom.**—The smallest, chemically indivisible, particle of an element.
2. **Molecule.**—The smallest particle of an element or compound that can normally lead a separate existence.
3. **Atomic Weight.**—The number of times the atom of an element is heavier than an **atom** of hydrogen.
4. **Molecular Weight.**—The number of times the molecule of an element or compound is heavier than an **atom** of hydrogen.
5. **Vapour Density.**—The number of times a certain volume of a substance in the state of gas is heavier than the same volume of hydrogen, under the same conditions of temperature and pressure.
6. **Relation between Molecular Weight and Vapour Density.**—The molecular weight of a substance is *twice* its vapour density.
7. **Gram-Molecular-Weight.**—The molecular weight expressed in grams, *e.g.* molecular weight of oxygen (O_2) is 32, hence G.M.W. is 32 *grams*.
8. **Gram-Molecular-Volume.**—The volume occupied by the G.M.W. of any gaseous substance. It is roughly 22·4 litres at N.T.P.
9. **Avogadro's Hypothesis.**—Equal volumes of all gases under the same conditions of temperature and pressure contain the same number of molecules.
10. **Equivalent.**—The *number* of units of weight of a substance that will cause one of the same units of weight

of hydrogen to take part in a chemical change either directly or indirectly.

11. **Gram-Equivalent.**—Equivalent in grams.

12. **Valency.**—Number of atoms of hydrogen with which 1 atom of the element concerned will unite.

13. **Relation between Valency, Atomic Weight and Equivalent.**—Atomic weight = Equivalent × Valency.

14. **Atomicity.**—Number of atoms per molecule.

15. **Basicity of an Acid.**—Number of atoms of hydrogen, replaceable by a metal, contained in 1 molecule of the acid.

16. **Normal Solution.**—A solution 1 litre of which contains the gram-equivalent of the dissolved substance (solute). *Deci-normal* = $\frac{1}{10}$ Normal, etc.

LAWS.

17. **Boyle's.**—The volume of a given mass of gas varies inversely as the pressure upon it if the temperature is constant.

18. **Charles's.**—The volume of a given mass of gas varies directly as the *absolute* temperature if the pressure is constant. [Absolute temperature = Centigrade temperature + 273°.]

19. **Gas-Equation.**—$PV = RT$, where R is a constant.

20. **Conservation of Matter.**—Matter can neither be created nor destroyed.

21. **Constant Composition.**—The same compound always consists of the same elements in a constant proportion by weight.

22. **Multiple Proportions.**—When two elements combine to form more than one compound, then the weights of one of those elements which combine with a fixed weight of the other are in a simple ratio to one another.

23. **Reciprocal Proportions.**—If an element A combines with an element B and also combines with an element C, then *if* B and C combine together, the proportion by weight in which they do so will be simply related to the ratio of the weights of B and C which combine with a fixed weight of A.

24. **Partial Pressures.**—In a mixture of gases, each gas exerts the same pressure as it would exert if it were alone in the same volume. Or—in a mixture of gases, the total pressure is equal to the sum of the partial pressures of the gases present.

25. **Gay-Lussac's.**—When gases react together their volumes are simply related to one another, and to the volumes of the products if these are gaseous.

26. **Dulong and Petit's.**—In a great many cases, the atomic weight of a solid element multiplied by its specific heat = 6·4 approximately.

27. **Mitscherlich's** [Law of Isomorphism].—Compounds of the same class which have analogous constitutions crystallize in the same form.

28. **Faraday's** [Laws of Electrolysis].—

First Law.—The weight of an ion liberated in electrolysis is proportional to the quantity of electricity which has passed through the electrolyte (*i.e.* to current × time).

Second Law.—The quantity of electricity required to deposit the gram-equivalent of an ion is 96,000 coulombs (or 1 "faraday").

29. **Guldberg and Waage's** [Law of Mass Action].—The rate of a chemical change at a given moment is directly proportional to the concentrations at that moment of the substances taking part in the change.

ACIDS, BASES AND SALTS.

30. *General Methods of preparing Acids.*

(i) By acting upon their salts with sulphuric acid, *e.g.*—

$$KNO_3 + H_2SO_4 = HNO_3 + KHSO_4.$$
$$NaCl + H_2SO_4 = HCl + NaHSO_4.$$

(ii) By dissolving the oxide of a non-metal in water, *e.g.*—

$$SO_3 + H_2O = H_2SO_4.$$
$$P_2O_5 + 3H_2O = 2H_3PO_4.$$

(iii) By acting upon a salt of the acid, in solution, with another acid which forms an *insoluble* salt with the metal of the original salt, *e.g.*—

$$\underset{\text{barium chlorate}}{Ba(ClO_3)_2} + H_2SO_4 = \underset{\text{chloric acid}}{2HClO_3} + BaSO_4\downarrow$$

(iv) To make the halogen hydracids act upon the halogen dissolved or suspended in water with hydrogen sulphide—

$$X_2 + H_2S = 2HX + S \downarrow. \quad (X = Cl, Br, I).$$

(v) If the acid consists of hydrogen and one other element only, by direct combination, *e.g.*—

$$Cl_2 + H_2 = 2HCl.$$

31. *General Methods of preparing Bases.*

(i) By the action of a metal upon water, *e.g.*—

$$2Na + 2H_2O = 2NaOH + H_2.$$

(ii) By burning a metal in air or oxygen, *e.g.*—

$$2Mg + O_2 = 2MgO.$$

(iii) By heating an unstable salt of the metal, *e.g.* the carbonate or nitrate—

$$2Pb(NO_3)_2 = 2PbO + 4NO_2 + O_2.$$
$$CuCO_3 = CuO + CO_2.$$

(iv) By precipitation with caustic soda solution if the base is insoluble, *e.g.*—

$$FeCl_3 + 3NaOH = Fe(OH)_3 + 3NaCl.$$

(v) By dissolving a *basic anhydride* in water—

$$NH_3 + H_2O = NH_4OH.$$

32. *General Methods of preparing Salts.*

(i) By neutralization of an acid with an alkali, *e.g.*—

$$KOH + HNO_3 = KNO_3 + H_2O.$$

(ii) By dissolving the oxide or hydroxide of a metal in an acid, *e.g.*—

$$CuO + H_2SO_4 = CuSO_4 + H_2O.$$
$$Fe(OH)_3 + 3HCl = FeCl_3 + 3H_2O.$$

(iii) By dissolving the carbonate of a metal in an acid, *e.g.*—

$$PbCO_3 + 2HNO_3 = Pb(NO_3)_2 + H_2O + CO_2.$$

(iv) By dissolving a metal in an acid, *e.g.*—

$$Zn + H_2SO_4 = ZnSO_4 + H_2.$$
$$Cu + 2H_2SO_4 = CuSO_4 + 2H_2O + SO_2.$$

(v) By double decomposition, *e.g.*—

$$NaCl + AgNO_3 = AgCl \downarrow + NaNO_3.$$

(vi) By direct synthesis, *e.g.*—

$$2Na + Cl_2 = 2NaCl.$$

33. *Chief Properties of Acids.*

(i) Sour taste.
(ii) Turn blue litmus red.
(iii) Corrode and dissolve metals, often with evolution of hydrogen.
(iv) Cause effervescence with a carbonate, owing to liberation of carbon dioxide.
(v) Contain hydrogen which can be replaced by a metal.

34. *Chief Properties of Bases.*

(i) Oxides or hydroxides of metals.
(ii) Will react with an acid to form a ***salt*** + ***water***.
(iii) If soluble, will turn red litmus blue.
(iv) If heated with an ammonium salt, cause liberation of ammonia.

[*N.B.*—Soluble bases, together with carbonates of sodium, potassium and ammonium, constitute class of compounds known as *alkalis.*]

35. *Chief Properties of Salts.*

(i) Consist of metal + acid radical.
(ii) Very often neutral to litmus.
(iii) Although many are insoluble, the majority are soluble.

36. *Acid Salts and Basic Salts.*

An *acid salt* is a compound formed from an acid by replacement of only *part* of its replaceable hydrogen by a metal, *e.g.*, $NaHSO_4$, acid sodium sulphate ; $Ca(HCO_3)_2$, calcium bicarbonate.

A *basic salt* may be regarded as a normal salt which has combined with excess of the oxide or hydroxide of the metal present, *e.g.* $CuCO_3.Cu(OH)_2$, basic copper carbonate ; $BiCl_3.Bi_2O_3$, basic bismuth chloride.

PREPARATION OF COMMON GASES.

37. **Hydrogen.**—Dilute sulphuric acid upon zinc—

$$Zn + H_2SO_4 = ZnSO_4 + H_2.$$

38. **Oxygen.**—Heat on potassium chlorate—

$$2KClO_3 = 2KCl + 3O_2.$$

39. **Nitrogen.**—Heat on ammonium nitrite solution—

$$NH_4NO_2 = N_2 + 2H_2O.$$

40. **Chlorine.**—Manganese dioxide on concentrated hydrochloric acid. Heat—

$$MnO_2 + 4HCl = MnCl_2 + 2H_2O + Cl_2.$$

41. **Hydrogen chloride.**—Concentrated sulphuric acid on sodium chloride—

$$NaCl + H_2SO_4 = NaHSO_4 + HCl.$$

42. **Carbon dioxide.**—Dilute hydrochloric acid upon marble—

$$CaCO_3 + 2HCl = CaCl_2 + H_2O + CO_2.$$

43. **Carbon monoxide.**—Heat oxalic acid with concentrated sulphuric acid and pass gases through caustic soda solution to absorb the carbon dioxide—

$$H_2C_2O_4 = H_2O + CO_2 + CO.$$

44. **Nitrous oxide.**—Heat on ammonium nitrate—

$$NH_4NO_3 = N_2O + 2H_2O.$$

45. **Nitric oxide.**—Nitric acid upon copper—

$$3Cu + 8HNO_3 = 3Cu(NO_3)_2 + 4H_2O + 2NO.$$

46. **Nitrogen peroxide.**—Heat on lead nitrate. Pass gases through freezing mixture, where nitrogen peroxide condenses—

$$2Pb(NO_3)_2 = 2PbO + O_2 + 4NO_2.$$

47. **Ammonia.**—Heat mixture of ammonium chloride and slaked lime—

$$2NH_4Cl + Ca(OH)_2 = CaCl_2 + 2H_2O + 2NH_3.$$

48. **Sulphur dioxide.**—Heat copper with concentrated sulphuric acid—

$$Cu + 2H_2SO_4 = CuSO_4 + 2H_2O + SO_2.$$

49. **Hydrogen sulphide.**—Hydrochloric acid on ferrous sulphide—

$$2HCl + FeS = FeCl_2 + H_2S.$$

50. **Methane.**—Heat mixture of anhydrous sodium acetate and soda-lime—

$$C_2H_3O_2Na + NaOH = Na_2CO_3 + CH_4.$$

51. **Ethylene.**—Heat alcohol with concentrated sulphuric acid—

$$C_2H_6O = C_2H_4 + H_2O.$$

52. **Acetylene.**—Water on calcium carbide—

$$CaC_2 + 2H_2O = Ca(OH)_2 + C_2H_2.$$

To collect and dry Common Gases.

53.

Gas.	To collect ordinarily.	To dry.	To collect when dry.
Hydrogen . .	Over water	Sulphuric acid	Upward displacement
Oxygen . .	,, ,,	,, ,,	Over mercury
Nitrogen . .	,, ,,	,, ,,	,, ,,
Chlorine . .	Downward displacement	,, ,,	Downward displacement
Hydrogen chloride	,, ,,	,, ,,	Over mercury
Carbon dioxide	,, ,,	,, ,,	Downward displacement
,, monoxide	Over water	,, ,,	Over mercury
Nitrous oxide .	,, hot water	Calcium chloride	,, ,,
Nitric oxide .	,, water	,, ,,	,, ,,
Nitrogen peroxide	In freezing mixture	,, ,,	,, ,,
Ammonia . .	Upward displacement	Quicklime	Upward displacement
Sulphur dioxide	Downward displacement	Sulphuric acid	Downward displacement
Hydrogen sulphide	,, ,,	Calcium chloride	,, ,,
Methane . .	Over water	Sulphuric acid	Over mercury
Ethylene . .	,, ,,	Calcium chloride	,, ,,
Acetylene . .	,, ,,	,, ,,	,, ,,

54. **Factors which may affect Rate of Chemical Change.**

(i) Temperature.
(ii) Concentration of reacting substances.
(iii) Pressure (in case of gaseous substances).
(iv) Presence of a catalyst.
(v) Presence of moisture.

54a. **Catalysis.**

(i) A catalyst is a substance which will alter the rate of a chemical change without itself being changed in weight or in chemical composition during the reaction.

EXAMPLES.—(*a*) Manganese dioxide on decomposition of potassium chlorate by heat (p. 172).

(*b*) Copper chloride in Deacon's process (p. 220).

(*c*) Platinized asbestos on combination of sulphur dioxide with oxygen (p. 308).

(*d*) Nitric oxide in lead chamber process (p. 305).

(ii) A catalyst, in a reversible action, increases the rates of both the forward and backward reactions equally.

(iii) A catalyst makes no difference in the *products* of the reaction.

(iv) Some catalysts are positive, others are negative.

(v) A substance which is a catalyst in one reaction is not necessarily so in another, *e.g.* manganese dioxide (*a*) in preparation of oxygen (p. 172) and (*b*) in preparation of chlorine (p. 209).

55. **Allotropy.**—When an element exists in two or more forms, those forms being physically and often chemically distinct, it is said to exhibit allotropy, and the different forms are called *allotropes* or *allotropic forms* of the element. *E.g.* sulphur, oxygen, phosphorus, carbon.

DETERMINATION OF FORMULÆ OF COMMON GASES.

56. **Hydrogen chloride**, p. 230.

57. **Carbon dioxide**, p. 328.

58. **Carbon monoxide**, p. 332.

59. **Nitrous oxide**, p. 276.

60. **Nitric oxide**, p. 277.

61. **Nitrogen peroxide**, p. 278.

62. **Ammonia**, p. 263.

63. **Sulphur dioxide**, p. 304.

64. **Hydrogen sulphide**, p. 299.

65. **Methane**, p. 335.

66. **Ethylene**, p. 337.

67. **Acetylene**, p. 338.

METHODS OF DETERMINING EQUIVALENTS.

I. Of Metals.

68. (i) Dissolve known weight of metal in a dilute acid and measure volume of hydrogen evolved (*e.g.* Mg, Zn, Fe, Al).

(ii) Convert weighed quantity of metal into its oxide, either by heating in oxygen, or by action of nitric acid (see p. 66). *E.g.* Mg, Cu, Sn, Pb.

(iii) Reduce weighed quantity of oxide to metal, in a stream of hydrogen or purified coal-gas. *E.g.* CuO, PbO, Fe_3O_4.

(iv) Displace metal from a solution of one of its salts with a weighed quantity of another metal of known equivalent. *E.g.* Cu and Ag by Zn.

(v) By electrolysis; measure weight of metal deposited in an electrolytic cell and weight of hydrogen liberated in another (or the same) cell by the same quantity of electricity.

(vi) By converting a compound of the metal with an element of known equivalent into another compound of the metal with other elements of known equivalent.

(vii) By converting the metal into its chloride (*e.g.* Ag).

II. Of Non-Metals.

69. (i) By direct combination of a known weight of the element with hydrogen (*e.g.* oxygen, chlorine).

(ii) By formation and analysis of the oxide or chloride.

(iii) By method (vi) as given for metals.

Methods of Determining Molecular Weights.

70. (i) Find vapour density and multiply by 2. (See p. 94.)

(ii) Depression of Freezing-point. (See p. 97.)

Methods of Determining Atomic Weights.

71. (i) (*a*) Find equivalent. (*b*) Find specific heat. (*c*) Hence by Dulong and Petit's Law find approximate atomic weight. (*d*) Divide approximate atomic weight by exact equivalent, and thus get approximate valency. (*e*) Take nearest whole number

as true valency. (*f*) Multiply exact equivalent by true valency.

(ii) (*a*) Find molecular weights of large number of compounds of the element. (*b*) Analyse these compounds and find smallest weight of element present in M.W. of any of its compounds.

(iii) By method of isomorphism (see p. 145).

OXIDATION AND REDUCTION.

72. By *oxidation* is meant an increase in the proportion of the electronegative constituent of a substance, or a decrease in the proportion of the electropositive constituent. *Reduction* is the reverse of oxidation.

An *oxidizing agent* is a substance capable of bringing about oxidation.

A *reducing agent* is a substance capable of bringing about reduction.

Examples of—

Oxidizing Agents.

1. Oxygen.
2. Ozone.
3. Chlorine.
4. Nitric acid.
5. Potassium chlorate.
6. „ nitrate.
7. „ permanganate.
8. Manganese dioxide.
9. Hydrogen peroxide.
10. Sodium peroxide.
11. Potassium dichromate.

Reducing Agents.

1. Hydrogen.
2. Carbon.
3. Carbon monoxide.
4. Sulphur dioxide.
5. Hydrogen sulphide.
6. Any mixture which evolves hydrogen, *e.g.*—
   $Zn + H_2SO_4$.
   $Na + H_2O$.
7. Hydriodic acid.
8. Zinc dust.
9. Stannous chloride.

Appendix III

BIOGRAPHICAL NOTES ON SOME FAMOUS CHEMISTS

ARISTOTLE.—The greatest scientist of Ancient Greece. Pupil of Plato. He was born in 384 B.C., and died in 322. Friend and counsellor of Alexander the Great. Considered that all matter was composed of four " elements," namely *fire*, *air*, *earth* and *water*. Did not believe in the atomic theories of other Greek philosophers. Realized the value of experiments in science. His views greatly influenced chemistry right up to the age of Boyle.

AVOGADRO, AMEDEO, Conte di Quaregna.—Born at Turin, June 9, 1776, and died there July 9, 1856. Professor of Physics at Turin University. His chief work was on physics, but he made a contribution of the highest possible importance to chemistry in his famous Hypothesis, 1811 (see p. 92).

BECHER, JOHANN JOACHIM.—German chemist, born at Spires in 1635. Died in London in 1682. Professor of Medicine in University of Mainz. Famous as the originator of the Phlogiston Theory of Combustion, later developed and extended by his follower and pupil G. E. Stahl. Discovered boric acid and ethylene.

BERZELIUS, JÖNS JAKOB.—Swedish chemist. Born 1779, died at Stockholm in 1848. Professor of Chemistry in the medical school at Stockholm. Created a Baron in 1835. Determined atomic weights of many elements with the greatest care and accuracy ; also the molecular weights of hundreds of compounds. Introduced the use of the present symbols and formulæ. Put forward an electrical theory of chemical combination. Analysed innumerable compounds. Helped very much in getting Dalton's Atomic Theory generally accepted.

BLACK, JOSEPH.—Born 1728, died 1799. Educated at Belfast and Glasgow. Showed true relationship between carbon dioxide, quicklime and chalk, and also explained in the modern way the action of lime upon sodium and potassium carbonates. Also did much useful work in physics, upon latent and specific heats.

BOYLE, THE HON. ROBERT.—Born 1627, died 1691. Son of the Earl of Cork. Educated Eton and Oxford. Did much to overthrow Aristotle's idea of the Four Elements, and defined "element" in the modern way. Discovered how to prepare phosphorus. Worked on gases and discovered "Boyle's Law." Introduced into England the air-pump and thermometer, and improved both. First prepared methyl alcohol. One of the founders of the Royal Society.

CANNIZZARO, STANISLAO.—Brilliant Italian chemist. Born at Palermo, 1826. Died in 1910. Professor of Chemistry at Rome University and a Roman Senator. In 1858 showed chemists that many of their chief difficulties over the Atomic Theory would vanish if they admitted Avogadro's Hypothesis, till then not widely known. For this service the Royal Society gave him a medal in 1891. He also carried out important work on organic chemistry.

CAVENDISH, HENRY.—Born 1731, died 1810. Educated at Peterhouse, Cambridge. A brilliant chemist and physicist, but shunned publicity and led a very retired life. Investigated hydrogen and discovered the composition of water and nitric acid. Was the first to dry gases, by passing them over anhydrous potassium carbonate. Found specific gravity of many gases. Never gave up his belief in the Phlogiston Theory.

DALTON, JOHN.—Born 1766 at Eaglesfield in Cumberland. Died 1844. Founded the modern Atomic Theory by re-shaping the older theories of the Greek philosophers into a form capable of being tested experimentally. Discovered Law of Multiple Proportions and Law of Partial Pressures. First clearly distinguished between elements, compounds, and mixtures.

DAVY, SIR HUMPHRY.—Born at Penzance in 1778. Died in 1829. Discovered sodium and potassium, which he prepared by the electrolysis of their fused hydroxides. Showed that chlorine is an element, and gave it its present name. Invented the miners' safety-lamp. Investigated iodine and its compounds. Showed that nitrous oxide could be used as an anæsthetic.

DEMOCRITUS.—Probably born about 470 or 460 B.C., and lived about 100 years. One of the greatest of the Greek philosophers. Put forward an atomic theory of matter; he thought that the atoms were eternal, invisible, and indivisible, and that they differed in size, weight, and shape. He had some idea of the modern conceptions of the conservation of matter and of energy.

DUMAS, JEAN-BAPTISTE ANDRÉ.—Born 1800, died 1884. Famous French chemist and statesman. Invented a method for determining vapour densities which is still in use. Carried out much work on organic compounds, and made many accurate determinations of atomic weights. Became Master of the (French) Mint in 1868.

EMPEDOCLES.—Lived about 490–430 B.C. Greek philosopher, born at Agrigentum in Sicily. Thought that all matter was composed of four elements, fire, air, earth and water, and that chemical combination and decomposition were brought about by "love" and "discord." Believed that nothing new can come into existence, and that change was merely change in position of the four elements with regard to one another.

GAY-LUSSAC, JOSEPH LOUIS.—Born 1778. Died in Paris in 1850. Professor of Chemistry at the Jardin des Plantes and of Physics at the Sorbonne (University of Paris). Discovered the Law of Gaseous Volumes. First investigated iodine and its compounds, and cyanogen (C_2N_2). Introduced the "Gay-Lussac Tower" in the manufacture of sulphuric acid by the lead-chamber process. Worked out a method of determining the percentage of chlorine in bleaching-powder by means of a standard solution of arsenious acid. Invented volumetric analysis.

GEBER.—*See* JABIR IBN HAYYAN.

JABIR IBN HAYYAN ("GEBER").—A celebrated Muslim chemist, possibly son of an Arab druggist, born at Tus in Persia about 722 A.D., and died about 803. Lived at Baghdad, under the Caliph Harun al-Rashid. Wrote numerous books on chemistry, some of which we still have. Put forward the theory that all metals are composed of mercury and sulphur. Described clearly the preparation of many chemical compounds, including lead carbonate and mercuric sulphide (HgS). Knew also how to concentrate acetic acid by distillation of vinegar.

LAVOISIER, ANTOINE LAURENT.—Born at Paris in 1743. Guillotined during French Revolution, in 1794. Overthrew the Phlogiston Theory and substituted for it the present theory of combustion. Gave the name *oxygen* to the gas which still bears it. Carried out much research on the composition of water. Discovered the composition of the atmosphere. First to analyse organic compounds (compounds of carbon). Showed that sulphur is an element. Believed that lime was the oxide of an element.

Incurred the enmity of the Revolutionists, who executed him in 1794. In his work he was greatly assisted by his wife.

LUCRETIUS.—Lived about 98–55 B.C. Latin poet. His poem, *De rerum natura* ("On the Nature of Things"), gives an account of an atomic theory of matter, based on an earlier theory of Epicurus.

MEYER, VICTOR.—German chemist. Born at Berlin in 1848, died at Heidelberg in 1897. Invented the famous method of determining the vapour densities of volatile liquids (see p. 95). Also did much work on the constitution of ammonium salts and upon organic compounds. Investigated the dissociation of hydrogen iodide ($2HI \rightleftharpoons H_2 + I_2$).

PARACELSUS.—Swiss physician and chemist born at Einsiedeln in 1493. In 1527 appointed physician to the town of Basle. Had a great contempt for earlier workers and struck out a new line. Believed that the aim of chemistry should be to provide drugs, etc., for use in medicine. Did great service to chemistry by stirring it up when it was very sluggish. Was the first to apply the name *alcohol* to spirit of wine. Died 24 Sept., 1541.

PRIESTLEY, REV. JOSEPH.—Born 1733, near Leeds. Died 1804, in U.S.A. Discovered oxygen in 1774; also ammonia, nitrous oxide, hydrogen chloride, sulphur dioxide, and hydrofluoric acid. Showed similarity between combustion and respiration, and part played by oxygen therein. Sympathized with French Revolutionists, and had his house sacked by an angry crowd at Birmingham (1791). Afterwards emigrated to America.

RAMSAY, SIR WILLIAM.—Born at Glasgow, October 2, 1852. Died at High Wycombe, July 23, 1916. Professor of Chemistry at University College, Bristol, and afterwards at University College, London. Discovered the existence of helium upon the earth. With Lord Rayleigh, discovered argon. With M. W. Travers discovered neon, krypton, and xenon. Also worked on organic chemistry and upon surface tension and other properties of liquids. His book, *The Gases of the Atmosphere*, should be read by all students of chemistry: though it is unfortunately out of print.

ROBERT OF CHESTER.—Lived in the twelfth century A.D. Famous scholar, renowned for his translations from the Arabic into Latin. Translated the Koran, also the first books on Algebra and Chemistry. Was Archdeacon of Pampeluna in Northern Spain. Returned to his native country, England, in 1150.

SCHEELE, CARL WILHELM.—Swedish chemist. Kept an apothecary's shop. Discovered oxygen independently of, and slightly before, Priestley. Also discovered chlorine, tungsten, prussic acid, glycerol, barium oxide, barium sulphate, the manganates and permanganates, hydrogen sulphide, and benzoic, citric, malic, oxalic, and gallic acids. Probably the greatest experimental chemist of all time. Born at Stralsund in 1742 and died at Köping in 1786.

STAHL, GEORG ERNST.—Born 1660, died 1734. Professor of Medicine in University of Halle, and Physician to the King of Prussia. Developed the Theory of Phlogiston put forward by Becher. Was a brilliant chemist, and did much to advance the cause of the science.

SHORT LIST OF BOOKS ON THE HISTORY OF CHEMISTRY

J. Campbell Brown, *History of Chemistry* (J. and A. Churchill).
T. M. Lowry, *Historical Introduction to Chemistry* (Macmillan).
J. M. Stillman, *The Story of Early Chemistry* (Appleton, 1924).
J. A. Cochrane, *A School History of Science* (Arnold).
E. J. Holmyard, *History of Chemistry to the Time of Dalton* (Oxford Univ. Press, 1925).
E. J. Holmyard, *Makers of Chemistry* (Oxford Univ. Press, 1931).

Appendix IV

USEFUL DATA AND FORMULÆ

1. Weight of 1 litre of some Gases at N.T.P.

Hydrogen . .	0·09 gm.	Carbon dioxide .	1·98 gm.
Oxygen . . .	1·43 ,,	Ammonia . .	0·77 ,,
Nitrogen . . .	1·25 ,,	Sulphur dioxide.	2·93 ,,
Chlorine . . .	3·22 ,,	Hydrogen sulphide . .	1·54 ,,
Air	1·29 ,,		
Hydrogen chloride . .	1·64 ,,		

2. Valencies of Common Elements and Radicals.

Element.	Valency.	Element or Radical.	Valency.
Aluminium . . .	3	Oxygen.	2
Barium	2	Phosphorus . . .	3 or 5
Boron	3	Potassium	1
Bromine	1	Silicon	4
Calcium	2	Silver	1
Carbon	4	Sodium	1
Chlorine	1	Sulphur	2, 4 or 6
Copper	1 or 2	Tin	2 or 4
Hydrogen	1	Zinc.	2
Iodine	1	———	
Iron.	2 or 3	Ammonium, NH_4— .	1
Lead	2 or 4	Sulphate group, SO_4 .	2
Magnesium . . .	2	Nitrate ,, NO_3	1
Mercury	1 or 2	Carbonate ,, CO_3 .	2
Nitrogen	3 or 5	Hydroxyl ,, —OH	1

3. Formulæ of some Common Compounds.

Element.	Oxides.	Hydrides.	Hydroxides.	Chlorides.	Carbonates.	Sulphates.	Nitrates.
Aluminium	Al_2O_3	—	$Al(OH)_3$	$AlCl_3$	—	$Al_2(SO_4)_3$	$Al(NO_3)_3$
Barium .	BaO	—	$Ba(OH)_2$	$BaCl_2$	$BaCO_3$	$BaSO_4$	$Ba(NO_3)_2$
Boron . .	B_2O_3	BH_3	—	BCl_3	—	—	—
Bromine .	—	HBr	—	—	—	—	—
Calcium .	CaO	CaH_2	$Ca(OH)_2$	$CaCl_2$	$CaCO_3$	$CaSO_4$	$Ca(NO_3)_2$
Carbon. .	CO CO_2	CH_4 C_2H_4	—	CCl_4	—	—	—
		C_2H_2					
Chlorine .	Cl_2O ClO_2	HCl	—	—	—	—	—
Copper .	Cu_2O CuO	—	$Cu(OH)_2$	Cu_2Cl_2 $CuCl_2$	$CuCO_3$	$CuSO_4$	$Cu(NO_3)_2$
Hydrogen .	H_2O H_2O_2	—	$HOH(H_2O)$	HCl	H_2CO_3	H_2SO_4	HNO_3
Iodine . .	I_2O_5	HI	—	ICl	—	—	—
Iron . .	FeO Fe_3O_4	—	$Fe(OH)_2$	$FeCl_2$	—	$FeSO_4$	—
	Fe_2O_3	—	$Fe(OH)_3$	$FeCl_3$	—	$Fe_2(SO_4)_3$	—
Lead . .	PbO PbO_2	—	$Pb(OH)_2$	$PbCl_2$	$PbCO_3$	$PbSO_4$	$Pb(NO_3)_2$
	Pb_3O_4						
Magnesium	MgO	—	$Mg(OH)_2$	$MgCl_2$	$MgCO_3$	$MgSO_4$	$Mg(NO_3)_2$
Mercury .	Hg_2O	—	—	Hg_2Cl_2	—	Hg_2SO_4	$Hg_2(NO_3)_2$
	HgO			$HgCl_2$		$HgSO_4$	$Hg(NO_3)_2$
Nitrogen .	N_2O NO	NH_3	—	NCl_3	—	—	—
	NO_2 N_2O_5						
Oxygen .	—	H_2O H_2O_2	—	Cl_2O ClO_2	—	—	—
Phosphorus	P_2O_3 P_2O_5	PH_3	—	PCl_3 PCl_5	—	—	—
Potassium	K_2O K_2O_4	—	KOH	KCl	K_2CO_3	K_2SO_4	KNO_3
Silicon . .	SiO_2	SiH_4	—	$SiCl_4$	—	—	—
Silver . .	Ag_2O	—	—	$AgCl$	Ag_2CO_3	Ag_2SO_4	$AgNO_3$
Sodium .	Na_2O Na_2O_2	—	$NaOH$	$NaCl$	Na_2CO_3	Na_2SO_4	$NaNO_3$
Sulphur .	SO_2 SO_3	H_2S	—	S_2Cl_2	—	—	—
Tin . .	SnO	—	$Sn(OH)_2$	$SnCl_2$	—	$SnSO_4$	$Sn(NO_3)_2$
	SnO_2		$Sn(OH)_4$	$SnCl_4$			
Zinc . .	ZnO	—	$Zn(OH)_2$	$ZnCl_2$	$ZnCO_3$	$ZnSO_4$	$Zn(NO_3)_2$

4. Pressure of Aqueous Vapour.

Temp. °C.	Press. in mm.	Temp. °C.	Press. in mm.
0	4·6	18	15·5
1	4·9	19	16·5
2	5·3	20	17·5
3	5·7	21	18·5
4	6·1	22	19·6
5	6·5	23	20·9
6	7·0	24	22·2
7	7·5	25	23·5
8	8·0	26	25·0
9	8·6	27	26·5
10	9·2	28	28·1
11	9·8	29	29·7
12	10·5	30	31·5
13	11·2	40	54·9
14	12·0	50	92·0
15	12·8	60	148·9
16	13·6	80	354·9
17	14·5	100	760·0

5. Specific Gravities of Common Substances.

Sulphuric acid, 1·8.
Nitric acid, 1·42.
Hydrochloric acid (conc. aqueous solution), 1·2.
Alcohol, 0·8.

6. Specific Heats of Metals.

Aluminium . . .	0·214	Magnesium . . .	0·250
Barium	0·068	Mercury	0·033
Calcium . . .	0·149	Potassium . . .	0·198
Copper	0·095	Silver	0·057
Iron	0·114	Tin	0·056
Lead	0·031	Zinc	0·096

	0	1	2	3	4	5	6	7	8	9	1	2	3	4	5	6	7	8	9
10	0000	0043	0086	0128	0170						4	9	13	17	21	26	30	34	38
						0212	0253	0294	0334	0374	4	8	12	16	20	24	28	32	37
11	0414	0453	0492	0531	0569						4	8	12	15	19	23	27	31	35
						0607	0645	0682	0719	0755	4	7	11	15	19	22	26	30	33
12	0792	0828	0864	0899	0934	0969					3	7	11	14	18	21	25	28	32
							1004	1038	1072	1106	3	7	10	14	17	20	24	27	31
13	1139	1173	1206	1239	1271						3	7	10	13	16	20	23	26	30
						1303	1335	1367	1399	1430	3	7	10	12	16	19	22	25	29
14	1461	1492	1523	1553							3	6	9	12	15	18	21	24	28
					1584	1614	1644	1673	1703	1732	3	6	9	12	15	17	20	23	26
15	1761	1790	1818	1847	1875	1903					3	6	9	11	14	17	20	23	26
							1931	1959	1987	2014	3	5	8	11	14	16	19	22	25
16	2041	2068	2095	2122	2148						3	5	8	11	14	16	19	22	24
						2175	2201	2227	2253	2279	3	5	8	10	13	15	18	21	23
17	2304	2330	2355	2380	2405	2430					3	5	8	10	13	15	18	20	23
							2455	2480	2504	2529	2	5	7	10	12	15	17	19	22
18	2553	2577	2601	2625	2648						2	5	7	9	12	14	16	19	21
						2672	2695	2718	2742	2765	2	5	7	9	11	14	16	18	21
19	2788	2810	2833	2856	2878						2	4	7	9	11	13	16	18	20
						2900	2923	2945	2967	2989	2	4	6	8	11	13	15	17	19
20	3010	3032	3054	3075	3096	3118	3139	3160	3181	3201	2	4	6	8	11	13	15	17	19
21	3222	3243	3263	3284	3304	3324	3345	3365	3385	3404	2	4	6	8	10	12	14	16	18
22	3424	3444	3464	3483	3502	3522	3541	3560	3579	3598	2	4	6	8	10	12	14	15	17
23	3617	3636	3655	3674	3692	3711	3729	3747	3766	3784	2	4	6	7	9	11	13	15	17
24	3802	3820	3838	3856	3874	3892	3909	3927	3945	3962	2	4	5	7	9	11	12	14	16
25	3979	3997	4014	4031	4048	4065	4082	4099	4116	4133	2	3	5	7	9	10	12	14	15
26	4150	4166	4183	4200	4216	4232	4249	4265	4281	4298	2	3	5	7	8	10	11	13	15
27	4314	4330	4346	4362	4378	4393	4409	4425	4440	4456	2	3	5	6	8	9	11	13	14
28	4472	4487	4502	4518	4533	4548	4564	4579	4594	4609	2	3	5	6	8	9	11	12	14
29	4624	4639	4654	4669	4683	4698	4713	4728	4742	4757	1	3	4	6	7	9	10	12	13
30	4771	4786	4800	4814	4829	4843	4857	4871	4886	4900	1	3	4	6	7	9	10	11	13
31	4914	4928	4942	4955	4969	4983	4997	5011	5024	5038	1	3	4	6	7	8	10	11	12
32	5051	5065	5079	5092	5105	5119	5132	5145	5159	5172	1	3	4	5	7	8	9	11	12
33	5185	5198	5211	5224	5237	5250	5263	5276	5289	5302	1	3	4	5	6	8	9	10	12
34	5315	5328	5340	5353	5366	5378	5391	5403	5416	5428	1	3	4	5	6	8	9	10	11
35	5441	5453	5465	5478	5490	5502	5514	5527	5539	5551	1	2	4	5	6	7	9	10	11
36	5563	5575	5587	5599	5611	5623	5635	5647	5658	5670	1	2	4	5	6	7	8	10	11
37	5682	5694	5705	5717	5729	5740	5752	5763	5775	5786	1	2	3	5	6	7	8	9	10
38	5798	5809	5821	5832	5843	5855	5866	5877	5888	5899	1	2	3	5	6	7	8	9	10
39	5911	5922	5933	5944	5955	5966	5977	5988	5999	6010	1	2	3	4	5	7	8	9	10
40	6021	6031	6042	6053	6064	6075	6085	6096	6107	6117	1	2	3	4	5	6	8	9	10
41	6128	6138	6149	6160	6170	6180	6191	6201	6212	6222	1	2	3	4	5	6	7	8	9
42	6232	6243	6253	6263	6274	6284	6294	6304	6314	6325	1	2	3	4	5	6	7	8	9
43	6335	6345	6355	6365	6375	6385	6395	6405	6415	6425	1	2	3	4	5	6	7	8	9
44	6435	6444	6454	6464	6474	6484	6493	6503	6513	6522	1	2	3	4	5	6	7	8	9
45	6532	6542	6551	6561	6571	6580	6590	6599	6609	6618	1	2	3	4	5	6	7	8	9
46	6628	6637	6646	6656	6665	6675	6684	6693	6702	6712	1	2	3	4	5	6	7	7	8
47	6721	6730	6739	6749	6758	6767	6776	6785	6794	6803	1	2	3	4	5	5	6	7	8
48	6812	6821	6830	6839	6848	6857	6866	6875	6884	6893	1	2	3	4	4	5	6	7	8
49	6902	6911	6920	6928	6937	6946	6955	6964	6972	6981	1	2	3	4	4	5	6	7	8
50	6990	6998	7007	7016	7024	7033	7042	7050	7059	7067	1	2	3	3	4	5	6	7	8

	0	1	2	3	4	5	6	7	8	9	1	2	3	4	5	6	7	8	9
51	7076	7084	7093	7101	7110	7118	7126	7135	7143	7152	1	2	3	3	4	5	6	7	8
52	7160	7168	7177	7185	7193	7202	7210	7218	7226	7235	1	2	2	3	4	5	6	7	7
53	7243	7251	7259	7267	7275	7284	7292	7300	7308	7316	1	2	2	3	4	5	6	6	7
54	7324	7332	7340	7348	7356	7364	7372	7380	7388	7396	1	2	2	3	4	5	6	6	7
55	7404	7412	7419	7427	7435	7443	7451	7459	7466	7474	1	2	2	3	4	5	5	6	7
56	7482	7490	7497	7505	7513	7520	7528	7536	7543	7551	1	2	2	3	4	5	5	6	7
57	7559	7566	7574	7582	7589	7597	7604	7612	7619	7627	1	2	2	3	4	5	5	6	7
58	7634	7642	7649	7657	7664	7672	7679	7686	7694	7701	1	1	2	3	4	4	5	6	7
59	7709	7716	7723	7731	7738	7745	7752	7760	7767	7774	1	1	2	3	4	4	5	6	7
60	7782	7789	7796	7803	7810	7818	7825	7832	7839	7846	1	1	2	3	4	4	5	6	6
61	7853	7860	7868	7875	7882	7889	7896	7903	7910	7917	1	1	2	3	4	4	5	6	6
62	7924	7931	7938	7945	7952	7959	7966	7973	7980	7987	1	1	2	3	3	4	5	6	6
63	7993	8000	8007	8014	8021	8028	8035	8041	8048	8055	1	1	2	3	3	4	5	5	6
64	8062	8069	8075	8082	8089	8096	8102	8109	8116	8122	1	1	2	3	3	4	5	5	6
65	8129	8136	8142	8149	8156	8162	8169	8176	8182	8189	1	1	2	3	3	4	5	5	6
66	8195	8202	8209	8215	8222	8228	8235	8241	8248	8254	1	1	2	3	3	4	5	5	6
67	8261	8267	8274	8280	8287	8293	8299	8306	8312	8319	1	1	2	3	3	4	5	5	6
68	8325	8331	8338	8344	8351	8357	8363	8370	8376	8382	1	1	2	3	3	4	4	5	6
69	8388	8395	8401	8407	8414	8420	8426	8432	8439	8445	1	1	2	2	3	4	4	5	6
70	8451	8457	8463	8470	8476	8482	8488	8494	8500	8506	1	1	2	2	3	4	4	5	6
71	8513	8519	8525	8531	8537	8543	8549	8555	8561	8567	1	1	2	2	3	4	4	5	5
72	8573	8579	8585	8591	8597	8603	8609	8615	8621	8627	1	1	2	2	3	4	4	5	5
73	8633	8639	8645	8651	8657	8663	8669	8675	8681	8686	1	1	2	2	3	4	4	5	5
74	8692	8698	8704	8710	8716	8722	8727	8733	8739	8745	1	1	2	2	3	4	4	5	5
75	8751	8756	8762	8768	8774	8779	8785	8791	8797	8802	1	1	2	2	3	3	4	5	5
76	8808	8814	8820	8825	8831	8837	8842	8848	8854	8859	1	1	2	2	3	3	4	5	5
77	8865	8871	8876	8882	8887	8893	8899	8904	8910	8915	1	1	2	2	3	3	4	4	5
78	8921	8927	8932	8938	8943	8949	8954	8960	8965	8971	1	1	2	2	3	3	4	4	5
79	8976	8982	8987	8993	8998	9004	9009	9015	9020	9025	1	1	2	2	3	3	4	4	5
80	9031	9036	9042	9047	9053	9058	9063	9069	9074	9079	1	1	2	2	3	3	4	4	5
81	9085	9090	9096	9101	9106	9112	9117	9122	9128	9133	1	1	2	2	3	3	4	4	5
82	9138	9143	9149	9154	9159	9165	9170	9175	9180	9186	1	1	2	2	3	3	4	4	5
83	9191	9196	9201	9206	9212	9217	9222	9227	9232	9238	1	1	2	2	3	3	4	4	5
84	9243	9248	9253	9258	9263	9269	9274	9279	9284	9289	1	1	2	2	3	3	4	4	5
85	9294	9299	9304	9309	9315	9320	9325	9330	9335	9340	1	1	2	2	3	3	4	4	5
86	9345	9350	9355	9360	9365	9370	9375	9380	9385	9390	1	1	2	2	3	3	4	4	5
87	9395	9400	9405	9410	9415	9420	9425	9430	9435	9440	0	1	1	2	2	3	3	4	4
88	9445	9450	9455	9460	9465	9469	9474	9479	9484	9489	0	1	1	2	2	3	3	4	4
89	9494	9499	9504	9509	9513	9518	9523	9528	9533	9538	0	1	1	2	2	3	3	4	4
90	9542	9547	9552	9557	9562	9566	9571	9576	9581	9586	0	1	1	2	2	3	3	4	4
91	9590	9595	9600	9605	9609	9614	9619	9624	9628	9633	0	1	1	2	2	3	3	4	4
92	9638	9643	9647	9652	9657	9661	9666	9671	9675	9680	0	1	1	2	2	3	3	4	4
93	9685	9689	9694	9699	9703	9708	9713	9717	9722	9727	0	1	1	2	2	3	3	4	4
94	9731	9736	9741	9745	9750	9754	9759	9763	9768	9773	0	1	1	2	2	3	3	4	4
95	9777	9782	9786	9791	9795	9800	9805	9809	9814	9818	0	1	1	2	2	3	3	4	4
96	9823	9827	9832	9836	9841	9845	9850	9854	9859	9863	0	1	1	2	2	3	3	4	4
97	9868	9872	9877	9881	9886	9890	9894	9899	9903	9908	0	1	1	2	2	3	3	4	4
98	9912	9917	9921	9926	9930	9934	9939	9943	9948	9952	0	1	1	2	2	3	3	4	4
99	9956	9961	9965	9969	9974	9978	9983	9987	9991	9996	0	1	1	2	2	3	3	3	4

	0	1	2	3	4	5	6	7	8	9	1	2	3	4	5	6	7	8	9
·00	1000	1002	1005	1007	1009	1012	1014	1016	1019	1021	0	0	1	1	1	1	2	2	2
·01	1023	1026	1028	1030	1033	1035	1038	1040	1042	1045	0	0	1	1	1	1	2	2	2
·02	1047	1050	1052	1054	1057	1059	1062	1064	1067	1069	0	0	1	1	1	1	2	2	2
·03	1072	1074	1076	1079	1081	1084	1086	1089	1091	1094	0	0	1	1	1	1	2	2	2
·04	1096	1099	1102	1104	1107	1109	1112	1114	1117	1119	0	1	1	1	1	2	2	2	2
·05	1122	1125	1127	1130	1132	1135	1138	1140	1143	1146	0	1	1	1	1	2	2	2	2
·06	1148	1151	1153	1156	1159	1161	1164	1167	1169	1172	0	1	1	1	1	2	2	2	2
·07	1175	1178	1180	1183	1186	1189	1191	1194	1197	1199	0	1	1	1	1	2	2	2	2
·08	1202	1205	1208	1211	1213	1216	1219	1222	1225	1227	0	1	1	1	1	2	2	2	3
·09	1230	1233	1236	1239	1242	1245	1247	1250	1253	1256	0	1	1	1	1	2	2	2	3
·10	1259	1262	1265	1268	1271	1274	1276	1279	1282	1285	0	1	1	1	1	2	2	2	3
·11	1288	1291	1294	1297	1300	1303	1306	1309	1312	1315	0	1	1	1	2	2	2	2	3
·12	1318	1321	1324	1327	1330	1334	1337	1340	1343	1346	0	1	1	1	2	2	2	2	3
·13	1349	1352	1355	1358	1361	1365	1368	1371	1374	1377	0	1	1	1	2	2	2	3	3
·14	1380	1384	1387	1390	1393	1396	1400	1403	1406	1409	0	1	1	1	2	2	2	3	3
·15	1413	1416	1419	1422	1426	1429	1432	1435	1439	1442	0	1	1	1	2	2	2	3	3
·16	1445	1449	1452	1455	1459	1462	1466	1469	1472	1476	0	1	1	1	2	2	2	3	3
·17	1479	1483	1486	1489	1493	1496	1500	1503	1507	1510	0	1	1	1	2	2	2	3	3
·18	1514	1517	1521	1524	1528	1531	1535	1538	1542	1545	0	1	1	1	2	2	2	3	3
·19	1549	1552	1556	1560	1563	1567	1570	1574	1578	1581	0	1	1	1	2	2	3	3	3
·20	1585	1589	1592	1596	1600	1603	1607	1611	1614	1618	0	1	1	1	2	2	3	3	3
·21	1622	1626	1629	1633	1637	1641	1644	1648	1652	1656	0	1	1	2	2	2	3	3	3
·22	1660	1663	1667	1671	1675	1679	1683	1687	1690	1694	0	1	1	2	2	2	3	3	3
·23	1698	1702	1706	1710	1714	1718	1722	1726	1730	1734	0	1	1	2	2	2	3	3	4
·24	1738	1742	1746	1750	1754	1758	1762	1766	1770	1774	0	1	1	2	2	2	3	3	4
·25	1778	1782	1786	1791	1795	1799	1803	1807	1811	1816	0	1	1	2	2	2	3	3	4
·26	1820	1824	1828	1832	1837	1841	1845	1849	1854	1858	0	1	1	2	2	3	3	3	4
·27	1862	1866	1871	1875	1879	1884	1888	1892	1897	1901	0	1	1	2	2	3	3	3	4
·28	1905	1910	1914	1919	1923	1928	1932	1936	1941	1945	0	1	1	2	2	3	3	4	4
·29	1950	1954	1959	1963	1968	1972	1977	1982	1986	1991	0	1	1	2	2	3	3	4	4
·30	1995	2000	2004	2009	2014	2018	2023	2028	2032	2037	0	1	1	2	2	3	3	4	4
·31	2042	2046	2051	2056	2061	2065	2070	2075	2080	2084	0	1	1	2	2	3	3	4	4
·32	2089	2094	2099	2104	2109	2113	2118	2123	2128	2133	0	1	1	2	2	3	3	4	4
·33	2138	2143	2148	2153	2158	2163	2168	2173	2178	2183	0	1	1	2	2	3	3	4	4
·34	2188	2193	2198	2203	2208	2213	2218	2223	2228	2234	1	1	2	2	3	3	4	4	5
·35	2239	2244	2249	2251	2259	2265	2270	2275	2280	2286	1	1	2	2	3	3	4	4	5
·36	2291	2296	2301	2307	2312	2317	2323	2328	2333	2339	1	1	2	2	3	3	4	4	5
·37	2344	2350	2355	2360	2366	2371	2377	2382	2388	2393	1	1	2	2	3	3	4	4	5
·38	2399	2404	2410	2415	2421	2427	2432	2438	2443	2449	1	1	2	2	3	3	4	4	5
·39	2455	2460	2466	2472	2477	2483	2489	2495	2500	2506	1	1	2	2	3	3	4	5	5
·40	2512	2518	2523	2529	2535	2541	2547	2553	2559	2564	1	1	2	2	3	4	4	5	5
·41	2570	2576	2582	2588	2594	2600	2606	2612	2618	2624	1	1	2	2	3	4	4	5	5
·42	2630	2636	2642	2649	2655	2661	2667	2673	2679	2685	1	1	2	2	3	4	4	5	6
·43	2692	2698	2704	2710	2716	2723	2729	2735	2742	2748	1	1	2	3	3	4	4	5	6
·44	2754	2761	2767	2773	2780	2786	2793	2799	2805	2813	1	1	2	3	3	4	4	5	6
·45	2818	2825	2831	2838	2844	2851	2858	2864	2871	2877	1	1	2	3	3	4	5	5	6
·46	2884	2891	2897	2904	2911	2917	2924	2931	2938	2944	1	1	2	3	3	4	5	5	6
·47	2951	2958	2965	2972	2979	2985	2992	2999	3006	3013	1	1	2	3	3	4	5	5	6
·48	3020	3027	3034	3041	3048	3055	3062	3069	3076	3083	1	1	2	3	4	4	5	6	6
·49	3090	3097	3105	3112	3119	3126	3133	3141	3148	3155	1	1	2	3	4	4	5	6	6

	0	1	2	3	4	5	6	7	8	9	1	2	3	4	5	6	7	8	9
·50	3162	3170	3177	3184	3192	3199	3206	3214	3221	3228	1	1	2	3	4	4	5	6	7
·51	3236	3243	3251	3258	3266	3273	3281	3289	3296	3304	1	2	2	3	4	5	5	6	7
·52	3311	3319	3327	3334	3342	3350	3357	3365	3373	3381	1	2	2	3	4	5	5	6	7
·53	3388	3396	3404	3412	3420	3428	3436	3443	3451	3459	1	2	2	3	4	5	6	6	7
·54	3467	3475	3483	3491	3499	3508	3516	3524	3532	3540	1	2	2	3	4	5	6	6	7
·55	3548	3556	3565	3573	3581	3589	3597	3606	3614	3622	1	2	2	3	4	5	6	7	7
·56	3631	3639	3648	3656	3664	3673	3681	3690	3698	3707	1	2	3	3	4	5	6	7	8
·57	3715	3724	3733	3741	3750	3758	3767	3776	3784	3793	1	2	3	3	4	5	6	7	8
·58	3802	3811	3819	3828	3837	3846	3855	3864	3873	3882	1	2	3	4	4	5	6	7	8
·59	3890	3899	3908	3917	3926	3936	3945	3954	3963	3972	1	2	3	4	5	5	6	7	8
·60	3981	3990	3999	4009	4018	4027	4036	4046	4055	4064	1	2	3	4	5	6	6	7	8
·61	4074	4083	4093	4102	4111	4121	4130	4140	4150	4159	1	2	3	4	5	6	7	8	9
·62	4169	4178	4188	4198	4207	4217	4227	4236	4246	4256	1	2	3	4	5	6	7	8	9
·63	4266	4276	4285	4295	4305	4315	4325	4335	4345	4355	1	2	3	4	5	6	7	8	9
·64	4365	4375	4385	4395	4406	4416	4426	4436	4446	4457	1	2	3	4	5	6	7	8	9
·65	4467	4477	4487	4498	4508	4519	4529	4539	4550	4560	1	2	3	4	5	6	7	8	9
·66	4571	4581	4592	4603	4613	4624	4634	4645	4656	4667	1	2	3	4	5	6	7	9	10
·67	4677	4688	4699	4710	4721	4732	4742	4753	4764	4775	1	2	3	4	5	7	8	9	10
·68	4786	4797	4808	4819	4831	4842	4853	4864	4875	4887	1	2	3	4	6	7	8	9	10
·69	4898	4909	4920	4932	4943	4955	4966	4977	4989	5000	1	2	3	5	6	7	8	9	10
·70	5012	5023	5035	5047	5058	5070	5082	5093	5105	5117	1	2	4	5	6	7	8	9	11
·71	5129	5140	5152	5164	5176	5188	5200	5212	5224	5236	1	2	4	5	6	7	8	10	11
·72	5248	5260	5272	5284	5297	5309	5321	5333	5346	5358	1	2	4	5	6	7	9	10	11
·73	5370	5383	5395	5408	5420	5433	5445	5458	5470	5483	1	3	4	5	6	8	9	10	11
·74	5495	5508	5521	5534	5546	5559	5572	5585	5598	5610	1	3	4	5	6	8	9	10	12
·75	5623	5636	5649	5662	5675	5689	5702	5715	5728	5741	1	3	4	5	7	8	9	10	12
·76	5754	5768	5781	5794	5808	5821	5834	5848	5861	5875	1	3	4	5	7	8	9	11	12
·77	5888	5902	5916	5929	5943	5957	5970	5984	5998	6012	1	3	4	5	7	8	10	11	12
·78	6026	6039	6053	6067	6081	6095	6109	6124	6138	6152	1	3	4	6	7	8	10	11	13
·79	6166	6180	6194	6209	6223	6237	6252	6266	6281	6295	1	3	4	6	7	9	10	11	13
·80	6310	6324	6339	6353	6368	6383	6397	6412	6427	6442	1	3	4	6	7	9	10	12	13
·81	6457	6471	6486	6501	6516	6531	6546	6561	6577	6592	2	3	5	6	8	9	11	12	14
·82	6607	6622	6637	6653	6668	6683	6699	6714	6730	6745	2	3	5	6	8	9	11	12	14
·83	6761	6776	6792	6808	6823	6839	6855	6871	6887	6902	2	3	5	6	8	9	11	13	14
·84	6918	6934	6950	6966	6982	6998	7015	7031	7047	7063	2	3	5	6	8	10	11	13	15
·85	7079	7096	7112	7129	7145	7161	7178	7194	7211	7228	2	3	5	7	8	10	12	13	15
·86	7244	7261	7278	7295	7311	7328	7345	7362	7379	7396	2	3	5	7	8	10	12	13	15
·87	7413	7430	7447	7464	7482	7499	7516	7534	7551	7568	2	3	5	7	9	10	12	14	16
·88	7586	7603	7621	7638	7656	7674	7691	7709	7727	7745	2	4	5	7	9	11	12	14	16
·89	7762	7780	7798	7816	7834	7852	7870	7889	7907	7925	2	4	5	7	9	11	13	14	16
·90	7943	7962	7980	7998	8017	8035	8054	8072	8091	8110	2	4	6	7	9	11	13	15	17
·91	8128	8147	8166	8185	8204	8222	8241	8260	8279	8299	2	4	6	8	9	11	13	15	17
·92	8318	8337	8356	8375	8395	8414	8433	8453	8472	8492	2	4	6	8	10	12	14	15	17
·93	8511	8531	8551	8570	8590	8610	8630	8650	8670	8690	2	4	6	8	10	12	14	16	18
·94	8710	8730	8750	8770	8790	8810	8831	8851	8872	8892	2	4	6	8	10	12	14	16	18
·95	8913	8933	8954	8974	8995	9016	9036	9057	9078	9099	2	4	6	8	10	12	15	17	19
·96	9120	9141	9162	9183	9204	9226	9247	9268	9290	9311	2	4	6	8	11	13	15	17	19
·97	9333	9354	9376	9397	9419	9441	9462	9484	9506	9528	2	4	7	9	11	13	15	17	20
·98	9550	9572	9594	9616	9638	9661	9683	9705	9727	9750	2	4	7	9	11	13	16	18	20
·99	9772	9795	9817	9840	9863	9886	9908	9931	9954	9977	2	5	7	9	11	14	16	18	20

ANSWERS TO NUMERICAL EXAMPLES

CHAP. V, pp. 52–53.

3. 20 c.c.
4. 33·6.
5. 770 mm.
6. 119 c.c.
7. 53 c.c.
8. 22·75 c.c.
9. 91 c.c.
10. 184 c.c.
11. 29·6° C.
12. 96 c.c.
13. 93 c.c.
14. 34 c.c.
15. 353 c.c.
16. 21 c.c.
17. 48 c.c.
18. 36 c.c.
19. 125·7 c.c.
20. 54·6 c.c.
21. 146·1 c.c.
22. 60·5 c.c.
23. 21·7 c.c.

CHAP. VI, pp. 72–73.

7. 21·1 c.c.
8. 54·5 c.c.
9. 12·1.
10. 27·6.
11. 32·7.
12. 59·4.
13. 9·0.
14. 12·1.
15. 9·0.
16. 32·7.
17. 31·8.
18. 100·3.
19. 56·2.
20. 59·4.
21. 31·8.
22. 107·9.
23. 27·92.
24. 103·6.
25. 107·8.
26. 10·35.
27. Silver, 108·2; copper, 31·9.

CHAP. VII, p. 89.

17. (i) 31·8. (ii) 63·4. Ratio 1 : 2.

CHAP. VIII. pp. 107–108.

13. 58·0.
14. 36·5.
15. 126·8.
16. 96.4.
17. 51·7.
18. 342·
19. 60.

CHAP. IX, pp. 123–125.

5. (i) 11·2. (ii) 5·6. (iii) 5·6. (iv) 44·8. (v) 2·24. (vi) 2·8 litres.
8. (i) Ca 40, C 12, O 48. (ii) K 39, H 1, C 12, O 48. (iii) Cu 33·9, N 14·9, O 51·2. (iv) C 78·94, H 10·53, O 10·53. (v) C 93·75, H 6·25. (vi) K 24·7, Mn 34·8, O 40·5. (vii) K 26·5, Cr 35·4, O 38·1. (viii) Pb 90·7, O 9·3. (ix) K 31·84, Cl 28·9, O 39·2. (x) H 11·1, O 88·9.
9. (i) 3·825 grams. (ii) 7·59 grams.
10. 2·76 litres.
11. 41·9 litres.
12. NaCl.
13. K_2CO_3.
14. (*a*) $C_2H_3O_3$. (*b*) $C_4H_6O_6$.
15. $ZnSO_4$.
16. (*a*) KSO_4. (*b*) $K_2S_2O_8$.
17. $Na_2S_2O_3$.
18. (*a*) CHO_2. (*b*) $C_2H_2O_4$.
19. Ag_2SO_4.
20. $K_4FeC_6N_6$.

CHAP. X, p. 135.

4. 94·6.

CHAP. XIII, p. 164.

2. (*a*) 3250 tons. (*b*) 290 grams.

CHAP. XV, p. 251.

13. 3·23 litres.
23. 5·17 grams.
32. 4·05 grams.
34. (*a*) 24·6. (*b*) 5,040,000 litres.
35. 7·55 litres.

CHAP. XIX, p. 387.

11. (*a*) 13·25 kilograms. (*b*) 28,000 litres.
12. 12·3 litres.

CHAP. XX, p. 406.

9. (*a*) 32·8 grams. (*b*) 117·6 grams. (*c*) 2·69 litres.
11. (*a*) 3·38 kilograms. (*b*) 104 grams.

INDEX OF NAMES

SUBJECT INDEX